D0968543

Rocket Development

Robert H. Goddard

Rocket Development

Liquid-Fuel Rocket Research
1929-1941

edited by

Esther C. Goddard

and

G. Edward Pendray

Prentice-Hall, Inc.

Englewood Cliffs, N. J.

1961

Copyright, 1948, by

ESTHER C. GODDARD

The Man Who Ushered in the Space Age, by G. Edward Pendray
Copyright, 1960, by G. EDWARD PENDRAY

Reprinted by permission from American Legion Magazine

All rights reserved. No part of this book may be
reproduced in any form, by mimeograph or any
other means, without permission in writing from
Esther C. Goddard and the publishers.

LIBRARY OF CONGRESS
CARD CATALOG NO.: 61-9221

PRINTED IN THE UNITED STATES OF AMERICA
78219-C

T.L 783.4
.G6
1961

Nicht Kunst und Wissenschaft allein,
Geduld will bei dem Werke sein.
—Goethe

The Editors

ESTHER C. GODDARD is Mrs. Robert H. Goddard; before her marriage Esther Christine Kisk. Mrs. Goddard was born in Worcester, Mass., attended Bates College, was graduated from the Johns Hopkins University, and holds a master's degree from Clark University. She first met Dr. Goddard at Clark University. They were married in 1924, and Mrs. Goddard subsequently attended virtually every one of Dr. Goddard's rocket experiments, serving as photographer. Her life has been so closely associated with Dr. Goddard's work that she knows in intimate detail most of the experiments recorded in this book. As executor of Dr. Goddard's estate, she is now engaged in making available to the technical and reading public the important data, both in text and pictures, which he left behind as a record of his fruitful life.

G. EDWARD PENDRAY, formerly assistant to the president of the Westinghouse Electric Corporation, has been closely associated with the development of rockets since 1929. He was one of the founders, served several terms as a director, and at present is an advisor to the American Rocket Society. Himself a rocket experimenter of many years' standing, he was well acquainted with Dr. Goddard and his work, and they were fellow directors of the American Rocket Society at the time of Dr. Goddard's death. He is the author of *The Coming Age of Rocket Power* (Harper & Brothers), edited the reprint of Dr. Goddard's two reports issued under the title of *Rockets* by the American Rocket Society, and has contributed largely to both technical and popular literature on the subject of rockets and jet propulsion. At present he is senior partner of Pendray & Company, counsel on public relations and management to a number of industrial companies and technical organizations, and is consultant on rockets to The Daniel and Florence Guggenheim Foundation.

Contents

Foreword

When Dr. Robert H. Goddard first began his monumental work on the development of rockets, about 1909, there was no real technical information anywhere on the subject. In the thirty-five years that followed, he brought a new science and a new branch of engineering into being, launched a new industry, and probably changed the course of human history.

At his death, in 1945, he left behind a voluminous collection of notes, records, photographs, patents, ideas, and experimental data, representing a remarkably active lifetime of devotion to a single purpose: the development of rockets for practical use. Though his achievements were widely known among technical men, none of his experimental data, and little of his other material, has been made public until now, except his numerous patents and two brief progress reports.

The purpose of this book is to make available for general readers the Goddard data on experiments performed during the fruitful period from 1929 until 1941. The series covers experiments which were sponsored for the most part by my father, Daniel Guggenheim, and subsequently by The Daniel and Florence Guggenheim Foundation.

The Goddard data given here are condensations of Dr. Goddard's own experimental notebooks for this period. The condensations are Dr. Goddard's own work.

In view of the great world-wide interest in the development of rockets and space flight, the publication of this book just now is especially timely. Many of the most modern ideas currently under study by rocket engineers were first proposed by Dr. Goddard. A great number of them, as these pages show, were tried out by him in rocket flights or on the proving stand.

There is evidence that the German rocket engineers followed Dr. Goddard's work very closely from the time of publication of his first Smithsonian report in 1919 until his death. They were familiar with his patents, all his published material, and any additional data which they were able to obtain by correspondence.

It will also be apparent that the German V–2 rockets, though larger, were almost identical versions of some of Dr. Goddard's rockets tested in flight. Rockets of the V–2 type were within our grasp in this country long before the Germans used them.

All of the Goddard experiments and patents were made available to our Government before Pearl Harbor by Dr. Goddard and The Daniel and Florence Guggenheim Foundation.

Dr. Goddard was the undisputed father of modern rocketry, and like many another pioneer his genius was not at first widely recognized. Now, however, the world, and particularly his own country, is beginning to take signal notice of the man and his accomplishments.

Among many honors and recognitions that have come to him posthumously are the establishment of Robert H. Goddard Professorships at the Daniel and Florence Guggenheim Jet Propulsion Centers at Princeton University and California Institute of Technology; the Goddard Gold Medal awarded annually by the American Rocket Society for outstanding achievements in rocketry and space flight; permanent exhibits on his life and work at the Smithsonian Institution (National Air Museum) in Washington, D.C., the Roswell Museum at Roswell, New Mexico, and at Clark University and Worcester Polytechnic Institute at Worcester, Mass. In 1960 Dr. Goddard was voted a Congressional Medal, and in the same year was awarded the Langley Medal, of which he was the ninth recipient. The Goddard Space Flight Center of the National Aeronautics and Space Administration at Greenbelt, Md., was named for him, and the Department of Defense awarded $1,000,000 for the use of his patents. Honors, awards and recognition continue to pile up as the importance of Dr. Goddard's work steadily becomes more and more clear to the nation and the world.

Dr. Goddard's technical material and research data, as published in this volume, is rich in information, suggestions and imaginative departures. It will unquestionably prove a mine of ideas for rocket, jet propulsion and space flight engineers and scientists for years to come; a continual inspiration and reminder that there is no force on earth so powerful as a determined, persistent and imaginative man with an important new idea.

HARRY F. GUGGENHEIM, *President*
The Daniel and Florence
Guggenheim Foundation

The Man Who Ushered in
the Space Age*

By G. EDWARD PENDRAY

The year 1909 is not one you would normally pick out of history, but it did produce several signal world events. Admiral Robert E. Peary, on his sixth attempt, reached the North Pole. Louis Bleriot flew across the English Channel, a distance of 31 miles, in the amazing time of 37 minutes. And in Worcester, Massachusetts, a quiet young man of 27 began a lifework that ultimately was to change the history of the human race.

In 1909, Robert H. Goddard, the man who launched the world into rocketry and space flight, was a slender, purposeful, shy young man; a bachelor, ambitious, frail in health—and a fellow with a dream so gigantic, so overwhelming he hardly dared confide it anywhere except in his diary.

The dream had been unfolding in his mind since he was 17, when on an autumn afternoon he climbed a cherry tree in his grandmother's yard in Worcester and caught a glimpse of the future. On that afternoon he visualized a kind of spaceship, propelled by a weight whirling around a cylinder or shaft, big enough to carry a man, and capable of flying upward through the atmosphere against the force of gravity.

The technical means by which such an object could be propelled was of course not clear to Goddard at 17. Just the same, he noted the idea in his diary, and firmly resolved to find a way to make it work. Subsequently he attended Worcester Polytechnic Institute, became a doctor of philosophy at Clark University, carried on a year of research in physics at Princeton University—and by that time he knew.

Goddard was not, of course, the inventor of the rocket. An unknown Chinese, or possibly Tartar, accomplished that feat more than 700 years ago. Rockets first flashed into written history at the battle of Kai-Feng, China, in the year 1232 A.D., when the city's defenders used them with telling effect against invading Mongol hordes led by the son of Genghis Khan. The rocket idea thereafter traveled all over the world. War rockets were used by the Indians against the British in 1799, by the

* Reprinted by permission from American Legion Magazine.

British against Napoleon in 1804, by the British against the Americans in the War of 1812, and by virtually all the armies of Europe against each other, until the late 1800's.

In all that time practically everything known scientifically about how and why a rocket operates was contained in Sir Isaac Newton's observation that in nature "every action hath an equal and opposite reaction." Starting with that general law, the youthful Goddard developed the basic mathematics of rocket operation. He followed up by testing and measuring the actual performance of rockets, both in the air and in a vacuum.

His experiments proved what theory predicted: that a sufficiently powerful rocket could go literally any distance into airless space. It could carry all of its propellants from the earth; and, unlike any other type of engine or prime mover, the rocket would need nothing to push against. It could work as well—even a little better—in a vacuum than in the atmosphere.

But how translate this preliminary and theoretical knowledge into something real? For an unknown, tubercular, and moneyless young physicist it was a problem.

Starting with his own very slender resources, Goddard resolutely began the task that was to be his lifework. It is not known exactly when he began experimenting with rockets, but classmates recall the excitement he caused during his senior year at Worcester Polytech, when he made unauthorized static rocket tests in the basement and filled the whole building with smoke. The following year, 1909, he definitely started his career by developing the idea of multiple or step rockets, and working out a plan for using hydrogen and oxygen as fuels for interplanetary flight.

Such powerful propellants were too ambitious for actual experiments at that early stage, however; so he purchased small ship rockets, and later carried on with larger ones he manufactured himself. By this time he was an assistant professor at Clark University, in Worcester. He made some of his experiments there, in the basement of the physics building.

His funds soon ran out. Undaunted, he put together a lengthy memorandum on the theory and possibilities of rockets, modestly entitled "A Method of Reaching Extreme Altitudes." This he sent to several scientific institutions, hoping someone would become interested in making money available for further research.

On his list of likely sources was the venerable Smithsonian Institution, in Washington, D. C., about as conservative an organization as one could imagine. To his happy surprise, the Smithsonian's secretary, after carefully checking Goddard's mathematics, wrote cautiously to ask how much he thought a real high-altitude rocket might cost.

Several governments have since spent billions to find the answer to this innocent question. Goddard pondered for several days and finally concluded he might need as much as $10,000. This seemed so large a sum, however, that he compromised on $5,000. The Smithsonion, accepting, sent him $1,000 for a start, not knowing what it was really getting into. Ultimately it invested more than $11,000 in Goddard's rockets—and this was still only a beginning.

Goddard had hardly started under the Smithsonian grants when an unexpected interruption came. The United States had entered the first World War, and the U. S. Army Signal Corps, on the advice of the Smithsonian, designated him to develop rockets that might be useful in battle. With two graduate students from Clark—one of whom was Dr. C. N. Hickman, who later played a significant part in the rocket story—Goddard went to the famous observatory at Mount Wilson, California. In a short time he came up with several solid propellant rockets he thought might be what the Army was asking for. One was a bombardment rocket with considerable range, which, unlike an artillery shell, required no cannon. Another was a rocket that could be launched from a light tube held in the hands or balanced on the shoulder of a soldier: a prototype of the modern bazooka.

These forerunners of modern rocket warfare were demonstrated before representatives of the Army, Navy, and Air Corps, at Aberdeen Proving Ground, Maryland, on November 6 and 7, 1918. The demonstrations went well. The military men were much impressed. There was talk of putting one or more of the new rockets into short-run production, for a possible tryout in actual combat. But only a few days later came the Armistice ending the war, and Goddard's war rockets were virtually forgotten for more than 20 years.

He happily resumed his experiments at Worcester, carrying on in such a way as to attract as little attention as possible. His reticence resulted partly from personal choice, and partly from the need to protect his scientific reputation. In modern times, when rocketry and space flight rank among the most respectable and glamorous of technical fields, it is hard to realize how utterly fantastic, how crackpot, how unbelievably ridiculous the whole idea of space flight appeared to the average American—even to scientists and engineers—in the 1920's.

As late as 1945 Goddard was to write: " The subject of projection from the earth, and especially a mention of the moon, must still be avoided in dignified scientific and engineering circles." At the beginning of the 1920's he was to learn, to his cost, that it is painful to be a pioneer—especially the pioneer of a daring new idea.

In January 1920 the Smithsonian Institution got around to publishing the paper Goddard had submitted to it some time before, his treatise on "A Method of Reaching Extreme Altitudes." Dated as of the previous year, this rather remarkable essay on rockets and their possibilities is one of the classic documents in astronautics.

Goddard recounted in it the results of some of his early experiments, explained rocket principles, explored basic rocket mathematics, examined the theory of the step rocket (which he had previously patented), and presented some computations to indicate what really great heights a rocket could reach if it had an efficient engine and suitable propellants. In this last section he showed that even a rather modest rocket, in theory at least, could go as far as the moon. He suggested that a pound or two of photographic flash powder might be carried by such a rocket to signal its arrival on our satellite.

The newspapers of 1920 made little or nothing of Goddard's mathematics, experiments, or technical contributions—but they had a field day with his suggestion about a shot at the moon. In addition to deriding him as "the moon man," some challenged his scientific knowledge; worse, a few even suggested that he had deliberately distorted scientific facts to make his point. A writer in *The New York Times* scornfully remarked that Goddard "only seems to lack the knowledge ladled out daily in high schools."

The effect of this derisive copy on the still very shy and sensitive New Englander was to make him shun publicity all the rest of his life, to be wary in describing his work, and reluctant to grant interviews. He did send a signed statement to the Associated Press after the first flood of stories, and in it he tried calmly to take the public interest away from the moon rocket and direct it to the less spectacular portions of his report. In 1921 he again tried to clarify his position, this time in an article for the *Scientific American*.

Thereafter for a while public interest in rockets declined. Goddard was free to continue his experiments without embarrassment. By this time he had reached a major conclusion about propellants to be used in reaching really high altitudes.

His early experiments had been made with solid fuels—for the most part varieties of gunpowder. By 1920 he became convinced that he could not get sufficient altitude with such relatively weak propellants. He resolved to experiment with liquid-fuel rockets instead, fully realizing the hazards of working with these highly explosive and treacherous materials. From 1920 until about 1925 he carried on preliminary tests. And on March 16, 1926, at his Aunt Effie's farm at Auburn, Massachusetts, he shot the first liquid-propellant rocket. The site, now a golf course, today bears a granite marker raised there by the American Rocket Society.

That historic first liquid-fuel rocket justifies a little description. The propellants were gasoline and liquid oxygen, a combination that yields about five times as much energy pound for pound as TNT. Until Goddard began experimenting, nobody had put this tricky and dangerous combination together. The propellants, contained in separate small tanks near the rear of the rocket, were piped to the motor, up at the front, through slender tubes that served both to convey the propellants and transmit the thrust. In this rocket Goddard placed the motor ahead of the tanks because he felt a rocket's flight would be more stable if pulled instead of pushed. He was to discover later that it actually doesn't make any difference at what point the thrust is applied, so long as it pushes along the axis of flight. In subsequent designs Goddard set the style that has been followed in all rockets since: the motor at the rear end, behind the tanks.

His historic first liquid-propellant rocket was a strange-looking affair. It stood 10 feet high. The slender motor and its nozzle were two feet long. The tanks trailed five feet behind the end of the nozzle. The launching was from a light portable metal framework. Preliminary heating with a small alcohol stove was required to provide gas pressure to force the propellants into the motor. There was no complicated ignition system. The propellant valves were simply opened by turning, and the motor ignited by a blowtorch at the end of a long pole.

When all was ready, Goddard opened the valves. Henry Sachs, a machinist and instrument-maker in the shop at Clark University, applied the torch. Two other persons witnessed the test: P. M. Roope, of the Clark University physics department, and Mrs. Goddard.

Promptly upon ignition the rocket leaped out of the launcher with a whistling roar, and quickly built up a speed of more than 60 miles an hour. After two and a half seconds its propellants were exhausted. The rocket yawed and came to earth 184 feet away; a very modest shot indeed by today's standards, but historically without equal. It was the world's first liquid-propellant rocket shot.

This test was reported privately to the Smithsonian Institution, but no public announcement was made.

On July 17, 1929, Goddard launched another rocket at Aunt Effie's Auburn farm, one that made history in a somewhat different way. The shot was his fourth liquid-propellant flight, and the rocket was a pretty impressive affair. Eleven feet long, it carried instruments in its nose— a barometer and a thermometer, with a small camera hopefully focused to record their readings at maximum altitude.

The rocket took off with a tremendous racket, soared 90 feet, then nosed over and traveled 171 feet before dropping to earth. The noise it made, as reported by *The New York Times,* "was such that scores of residents called Police Headquarters, saying that an airplane was shooting along afire. Two police ambulances scoured the section looking for victims and an airplane left Grafton Airport to aid the search." A flood of new and unwelcome publicity resulted, and this time unpleasant official attention came as well. Goddard was summoned before the Massachusetts State Fire Marshal, and after a brief hearing agreed to discontinue his tests in the State.

Again the Smithsonian saved the day, this time by persuading the Army to allow Goddard to shoot rockets on the artillery range at Camp Devens, near Ayer, Massachusetts, which was, of course, Federal territory. Authorities there were also worried about fire, however, and would allow testing only after a rain or snowfall. This restriction, combined with the difficulties of transporting fragile equipment 25 miles or so from the University to the Fort, and the long trips back to the University shops for repairs, slowed matters considerably. It began to appear as though Goddard's work might have come to its end at last.

But among those who had seen the sensational newspaper stories was Charles A. Lindbergh, at the peak of the enormous popularity that followed his historic flight to Paris. He visited Goddard, was much impressed, and called Goddard's work to the attention of Daniel Guggenheim, head of the philanthropic family that had already done so much to aid the development of aviation and aeronautics.

Mr. Guggenheim—and later the famous Daniel and Florence Guggenheim Foundation headed by Daniel's son Harry Guggenheim—provided a series of grants enabling Goddard to devote his entire time to rockets and high-altitude research. After a study of possible sites for his experiments, he set up a shop and testing ground near Roswell, New Mexico—not far from today's White Sands Missile Range—an area so sparsely inhabited that rockets could endanger little but jackrabbits, scorpions, and snakes.

In New Mexico Goddard's work progressed rapidly. By December 1930 he had a new rocket ready for testing. This one leaped skyward for 2,000 feet, reaching a top speed of 500 miles an hour. Not satisfied with the motor, Goddard continued testing and improving it for some time. In September and October 1931 he successfully tested his first remotely controlled rocket. He then turned his attention to another pressing and difficult rocket problem: flight stabilizaton. By April 1932 he had developed and successfully shot the first rocket controlled by a gyroscope, a method used on all large rockets today. Pressure for the operation of this rocket was supplied by liquid nitrogen carried on the flight.

But by that time his initial grant was running out. A technical committee that had been studying his progress recommended extending the grant for another two years. But the great depression had begun, and renewal just then was impossible. So in June 1932 Goddard closed down his shop and returned to Clark University, where he had been a full professor since 1919. He did not give up his rocket work, however. A small new grant from the Smithsonian kept him going for a time, and one from the Daniel and Florence Guggenheim Foundation a short time later permitted renewed attack on the problem of flight stabilization.

In August 1934 Guggenheim grants again made it possible for the Goddards and their small crew of assistants to resume full-scale activities on the New Mexico testing ground. Goddard signaled his return with a spectacular test of a new rocket stabilized with a pendulum, which approached, or reached, the speed of sound in powered horizontal flight. It went so fast that the parachute cable snapped off. Goddard then constructed a large rocket controlled by an improved gyro, and again made a triumphantly successful shot. This rocket, affectionately nick-named "Nell," was steered in vertical flight by a small gyroscope linked to four moving vanes set in the jet exhaust stream—a device later used by the Germans on their V-2's.

Mrs. Goddard, who was photographer as well as chief cook and bottle washer of the experimental group, made a beautiful motion picture of Nell rising majestically from her 60-foot launching tower and climbing a sinuous path into the desert sky. The picture was shown in December 1935 at the annual meeting of the American Association for the Advancement of Science, the world's largest scientific society. It seemed as though Goddard and his rockets had arrived at last.

In the following year Goddard made a complete report on his liquid-fuel rocket work to the Smithsonian Institution. The report was published March 16, 1936, under the title: "Liquid-Propellant Rocket Development," and it appeared on the tenth anniversary of his historic first liquid-propellant rocket shot.

The work in New Mexico continued until October 1941. During this period Goddard constructed and tested a long series of liquid-propellant rockets, and tried out, in one form or another, practically every one of the ideas that have since been developed successfully in large rockets and guided missiles, including gyrocontrols, clustered rockets, research instrumentation, turbopumps for propellants, gimbal-mounted tail sections capable of being moved in flight for steering, and numerous other schemes.

He kept meticulous and detailed notebooks and diaries of his experiments, carefully jotting down all his numerous and varied ideas for rocket propulsion, design, launching, controls, and flight in space. Goddard received or applied for a total of 83 patents on these rocket and space ideas in his lifetime. His executors, combing his research notes and diaries, found additional ideas which have resulted in 131 more patents, 214 in all. Today it is virtually impossible to design, construct, or shoot a rocket without making use of ideas or devices covered by Goddard patents.

The culmination of Goddard's work in New Mexico was a rocket that made a successful altitude shot of some 9,000 feet, and that contained almost all of the features later incorporated into the German V-2 rockets —though the latter, of course, were much larger. When he had reached this stage, Goddard perceived that World War II was imminent; and for the second time in his life offered his work and services to his country.

In May 1940 Harry Guggenheim arranged a meeting in the office of Brigadier General George H. Brett in Washington. It was attended by representatives of the Navy's Bureau of Aeronautics, the Army's Ordnance Department, and the Air Corps. Goddard described his experiments and presented the possibilities, as he saw them, of long-range liquid-propellant rockets for military use.

At the end of the conference the Army representatives said they still felt that "the next war will be won with the trench mortar." The Air Corps and Navy people saw no possibilities in the rocket as a missile weapon, but thought liquid-fuel rocket motors might perhaps be developed to assist heavily loaded aircraft take off from water or short runways and to power fast climbs in emergencies. In September 1941 both branches engaged Goddard to carry on research for that pedestrian, unimaginative —and as it turned out, largely futile—purpose. It was like trying to harness Pegasus to a plow.

We know now that the German military had become strongly interested in rockets as early as 1930. By 1937—three years before the historic but unfruitful meeting of U. S. military men with Goddard—the Germans had established the huge liquid-propellant rocket research center at Peenemunde, and were well along the way toward an operational V-2.

In this country the Armed Forces had not a single rocket weapon as late as the time of Pearl Harbor. Then came the great awakening, impressed on us by the British, Russian, and German solid-propellant anti-aircraft and bombardment rockets. Though our own services plunged into rocket development several years late, they did it with zeal. By V-J Day, in September 1945, the U. S. Army was spending $150 million a year on rockets of the solid-fuel variety, and the Navy was spending eight times as much.

One cannot say that Goddard was directly responsible for this fantastic development, but certainly he was indirectly responsible. Its beginning was the work he had done during World War I. The publicity his later work received throughout the world gave it impetus. The followup came through one of the men he had trained and indoctrinated.

Dr. Hickman, Goddard's former graduate student and assistant at Mount Wilson, had by 1940 become a prominent engineer associated with the Bell Laboratories. When U. S. entry in the Second World War seemed inevitable, Hickman contacted Goddard and asked his permission to call those nearly forgotten 1918 experiments to the attention of the National Defense Research Committee. Goddard gave consent promptly, and Hickman's report was referred to Dr. R. C. Tolman, chairman of NDRC's Division of Armor and Ordnance.

As a result, Hickman was called to Washington to head rocket development in Dr. Tolman's division. Goddard's early work thus became the starting point for the huge U. S. solid-fuel rocket development that mushroomed into existence a short time later.

Goddard was working for the Navy at Annapolis in 1944, on variable-thrust liquid-propellant motors, when the Germans launched their first calamitous V-2 rockets into London. He thus lived to see his dream of man's conquest of space begin to come to fruition. But he was not fated to witness the later high-altitude rocket shots that zoomed up from White Sands Missile Range to the very edge of space, or the launching of the first satellites, or the blast-off of the space probes, or the first tries at the moon. He died on August 10, 1945, at the age of 63.

Throughout his life Goddard was a happy man, despite the obstacles he encountered. He was basically a research man, a seeker after truth, along whatever paths were necessary. The joy of the struggle and the mapping of new territory were for him more important than popular recognition or material success. And partly for that reason, perhaps, it took the American people a long time to realize that they had themselves brought the space age into being, in the person of this quiet, gentle, persistent, and dauntless man.

Many still believe the German V-2 engineers were the originators of the modern rocket age. In the boldness of their conception, in the quality of their engineering, in their ability to command men, money, and materials for a major development, possibly they were. But it was Goddard from whom they received their original inspiration. Those German engineers now living in the United States give credit to him for the ideas, the imagination—and perhaps most important of all, the moral courage to risk injury, health, and professional reputation when all others doubted—to make a practical start on man's journey toward the stars.

The United States has at last begun to take belated notice of Goddard and his accomplishments. In 1959 Congress voted him posthumously the Congressional Gold Medal, one of the Nation's highest civilian awards. The Langley Gold Medal, one of aviation's rarest and highest honors, which since its inception in 1910 has been granted to only nine men, was awarded to Goddard early in 1960. The huge new research and engineering center of the National Aeronautics and Space Administration at Greenbelt, Maryland, has been named the Goddard Space Flight Center in his honor. Awards and honors are beginning to pile up.

But perhaps his most fitting memorials are the gleaming giants that thunder skyward from their launching pads at Cape Canaveral and Vandenburg Air Force Base, arching over the oceans in 6,000-mile shots, or sending satellites—and soon men—into the interplanetary spaces that Goddard, as a 17-year-old boy, set out so long ago to bring within man's reach.

Introduction

I

The rocket experiments in the series reported in this volume began in the fall of 1929 and ended 12 years later, in October, 1941.

They comprise the entire Goddard rocket development from the time of Dr. Goddard's now historic liquid-fuel rocket flight of July 17, 1929, at Auburn, Mass., until his acceptance of an assignment to carry on experimental rocket work for the United States Army and Navy at the beginning of World War II.

The first test included in the series occurred on December 3, 1929. Dr. Robert H. Goddard was then a man of forty-seven, and he had already spent nearly 30 years in studying rockets and experimenting with them. He was born at Worcester, Mass., on October 5, 1882. His early schooling was obtained in Boston, where he lived until he was sixteen. His college work was taken at Worcester; he was graduated from Worcester Polytechnic Institute in 1908, and became an instructor in physics there while pursuing graduate studies at Clark University. He received the M.A. degree from Clark in 1910 and the Ph.D. in 1911. He later joined the Clark faculty, where he rose from instructor to assistant professor and finally to full professor. He continued to be connected with Clark until 1943, part of the time on leaves of absence.

As a young professor of physics, Dr. Goddard made important studies on the conduction of electricity in powders, the development of crystal rectifiers, the balancing of airplanes, and the production of gases by electrical discharges in vacuum tubes.

In the 1912-1913 season he served as research fellow at Princeton University. During this period he produced the first laboratory demonstration of mechanical force from a "displacement current" in a magnetic field.

These investigations, however, were only more or less incidental to the real interest and accomplishment of his life. As early as 1899, when he was only seventeen, he began to speculate about conditions in the upper atmosphere and beyond, and to evaluate various proposed methods of reaching these regions physically, for exploration. A notebook of his, dating back to October 19, 1899, contains such speculations and mentions the possibility of employing rockets for this work.

In 1907 he prepared and submitted for publication a manuscript suggesting that heat from radioactive materials could be used to expel substances at high velocity from an orifice, thus furnishing jet propulsion sufficient to navigate in interplanetary space. The manuscript, still in existence, is an interesting document. It was ahead of its time, however, and was forth-rightly refused when Dr. Goddard submitted it seriatim to the *Scientific American, Popular Science Monthly,* and *Popular Astronomy.*

The idea of using hydrogen and oxygen as fuels for an interplanetary rocket, and the construction of such a rocket according to the multiple or step-rocket principle, occurred to him in 1909. After considerable calcula-tion he put the theory into satisfactory form in the winter of 1912-1913. His computations included the possible use of smokeless powder for the propellant, as well as hydrogen and oxygen.

His actual experimental work began about 1914, upon his return to Clark University as an instructor and honorary fellow in physics. The first tests were made with various types of ship rockets and were con-tinued with larger solid-fuel rockets constructed by himself.

By 1916 he had nearly reached the limit of what he could do with his own resources. In that year he began to seek support for his work, his principal instrument of solicitation being a lengthy technical paper he had prepared on rocket possibilities, which he submitted to several foundations and other prospective donors.

It was as a result of sending this paper to Dr. Charles D. Walcott, then secretary of the Smithsonian Institution, that he obtained his first grant of funds from that source. Most of his paper was later incorporated in the report entitled *A Method of Reaching Extreme Altitudes,* pub-lished in 1919 as a part of the *Smithsonian Miscellaneous Collections,* Vol. 71, No. 2. It has since been republished by the American Rocket Society in book form.

Total grants from the Smithsonian amounted to about $11,000. With this small sum Dr. Goddard laid the foundation for virtually all of his later achievements, and initiated the world-wide interest in rockets and jet propulsion which has become of major importance not only to scientists and engineers but to all men and nations.

II

After the entry of the United States into World War I in 1917, Dr. Goddard was assigned to explore the military possibilities of rockets. He succeeded in developing a number of promising military rocket devices. One of these was a rocket for long-range bombardment, the motor of which operated intermittently during flight, solid-fuel propel-lant charges being injected rapidly into the combustion chamber by a method similar to that used in loading repeating rifles.

He also developed several types of relatively short-range rocket projectiles intended to be fired by infantrymen at tanks or other military objectives, the firing mechanism being a simple launching tube held in the hands and steadied by two short legs. Some of these devices were in many respects similar to the "bazooka" of World War II, and were, of course, that weapon's progenitors.*

A number of these new weapons were demonstrated at the Aberdeen Proving Grounds on November 6 and 7, 1918, before representatives of the Signal Corps, the Air Corps, the Army Ordnance, and others. The demonstrations went off quite successfully, and the Air Corps representatives particularly expressed interest in continuance of the work, with experimental trials of Goddard rockets in actual combat. The Armistice a few days later put an end to the war, however, and also ended Army interest in rocket experiments for more than 20 years.

Dr. Goddard eagerly returned to his work on the development of high-altitude rockets, and the following ten years saw rapid progress. In that fruitful decade he first successfully used liquid fuels for rocket propulsion, and made the world's first liquid-propellant rocket shot on a farm near Auburn, Mass., on March 16, 1926. The site is now marked by a granite shaft erected by the American Rocket Society. He also made the beginnings of rocket flight control by gyroscope, the first application of instruments to record conditions on the rocket during flight, and many other significant contributions.

The period culminated in the rocket flight of July 17, 1929, to which Dr. Goddard refers at the beginning of his text in this book. The importance of this shot was not so much its success as a flight—though within the experimental meaning of the term it was successful—as in the attention it aroused. It led to near disaster, and also, through an interesting chain of events, to more adequate support of Dr. Goddard's work.

The flight of July 17, 1929, was the last of a series of tests conducted at a site on the farm of a relative, Miss Effie Ward, at Auburn, Mass. In his notes Dr. Goddard designated this series thus: "Test of Medium-Sized Rocket Having High Center of Gravity and Low Center of Air Resistance."

The total length of the rocket was 11 ft 6 in., its greatest width 26 in. and its total weight, empty, about 32 lb. It was launched from a metal tower 60 ft high, the rocket being guided up the tower by two $\frac{3}{8}$-in. vertical pipes. As propellants, 14 lb of gasoline were used, and 11 lb

* Associated in his work with Dr. Goddard were H. S. Parker and C. N. Hickman, then graduate students at Clark University. Dr. Hickman, in 1940, became one of the principal directors of rocket research and development under the National Defense Research Committee.

of liquid oxygen. The rocket carried an aneroid barometer, a thermometer, and a camera focused on both of these instruments, to be operated by a trip lever at the time of ejection of the parachute.

The rocket fired a total of 18½ sec. It rose about 90 ft above the ground, and flew a horizontal distance of 171 ft.

In this short flight it made a very considerable noise—sufficient to alarm the neighborhood. Evidently that July 17 was the kind of day on which sound travels well, for no such attention had been attracted by numerous previous tests at the same spot, of approximately equal noise and duration. But on this occasion neighbors sent in calls for ambulances, believing that an airplane had caught fire and crashed. Two police ambulances searched through Auburn for victims. An airplane was sent to investigate. As a result of all this commotion the shot produced an astonishing amount of publicity.

The sequels are most interesting. One of them was that Dr. Goddard was requested to call on the Massachusetts state fire marshal and explain, with the result he recounts in his text. A much happier sequel also occurred. The attention of Colonel Charles A. Lindbergh was attracted to Dr. Goddard's work, and Colonel Lindbergh brought it to the notice of Harry F. Guggenheim and his father, Daniel Guggenheim. There followed an arrangement for financing the work which made possible the accomplisments recorded in this book.

III

Dr. Goddard's work on the development of rockets falls into four well-defined periods.

The first, extending from 1899 until after World War I, was one of speculation, mathematical and theoretical development, and experiment with solid-fuel propellants.

The second, financed by the Smithsonian Institution and Clark University, comprised the years from the end of World War I until the shot of July 17, 1929. In this period Dr. Goddard laid the experimental basis for his subsequent work and demonstrated the feasibility of liquid propellants for rockets.

The third was the period from 1929 to 1941, financed principally by Daniel Guggenheim and later by The Daniel and Florence Guggenheim Foundation, during which the experimenter made great strides in the development and flight of large gyro-controlled, pump-operated liquid-fuel rockets, and all but had within his grasp the long-range and high-altitude flights toward which he had been working, the feasibility of which later was so dramatically demonstrated by the Nazis, in their 250-mile, 12-ton V-2 rockets.

The fourth period comprises the time from the beginning of World

War II until Dr. Goddard's death on August 10, 1945, during which he worked on important rocket projects including variable-thrust rocket motors and liquid-propellant jet-assisted takeoff for aircraft, at the Naval Engineering Experiment Station at Annapolis, Md.

The enormous volume of work he accomplished during his lifetime is the more remarkable in view of the fact that he was a lifelong sufferer from tuberculosis, which first became manifest in early manhood. Not only was there ill-health to combat, but he was hampered by lack of sufficient funds during a large part of his productive life. Added to this was the constant skepticism of the technical world generally toward rockets, and the sensational, distorted publicity and ridicule that from time to time burst into the press.

Dr. Goddard was to strangers a quiet, sensitive, scholarly man, reluctant to draw attention to himself. To intimates he was warm, friendly, witty, and unruffled in spite of all obstacles and discouragements. He was an accomplished pianist and enjoyed playing for his own and his friends' entertainment. He was also an artist of ability, painting in both water colors and oils.

In addition to his active technical imagination and his overwhelming interest in rockets, he possessed two qualities that were of utmost importance in his work. He was persistent, and he was methodical. To the first of these qualities is owed his steady, determined progress in a field so complex that probably no other engineering area exceeds it for difficulty. To the second the world may long be indebted for clear and precise records of everything he did, and a great deal of what he thought, in connection with his chosen field.

Among the materials and data on his work in existence at his death were the following:

1. Two large complete rockets, and miscellaneous rocket materials, including motors, fuel pumps, parts of early experimental models, fuel tanks, valves, and the liquid-fuel rocket tested in May 1926.

2. One complete large rocket, at the Smithsonian Institution, Washington, D. C.

3. Set of early notebooks, from 1899 to 1910.

4. Set of notebooks containing ideas and suggestions for experiments from 1924 to 1942; these ideas mostly having been embodied in rockets and rocket patents later.

5. Set of original notebooks in Dr. Goddard's handwriting, with photographs and pen-drawn sketches of ideas and apparatus, describing in great detail the liquid-fuel experiments from 1920 to 1943. These notebooks, transcribed by Mrs. Goddard in 1947, comprise about 5500 typewritten pages, 2600 photographs, and 500 pages of photostats of drawings.

6. A series of reports to the Smithsonian Institution and The Daniel and Florence Guggenheim Foundation. These comprise not only progress reports of work done under grants from these institutions but also ideas, suggestions for further work, and theories, including Dr. Goddard's speculations and calculations regarding interplanetary flight, which he felt it unwise to publish at the time of writing, between 1918 and 1929.

7. Several book-length and shorter manuscripts, including ideas and suggestions regarding rocket motors, fuel pumps, and ultimate possibilities in rocket development, as well as summaries or condensations from his notes covering two experimental periods—from about 1920 until 1929, and from 1929 until 1941. The latter is the material comprising this book.

8. Papers on 214 patents on rockets and rocket apparatus granted to Dr. Goddard between 1914 and 1956.

9. Many other items, including motion pictures of all the rocket tests and flights; lantern slides of experimental work; about 3000 photographs; biographical material, diaries, correspondence, and a library of early rocket literature which was later presented to the Institute of the Aerospace Sciences.

IV

The summaries of his experimental notes presented in this volume were prepared by Dr. Goddard apparently in 1944 and 1945. Mrs. Goddard believes he prepared them as he could find time between tests and development work connected with his Navy projects.

Although the summaries as found were not in final shape for publication, only a minimum of editing was necessary to prepare them for the printer. The changes were principally to provide uniformity of presentation, some condensation, and minor clarification of certain passages.

The only important changes from the original Goddard text are in Sections 3 and 11. In Section 3 data have been omitted on a number of investigations because they seem of secondary interest, in the light of later developments. These have been listed in the editors' note at the beginning of the section. This section retains the data on work that became important to Goddard rocket developments later, and also the interesting and significant experiments made by Dr. Goddard in 1932-1933 on devices that must be looked upon as precursors of the resojet and ramjet engines.

Section 11, a condensation made by the editors from Dr. Goddard's original notebooks, follows his general style as far as possible. His own summary ends with the pump-rocket tests recorded in Section 10.

In his notebooks Dr. Goddard did not number his experiments or give them series names until after the resumption of his tests in New Mexico in September, 1934. The previous tests were identified by date only. After 1934 he carried out four series of tests, which he identified by the key letters A, K, L, and P. Dr. Goddard's earlier method of identifying each test by date has been preserved, but for convenience a few descriptive words suggesting the nature of the test have been added as a title. Subheads have been supplied in the text at many places in the earlier portion of the manuscript, following a style Dr. Goddard himself established in the latter parts.

In the later portions Dr. Goddard's letter and number identification of his tests have been retained, in parentheses, as a key to possible future cross references with the full text of his notebooks.

Limitations of space have precluded the use of any large portion of the drawings and photographs in Dr. Goddard's notebooks covering the period. We have selected illustrative material thought to be most useful in making the text clear and have regretfully omitted the rest.

The difficulties inherent in editing another person's work, especially when he is not available for counsel and guidance, have been abundantly brought home to us, as well as a sense of our own shortcomings in the face of so significant and important a task.

ESTHER C. GODDARD
G. EDWARD PENDRAY

Worcester, Mass., and New York, N. Y.

Rocket Development

two tangential holes, No. 60; and the axial hole in the small end plug, No. 79.

These small spray heads or plugs were mounted in square nickel tubes that supplied the two liquids, the ends of these tubes being closed. Between each pair of $7/16$-in.-O.D. square gasoline tubes, with bases in the plane of the head end of the chamber, a $1/2$-in.-O.D. square oxygen tube was placed, with the sides making 45 deg with this plane. By this arrangement the sprays were caused to intersect as described above. The proportion of oxygen to gasoline was made as nearly as possible that for complete combustion. The 28 liquid-oxygen orifices gave 10.9 oz/sec of water at 20 psi; and the 14 gasoline orifices gave 2.94 oz/sec of water at the same pressure.

The whole system of square tubes was mounted for convenience in a thin four-sided sheet-steel pyramid. All the surfaces of the square tubes except the orifices were encased in a refractory cement, two holes being provided to equalize the pressure on both sides of the cement covering. A liquid-curtain tube was located between the nozzle end of this pyramid, where the spray orifices were located, and each of the four walls of the square-sectioned chamber. This tube consisted of a square, formed of $1/4$-in.-O.D. steel tubing; it had No. 79 holes spaced $1/16$ in. apart and produced streams that struck the chamber wall at an angle of 16 deg, this angle having been found by experiment to produce the smoothest curtain on a flat piece of steel. The 272 holes gave a flow of 9.2 oz/sec for water at 20 psi. Strainers of 50-mesh copper gauze were used in both feed lines.

Chamber and nozzle. Both the chamber and the nozzle, of 24-gauge sheet steel, were of square cross section, the former being strengthened against bulging by two bands, each of 1- $\times$ $3/16$-in. iron. The chamber was $10\frac{1}{2}$ in. long and 5 in. wide, with a $2\frac{3}{4}$-in. long pyramidal part at the bottom, ending in a 1.05-in. square throat (equivalent to a $1\frac{3}{16}$-in. diameter circle) from which a 14-in. nozzle, $3\frac{1}{2}$ in. square at the end, projected. The completed chamber weighed 5 lb.

Test. In the test of December 3, no flame appeared until a short time after pressure had been applied, when the chamber exploded. This explosion was found to have been due to the long gasoline pipe line from the tank to the chamber. In order to avoid the use of a valve and at the same time to avoid siphoning, this line had passed up over the gasoline tank and hence had delayed the admission of the gasoline until a considerable amount of oxygen accumulated within the chamber.

Test of December 5, 1929:
Dent-Type Injector

A further test was attempted in which solid cones of spray were formed by injectors having less heat capacity than the plugs just described. These injectors consisted of conical dents, or depressions, in the square nickel tubes. Three equidistant holes were drilled in the side of each dent, halfway from base to vertex, these holes being normal to the surface. It will thus be seen that the heat capacity was no more than that for the plain square tubes.

The dents for the oxygen were 0.164 in. deep inside and contained three No. 75 holes. Those for the gasoline were 0.138 in. deep and contained three No. 77 holes. The holes in the four curtain tubes were No. 75 and were spaced $1/8$ in. apart.

Delay in bringing gasoline to the chamber, on starting, was avoided by connecting the gasoline delivery tube from the gasoline tank directly to the combustion chamber, a gasoline valve being used in this line. In the test, the gas-generator chamber vent was accidentally left open and the pressure thus rose to only 25 psi. The lift was 25 lb, and the chamber bulged somewhat between the reinforcing bands.

Test of December 7, 1929:
Dent-Type Injector

In this test the gasoline flow decreased soon after the start, thus allowing the nozzle to become overheated and to burn through just below the throat. The decreased gasoline flow appeared to be due to the orifice tubes having become cooled to such an extent, during the precooling of the oxygen orifice tubes that took place while the oxygen tank was being filled, as to freeze the gasoline, or at least to retard its flow.

Test of December 14, 1929:
Dent-Type Injector

At the start of the test the gasoline flame accompanying the opening of the gasoline valve was allowed to burn for 4 or 5 sec before gas pressure was applied, in order to avoid brittleness of the combustion chamber due to low temperature.

Soon after the gas pressure reached 50 psi, the combustion chamber broke and burned through on one side. Apparently the chamber wall gave way before it became red-hot, indicating a fracture rather than failure of the gasoline cooling curtain. The lift during the last 2 sec of run was 146 lb. Since the run lasted 6 sec, during which $2\frac{1}{2}$ lb of gasoline and 6 lb of liquid oxygen were consumed, an idea of the average jet velocity could be obtained by assuming that the average thrust was 100 lb and that the above weights of liquids were used during the propulsion period. This velocity was found to be 2250 ft/sec.

Test of December 23, 1929:
Dent-Type Injector, Cylindrical Chamber

A chamber and nozzle of circular cross section were used in this test, in order to reduce the danger of fracture. Both were made of 0.031-in. sheet spring steel. The injection system consisted of dent-type orifices, as above described. The thin steel frustum of cone in which the injection system was located was set in a circular steel band, outside of which was the circular curtain tube, this frustrum being brazed in a flat plate, or ring, itself welded to the circular wall of the chamber.

In the test the welded joint between the cylindrical part of the combustion chamber and the flat plate at the head, through which the cone frustum containing the injection system projected, broke at the edge when the gas pressure had risen to 150 psi and was still rising.

Tests of February 4, 1930

In order to make two tests of combustion chambers on the same day, duplicate rockets were constructed, these being the same in all respects except for the combustion chambers and the crosspiece at the top, to which the spring-balance chain was hooked. A single crosspiece was used, the two supports of the rocket consisting of piping and being bolted interchangeably to this crosspiece.

An indicator was made in order to show when the vent valve on the oxygen tank was closed at the beginning of the run.

First test: plug-type injectors. The combustion chamber, of circular cross section, used in the first test of February 4 was of the small plug injector type. The top plate, of $\frac{1}{32}$-in. sheet steel as before, was crimped along the edge so that the edge section was a quarter circle of $\frac{1}{4}$-in. radius, the change being made in order to avoid the severe stress along this edge that had occurred in the test of December 23. This crimped plate was brazed to the outside of the cylindrical wall of the chamber.

After 2 sec of 130 lb lift, the cylindrical wall of the combustion chamber burned through at two diametrically opposite places, each $3\frac{1}{2}$ in. below the top of the cylindrical part and at points farthest removed from the two entrance tubes supplying the circular curtain tube, where the pressure at the small holes of the curtain was least.

Second test: dent-type injectors. In this test the chamber was also of circular cross section, and the injection system consisted of the perforated dents in square nickel tubes as above described.

A run of 4 sec was obtained at a pressure varying from 75 to 150 psi, it being necessary to relieve the pressure in the gas-generating chamber occasionally. The lift reached 130 lb. At the end of the above period the chamber burned through at a point $2\frac{1}{2}$ in. below both the top of the cylindrical part and a corner of the square-tube injection system, the burning taking place soon after the chamber became red at this point.

The reason for the burnout did not appear to be related to the gasoline curtain but, instead, seemed due to the nature of the sprays produced by the dents, since the refractory cement between the square tubes was found to have been fused to a considerable extent. Inasmuch as drops accumulating on the walls of the dents amounted to somewhat under 10 per cent of the total flow, because of spray striking the inner wall of the dent, it appears likely that this runoff from the various dents collected on the cement and caused intense heating of the refractory surface.

Tests of March 4, 1930

In view of the rather serious heating in the preceding test with dent-type injectors, it was decided to test plug-type injectors in two ways: first, using a large number, mounted in square tubes as described, with several feed tubes supplying a ring-shaped gasoline-curtain tube; and second, using a comparatively small number of mixed sprays, all meeting at a common focus, with the gasoline introduced tangentially at the head end of the cylindrical part of the chamber, in order, if possible, to provide a more effective cooling means than the curtain described above.

In both tests the oxygen orifices were precooled by pouring liquid oxygen into a 4-in.-long side tube on the oxygen-supply line, just above the chamber. This tube extended upward at an angle of 45 deg with the horizontal. Further, an indicator was used to show when the gasoline valve had become fully open. This consisted of a 2- × 9-in. blackened steel strip on the arm of this valve, so positioned that it appeared edge-on when the valve was fully open.

First test: small number of plug-type injectors. The chamber having a small number of injectors was provided with an upper 60-deg end cone of $\frac{1}{32}$-in. sheet steel lined with a $\frac{1}{4}$-in.-thick Alundum cone. The side wall was cylindrical, 10 in. long and $4\frac{1}{8}$ in. in diameter, the throat was 1 in. and the 9-in. nozzle had an open-end diameter of $2\frac{5}{8}$ in.

Ten plug-type injectors were used alternately, five for each liquid and at equal distances apart, all being located $\frac{31}{64}$ in. above the base of the Alundum cone as measured upward along the inside. They were directed inward, perpendicularly to the wall. All these nozzles were of steel, $\frac{15}{64}$ in. I.D., with rounded ends having axial holes. The hole size was No. 52 for the liquid-oxygen nozzles and No. 65 for the gasoline.

The rotators, to produce solid spray cones, were of brass, $\frac{1}{4}$ in. in diameter and 0.08 in. thick, with inclined grooves. Those for the oxygen had grooves consisting of 10 saw cuts, 0.016 in. wide and 0.085 in. deep, making an angle of 30 deg with the plane of the disk. Those for the gasoline had 10 saw cuts, 0.016 in. wide and 0.035 in. deep, making an angle of 40 deg with the plane of the disk. All the nozzles gave spray cones of about 60-deg angle, and in water tests came together at a focus about 1 in. wide and 1 in. above the bottom of the Alundum cone. The rates of flow, with water at 20 psi, were 3.7 oz/sec for the oxygen orifices and 0.21 oz/sec for the gasoline orifices.

The tangential liquid sheet, replacing the curtain, was produced by two

⁷⁄₁₆-in.-O.D. steel tubes, each flattened at the end to form a slotlike opening
¹¹⁄₁₆ in. long and ¹⁄₆₄ in. wide. These tubes, located on opposite sides of the
cylinder of the chamber, together produced a tangential sheet of gasoline
covering the chamber wall and nozzle. For the tangential orifices the flow
for water at 20 psi was 5.36 oz/sec. The completed chamber weighed 4 lb
(Fig. 2).

In carrying out this test the gasoline valve was not fully opened at
first, and when it became opened a short time after the start, an explosion
was heard, followed immediately afterward by flame appearing from a
hole in the lower cone of the chamber. The flame seemed to take place
after a fracture of the chamber had occurred, rather than to be a burning
of the chamber, since it was preceded by no appreciable red color on the
surface. Possibly the explosion resulted from the sudden increase in rate
of gasoline flow when the valve opened fully. The pressure rose from 50
to 75 psi, the lift becoming 70 lb for a second or so.

It was suggested at the time that a large number of small sprays might
be employed, covering a large part of the chamber wall surface; that the
sprays might be directed toward a refractory wall, such as the Alundum
cone; and that possibly the sprays "do not intermingle, in the rocket, as
water sprays do in tests with water in both sets of nozzles."

Second test: large number of plug-type injectors. The spray system in
this test, in which a large number of injectors were used, consisted of the
small plug-type orifices in square tubes, as tested February 4 and already
described, with a round perforated curtain tube supplied by six feed
tubes, spaced at equal intervals instead of at the two diametrically opposite ends of the curtain tube as before. The priming tube, for cooling
the oxygen orifices, was not used in this run except for a short time after
the oxygen tank had been filled.

The lift rose to 150 lb in 3 sec and remained at this figure for 4 sec,
when the chamber burned through at the lower end of the cylindrical
part. A red color appeared for a short time before the burning through
took place. After the test it was found that parts of the refractory cement
covering over the square-tube system had melted and that the small flat
plug in one of the oxygen-orifice plugs had dropped off, thus producing a
stream, rather than a spray, from this particular orifice.

It appeared that precooling had not been adequate and that possibly
the gasoline tank had become empty sooner than the oxygen tank. The
protection afforded by the curtain was shown to have improved, however,
inasmuch as burning did not take place near the top of the cylindrical
part of the chamber.

Tests of March 13, 1930

From the tests made with a large number of small spray orifices, both
of the plug and of the dent types, it appeared likely that the jet velocity

obtainable in this way would not exceed that for the July 17, 1929 test, in which a single hollow spray cone of oxygen, and simple tangential feeding of the gasoline, were employed.

Hence it appeared desirable to check, as closely as possible, the performance of the chamber, using 10 spray nozzles in the upper cone, with that of a chamber made as nearly as possible like that of the July 17 test.

The small piece of sheet steel on the gasoline-valve arm, to indicate when this valve was opened, was painted white in order to give clearer visibility.

First test: single oxygen-orifice chamber. The combustion chamber used in this test was as nearly as possible like that used in the test of July 17, 1929. The cylindrical part was 10 in. long, of $\frac{1}{32}$-in. soft steel, $4\frac{1}{8}$ in. in diameter, with a 60-deg lower cone, a 1-in. throat, and a nozzle 10 in. long and of $2\frac{3}{4}$-in. large diameter.

The 60-deg upper cone was lined with an RA 98 Alundum cone, having a hole at the top for the liquid-oxygen injector, which consisted of a $\frac{1}{2}$-in.-I.D. steel plug having a hemispherical inner end in which was an axial No. 28 hole. A rotator in this orifice piece served to produce a hollow spray cone of nearly 60-deg angle, as tested with water. This rotator consisted of a $\frac{1}{64}$-in.-round disk, cut at eight places radially along the edge, with the tabs thereby produced twisted to make an angle of $27\frac{1}{2}$ deg with the plane of the disk.

The two gasoline orifices were on opposite sides of the top of the cylindrical part and consisted of tubes having flattened ends, providing slotlike orifices $\frac{1}{2}$ in. by $\frac{1}{64}$ in. In water tests at 20 psi pressure, the oxygen orifice gave 3.2 oz/sec, and the gasoline orifices, together, 5.4 oz/sec.

In this run the pressure produced by the gas-generator chamber rose above 150 psi, and when it reached 175 psi the liquid-oxygen tank broke. The lift, lasting about a second, was 100 lb, and the short white flame was not surrounded by a reddish gasoline-air flame.

Second test: multiple spray-nozzle chamber. The object of this test was to repeat the first test of March 4, 1930, in which five spray nozzles were used for each liquid, all having a common focus, together with tangential gasoline cooling of the chamber wall. The chamber was the same as before, except that in repairing it the length of the cylindrical part was reduced by $\frac{1}{2}$ in., that is, to $9\frac{1}{2}$ in.

In conducting the test it was observed that the flame was very small, even though the pressure was 150 to 175 psi, apparently due to a reduced gasoline flow, the lift being under 6 lb. After 4 sec the nozzle burned through, and the run was accordingly stopped. It appeared likely that the reason for the small flow of gasoline was the cork float in the gasoline tank, which possibly became wedged between the guide wires during transportation of the rocket to Camp Devens, thus constricting the tank outlet.

Tests of April 5, 1930

The plan was to repeat the first test of March 4, 1930, using the chamber with the 10 orifices in the 60-deg upper cone, with the addition of a turbine propeller, and also to repeat as nearly as possible the test of July 17, 1929, using a chamber having a single oxygen-inlet nozzle and tangential gasoline cooling.

In order to facilitate inspection of the cork float in the gasoline tank before a run, a ½-in. pipe nipple was brazed into the lower end of the cylindrical part of the tank.

First test: multiple spray-nozzle chamber and turbine propeller. The chamber was that used in the second test of March 13, after being repaired.

The turbine propeller consisted of two support rings of ¼-in.-O.D. steel tubing, 11½ in. in diameter, held 1⅛ in. apart by 20 turbine blades brazed, at the top and bottom of the inner ends, to the outside of these two rings, with the upper edges of the blades vertical and the lower edges about 45 deg with the horizontal. These blades were 2¾ in. long in the radial direction, and 1½ in. wide. Inside the ring were four small air vanes or propeller blades, each 5½ in. long and 1½ in. wide. All the blades were of ¼₆₄-in.-thick steel, and all the joints were brazed. Any lifting force produced by the propeller blades was made visible by mounting the steel-tube axis of the turbine propeller on a rod, allowing 3⅝ in. upward motion of the propeller, the latter being held down normally by a light coil compression spring. The propeller was mounted vertically, the periphery of the turbine blades being ¼ in. from the axis of the rocket, the blades themselves being 4¼ in. below the bottom of the nozzle. The propeller when at its highest possible position still cleared the nozzle.

As soon as pressure was applied, a large, somewhat whitish cloud appeared, changing after a few seconds to a white flame, with the lower conical part of the chamber burning through soon afterward. The pressure did not rise rapidly and was not over 100 psi when the chamber burned through. The lift became 90 lb at 6 sec after the start. It appears likely that the precooling was not sufficiently thorough.

The action of the turbine propeller was as follows: the propeller began to turn rapidly as soon as the flame appeared. As the flame became brighter it turned very rapidly, and the individual blades finally became lost to view. The propeller stopped when the flame ceased.

All but seven of the turbine blades were found to have been pulled off. They were picked up over a considerable area, the farthest being 47 ft from the rocket. The brazing had apparently been melted at the bottom corner of the blades, and the steel of the blades had been torn at the upper corner. The under sides of the blades were blistered by heat, whereas the upper sides were not. It therefore appeared likely that most of the heating of the turbine blades took place after the chamber had burned through, when a large white flame appeared that rose through the turbine from below.

Second test: single oxygen-orifice chamber. The object of this test was to repeat the first test of March 13, 1930, in which a single liquid-oxygen orifice was used in a 60-deg cone on the chamber, the side wall and nozzle being cooled tangentially with the gasoline. A pressure of 200 psi was used, a 250-psi safety valve being placed in the pipe line from the gas-generating chamber to the rocket.

In the test a white flame appeared as soon as pressure was applied. The pressure varied between 175 and 225 psi, and the lift was between 90 and 100 lb from 8 to 25 sec after the start, when the nozzle burned through and the test was stopped.

The behavior during precooling, and the appearance and sound of the flame, all indicated a clogging of the liquid-oxygen supply line. This explanation was verified on an examination of the liquid-oxygen orifice, which showed that two of the vanes on the $\frac{1}{64}$-in. steel-disk rotator had broken off and had partly choked the orifice.

Tests of April 21, 1930

In the first of these tests, the preceding single oxygen-orifice chamber test was repeated at 200 psi pressure, with a turbine propeller in which the turbine blades were welded to the two tubing support rings. In the second a test was made of a combustion chamber and nozzle having a porous wall or liner.

First test: single oxygen-orifice chamber and turbine propeller. The chamber employed in this test was the same as that used in the second test of April 5, having a single oxygen spray inlet and two tangential gasoline orifices.

The original turbine propeller was modified by having the turbine vanes inserted in saw cuts in the two support rings and in having these vanes welded, instead of brazed, to these rings.

The run started promptly, the flame soon becoming steady, showing white inside and yellowish outside. The pressure varied between 175 and 225 psi, averaging 200 psi. The lift was 170 lb for 10 sec, and the gas velocity was estimated as 5400 ft/sec. The chamber was undamaged. The turbine lifted a small amount, at one time, and all but three of the turbine blades were found to be undamaged. Of these three, one was broken off and recovered 10 ft away, and the two adjacent blades were found to have been softened by heat.

The rate of flow of the gasoline for the tangential cooling of the chamber appeared to be more than adequate. The injury to the three propeller blades appeared to have been caused by too slow a rotation at the start, due to the small pitch of the blades and to the relatively large distance apart. The lack of any considerable lift of the propeller may have been due partly to the downward force of the rocket blast on the turbine blades and partly to the fact that the air-propeller blades were rather narrow. Further, being closer to the axis than the turbine blades, the air blades had a considerably lower velocity.

Second test: chamber with porous-wall liner. The chamber used in this test was of a porous-wall construction, the oxygen entering through a porous refractory cylindrical wall, lower cone, and nozzle. The gasoline entered through a single conical spray nozzle in a 60-deg steel cone lined with an Alundum cone, similar to the head end in which oxygen was introduced in the preceding test. The gasoline nozzle was ⅜ in. I.D. with a rounded inner end having a No. 45 axial outlet hole. The rotator had eight blades, each making an angle of 20 deg with the plane of the disk.

The cylindrical part of the chamber wall consisted of a Norton RA 1063 porous cylinder, 10½ in. long, with 4-in. bore and ½-in.-thick wall. The lower 60-deg cone, of the same material, had a ⅜-in. wall and tapered to a 1-in.-diameter throat. The nozzle, 10⅜ in. long, also having a ⅜-in. wall, widened to 2½ in. I.D. at the open end.

These three porous units were held firmly together by means of four ½-in. steel rods passing through two flat steel rings, one at the upper end of the cylinder and the other at the lower end of the nozzle. They were bolted on the outside to these rings, the bolts later being covered with brazing.

The junctions between the three units were filled with Alundum cement. Further, the lower half of the nozzle, and also the upper half except for four lengthwise strips ¼ in. wide, were covered with the same cement, in order to avoid too great a flow of oxygen through the nozzle wall, within which the pressure was relatively low.

The liquid oxygen was supplied through a ¼-in. O.D. steel tube in the form of a ring, directly below the flat upper steel support ring just mentioned. It was supplied by four feed tubes at equal distances apart. Number 60 holes were drilled in this ring-shaped tube at intervals of ⅛ in., the streams being directed so as to strike the middle of the cylindrical porous wall.

The ¹⁄₃₂-in. sheet-nickel outside jacket, or chamber wall proper, consisted of a cylinder 5⅞ in. in diameter and 10¼ in. long, and a lower conical part 10 in. long and tapering from 5⅞ in. to 4 in. The porous parts were kept centered in the nickel jacket by four ½-in.-wide U-shaped steel strips, held on the four rods mentioned above by clamplike action, with the outer ends of the strips resting against the nickel jacket at the lower end of the inner cylindrical wall. Refractory cement was used on the upper surface of the flat ring, at the nozzle, to avoid too great cooling of this ring by any liquid oxygen that might accumulate at the bottom of the jacket space. The weight of the completed chamber was 15½ lb.

While the oxygen tank was being filled before the test, a considerable amount of liquid oxygen passed through the delivery tube to the chamber, the top and bottom of the nickel jacket thereby becoming covered with frost, with small drops of liquid oxygen actually falling from the nozzle.

In the test the flame was long and dazzlingly white, and remained unchanged during the entire run, the pressure varying from 50 to 100 psi. The lift reached 42 lb after 3 sec, remaining constant thereafter for 7 or 8 sec. The average gas velocity, estimated for an 8-sec run with 42-lb thrust and a mass of liquids of 7 lb, was 1500 ft/sec.

After the run the chamber appeared undamaged, the Alundum nozzle not having been melted or glazed as had occurred previously in all cases where an Alundum nozzle liner was uncooled by inward flow. The liner parts broke, however, during the return trip to the laboratory, possibly owing to cracks which had developed in the walls during the run but which had not been noticed immediately afterward. The low gas velocity and the large outside flame may have been due in part to too low a rate of gasoline flow for the large throat diameter. More braces between the jacket and porous wall seemed desirable; also thinner porous walls, for the sake of lightness; and possibly a large number of gasoline-spray orifices, in order to confine the flame within the chamber.

Test of June 30, 1930:
Liquid-Oxygen Evaporator

In this test a chamber with a single oxygen-spray injector, together with tangential gasoline admission, was used. An outer jacket was provided in which liquid oxygen could be evaporated, thereby maintaining a constant pressure in the oxygen and gasoline tanks.

Chamber and evaporating jacket. The chamber was the same as that used in the first test of April 21, with the addition of the outer jacket, of $\frac{1}{2}$ in. greater radius than the cylindrical part of the chamber, tapering to a $3\frac{1}{2}$-in. radius at the wide end of the nozzle. Both the chamber and the jacket were of sheet nickel, except for the 60-deg upper cone of the chamber, which was of steel as before.

Inasmuch as evaporation was to take place in the jacket space, thereby cooling the chamber and nozzle walls, the flat tangential gasoline nozzles were reduced in width from 0.0156 to 0.0125 in., thus reducing the water flow at 20 psi pressure from 5.4 to 3.30 oz/sec, or to 61 per cent of the flow for the test of April 21. The oxygen nozzle flow remained at 3.2 oz/sec.

The liquid oxygen to be evaporated entered the top of the cylindrical part of the jacket by way of four $\frac{1}{2}$-in.-O.D. steel entrance tubes, and the evaporated gas left the bottom of the jacket space through two $\frac{1}{2}$-in.-O.D. steel delivery tubes. The liquid oxygen was thrown against the chamber and nozzle wall, and was prevented from falling directly to the bottom of the jacket space by a series of inclined perforated baffles.

Baffles. These baffles consisted of frustums of 60-deg-angle cones, of

0.005-in. sheet copper having 1/8-in.-diameter perforations. Three of these were used around the cylindrical wall of the chamber, one around the lower cone, and three around the nozzle. Each extended from the chamber, or nozzle, to the outer jacket and, owing to the inward inclination, tended to throw the liquid oxygen against the chamber or nozzle wherever it did not pass directly downward through the perforations.

The chamber and nozzle were centered inside the jacket by two flat perforated sheet-nickel rings, one 1/2 in. above the bottom of the cylindrical part of the chamber and the other at the throat of the nozzle. Both were secured to the outer jacket by brazing through small holes drilled in the jacket at intervals where the perforated rings touched the jacket. The completed chamber and jacket weighed 7 1/4 lb.

Pressure regulator. The flow of liquid oxygen to the jacket space was controlled by a disk valve having a conical edge, this disk being kept pulled upward against a valve seat in the bottom of the liquid-oxygen tank, except when flow was needed. The liquid passed downward through a 5/8-in.-O.D. steel tube to the jacket.

The pressure regulator, operating on this valve and located at the top of the oxygen tank, consisted of a 1 1/8-in.-O.D. metal bellows in a guide tube, the upper or closed end of which was connected to a rod extending down to the valve. Another rod extended upward, through an aluminum guide tube, to a yoke to which two 13-in.-long coil tension springs were attached, these tending to keep the valve rod pushed down, that is, to keep the valve open.

A perforated steel tube inside the bellows, the lower end of which was fastened to the tank, prevented collapsing of the bellows by the tension springs. The valve rod was in two parts, joined by a stiff coil spring, in order to avoid great tension on the rod at pressures so high that the oxygen tank tended to expand. The oxygen tank was made 1/2 in. larger in radius than the tank previously used, in order to provide enough liquid oxygen to furnish pressure for the gasoline tank as well. The adjustment was such that the valve rod moved upward 3/16 in. for a tank pressure of 200 psi. This rod was kept pulled upward before a run, thus keeping the valve closed, by two toggles, which raised a movable yoke and thereby stretched the two tension springs.

Test. In the test the igniter failed to fire, apparently having become moist after a previous attempt. The oxygen-gas pressure rose considerably over 100 psi, probably as high as 200 psi. Soon a stream of oxygen vapor was seen to emerge from the chamber, and the run was stopped. An examination showed that the cylindrical part of the chamber had bulged inward lengthwise in three places, these bulges being about 1 in. wide near the top of the cylinder and tapering down nearly to the lower cone. Owing to this distortion, the chamber wall had become separated from the jacket at the top of the chamber cylinder, this separation having caused the observed escape of oxygen.

It was suggested that collapse of the chamber wall might be prevented by several methods: by providing transverse stiffening ribs on the outside of the chamber wall; by attaching the wall to the outside jacket at a number of points; or by using a jacket having an inner and outer wall, the inner wall being in good thermal contact with the chamber.

The tests at Camp Devens were discontinued after the run of June 30, 1930, owing to the transfer of the work to a new location.

2

Early Experiments in New Mexico

October 29, 1930 — May 20, 1932

As has been stated, in the fall of 1929 Colonel Charles A. Lindbergh, who had learned of the rocket work during a conference in which jet propulsion was discussed, called upon the writer at Clark University. An outline of the work in progress was presented to him, and motion pictures of liquid oxygen-gasoline rocket flights were shown.

Believing that work in this field would lead to important results, Colonel Lindbergh interested Mr. Daniel Guggenheim to the extent of agreeing to finance the rocket work for a 2-year period, to be followed by an additional 2 years if the members of an advisory committee decided that these were warranted by the results. Through the efforts of President Wallace W. Atwood, the trustees of the University voted to grant the 2 or 4 years as a leave of absence.

East central New Mexico was selected as being the most promising location, both in climate and terrain, after an investigation of weather records with Dr. Charles F. Brooks, then professor of meteorology at the University.

Fortunately there was an attractive city in the region decided upon, and the research group, together with a considerable amount of machinery and equipment, moved in July, 1930, from Worcester to Roswell, where the writer occupied a large Spanish-type house on Mescalero Ranch, an 8-acre plot about three miles from the city.

Here were erected a shop, of 35×50 ft floor space, at the rear of the ranch house; a 20-ft tower, for making static tests, about 200 ft from the shop; and the 60-ft tower formerly used at Camp Devens for flight tests, about 15 miles to the northwest of Roswell.

A number of static, or proving-stand, tests were first made, in the tower near the shop. This tower was constructed of ³⁄₁₆-in.-thick galvanized angle iron and was surrounded by a corrugated-iron shield, 20 ft high. The formation of a dust cloud around the tower during a run was avoided by the use of a concrete gas deflector, or block of concrete, of 3-ft-square cross section; the gases from the rocket were directed downward into an 8-in.-

diameter hole, beveled at the top, this hole turning and passing out at the rear of the sheet-iron shelter.

The gas-generating chamber from Camp Devens was bolted to the left front corner post of the tower, when in use. The testing crew remained within a wooden shelter covered with corrugated iron, located 55 ft from the tower. It was provided with a narrow horizontal slot for observation and a lower horizontal slot for the control cords.

Test of October 29, 1930:
Single Oxygen-Orifice Chamber, Liquid-Oxygen Evaporator

The chamber used in this test, of $\frac{1}{32}$-in. soft sheet steel, was of the type used previously in which the oxygen entered as a hollow spray cone, at the apex of a 60-deg Alundum-lined cone at the top of the chamber, and the gasoline entered tangentially at the top of a cylindrical part, at two diametrically opposite points. The dimensions were the same as for previous chambers having this construction.

Oxygen evaporator. A jacket in which oxygen-gas pressure was produced by evaporation, to supply the oxygen and gasoline tanks, was used again, but only around the nozzle and the lower cone of the chamber, in order to avoid possible collapse of the cylindrical wall. This jacket tapered from a diameter $\frac{1}{2}$ in. larger than the cylindrical part of the chamber, at the level of the upper cone edge, to $3\frac{1}{4}$ in. at the $2\frac{1}{2}$-in.-diameter nozzle opening. It was $12\frac{3}{8}$ in. high.

As before, there were three thin perforated-copper conical deflectors, to throw descending liquid oxygen inward against the nozzle, and one on the lower cone. The jacket was held, by brazing through holes, to a perforated sheet-nickel ring around the throat of the nozzle. The same four $\frac{1}{2}$-in. steel entrance tubes for the jacket were at the top of the jacket, but the two opposite outlet tubes previously at the bottom were now located at the top.

It was planned to apply pressure from the gas-generating chamber until the pressure rose to 100 psi, when the bellows pressure regulator, as previously used on the oxygen tank, was to take over and supply pressure from the nozzle jacket. A white strip was used on the top of the oxygen pressure regulator to indicate the motion of the latter.

Test. In the test the pressure rose rapidly to 200 psi, when the vent cord was pulled. The pressure fell to 150 psi and remained there. The lift rose to 140 lb after 9 sec, fell to 80 lb after 15 sec, and thereafter remained at 80 lb until a total of 20 sec had elapsed. The flame varied considerably, disappearing almost entirely during the final three seconds or so of the run.

Since the pressure-regulator valve appeared to have been closed during most of the run, the sustained pressure was probably produced by a considerable amount of liquid oxygen entering the jacket initially. The jacket, however, did not become covered with frost during the run. After

20 sec the gasoline tank exploded, probably owing to failure of the cork float to descend and shut off the gasoline.

After the run it was found that the nozzle had become nearly closed by collapsed places extending along the entire length. The gradual decrease of flame length indicated that these places were produced by heating rather than pressure, since the pressure was highest at the beginning.

Test of November 11, 1930:
Repeat Test, with Stronger Jacket and Higher Tank Pressure

The object of this test was to obtain tank pressure with a jacket capable of withstanding the required internal pressure without danger of collapsing, and also to operate the rocket at an increased tank pressure.

Changes and additions. The chamber was similar to that previously used. The jacket consisted of sixteen 1/4-in.-O.D., 1/32-in.-wall copper tubes extending axially between two 1/2-in.-O.D. steel manifold tubes located along the nozzle and the lower cone of the chamber. The oxygen entered the lower manifold through two tubes on opposite sides and left the upper manifold in the same manner. In order to break up drops, each copper tube was provided inside with a 1/32-in.-diameter galvanized-iron wire extending lengthwise and having occasional bent places extending from side to side. The chamber weighed 3 lb without the jacket and 5 lb with it.

The guides for the cork float in the gasoline tank were made more rigid, and a pipe plug was used in the side of the tank in order for the float to be observed just before the run. The crossbar support for the rocket was arranged to be held by chains, so that the rocket could be removed between runs, while the heavy side weights remained in place. There was also a lift recorder, consisting of a paper-covered tin drum on which the lift trace could be made by a pencil while the rocket was suspended from a 500-lb spring balance. This drum was driven at the rate of one revolution in 10 sec by the works of an alarm clock.

Test. In the test the pressure rose as usual when the pressure-generating tank was operated but fell as much as 50 psi each time the tank was shut off. For this reason the toggle holding the pressure-regulating valve open, thus allowing oxygen to pass to the copper-tube jacket, was not pulled to free the valve until the pressure had risen to 200 psi.

The chamber became red-hot within a short time and finally burned at the throat. This result appeared to be due to too meager a supply of gasoline, which in turn was due either to the gasoline orifices' being too small or to the gasoline valve's not opening fully when the control cord was pulled.

Test of November 24, 1930:
Repeat of Previous Test

A repetition of the previous test was attempted, precautions being taken to make certain that the rate of gasoline flow was adequate.

Changes and additions. New gasoline-entrance orifices were made, $\frac{1}{2}$ in. long as before but 0.014 in. wide instead of 0.0085 in., the total water flow for the two orifices being increased from 3.7 to 7.5 oz/sec at 20 lb pressure.

The iron baffle wires in the copper jacket tubes were modified by winding the wire into a spiral on an 0.08-in.-diameter rod flattening each half inch of length in alternate planes at right angles, and then pulling the resultant form out until the flattened corners became V's.

An electric contact arrangement was used to indicate, by means of a light at the shelter, when the gasoline-valve arm had been moved to the fully open position at the start.

Test. As soon as the pressure produced by the gas-generating tank had risen to 150 psi, the toggle joint allowing liquid oxygen to pass through the regulating valve to the copper-tube jacket was freed, the pressure then rising to 200 psi, where it remained for a number of seconds.

A large flame appeared, the color of which indicated an excess of gasoline, this being accompanied by a low lift. After the run the large gasoline excess was accounted for by one of the gasoline-entrance orifices, consisting of the usual flattened tube end. It had widened considerably, becoming over $\frac{1}{32}$ in. wide at the middle. The change of shape had evidently been produced by heating when the upper cone was brazed to the cylindrical part of the chamber.

Test of November 26, 1930:
Repeat Test

In this test, no changes were made except to prepare new gasoline-entrance orifices in the chamber, these being $\frac{1}{2}$ in. long, as usual, and 0.0125 in. wide, giving 6.5 oz/sec of water at 20 psi for both orifices together.

Five seconds after the start of the test the gas-generating tank was shut off and the toggle was freed. The pressure rose to 200 psi at 12 sec and was 250 psi at the end of the 18-sec run.

The toggle, or regulator, valve remained open for only 3 sec—long enough, however, for the liquid oxygen remaining in the tubes leading from the tank to the bottom of the copper-tube jacket to maintain the pressure thereafter. This valve may have opened slightly during the last few seconds of the run, thus accounting for the final rise of pressure.

The lift varied considerably but averaged about 100 lb.

Test of December 10, 1930:
Static Test of Pressure Rocket

The object of this test was to determine whether sufficient pressure for flight tests could be obtained by the simple means of a large gas pressure-storage tank, together with the removal of the felt insulation around the oxygen tank just before the start.

Tanks and equipment. It was first planned to store the gas in a large liquid-oxygen tank containing a relatively small amount of liquid oxygen. The pressure in such a tank fell considerably, however, although reaching a fairly constant value, and it was therefore decided to use gas at normal temperature. The pressure-storage tank for this purpose was located in the middle of the rocket, the gasoline tank being above and the oxygen tank below, with the combustion chamber at the bottom. A 5-in. space was allowed between the tanks.

The oxygen tank was a cylinder with conical ends, of the same dimensions as before, namely, 5⅜ in. in diameter and 9½ in. long. Without the felt covering, it weighed 3½ lb. The gasoline tank was of approximately the same capacity as that previously used, having a cylindrical part 6 in. in diameter and 13½ in. long, provided with 60-deg conical ends. The weight was 4½ lb. The gas or pressure-storage tank had a 9-in.-diameter cylinder 20 in. long, with 60-deg conical ends, and weighed 10 lb. Both liquid tanks were baffled by the use of floats, each consisting of a 0.020-in. duralumin disk with corks wired to the top and having ³⁄₁₆-in.-O.D. duralumin guide tubes riveted underneath.

The pressure-storage tank was provided with a 350-psi pressure gauge, with a black mark at 225 psi to facilitate reading the pressure within the rocket tanks at the moment of release.

The gasoline line from the tank to the chamber was provided with a valve that could be opened by a control cord. The felt-wrapped liquid-oxygen line was used without valves. Draining or siphoning through the chamber was prevented by having the oxygen tube pass 7 in. above the top of the oxygen tank and thence down to the combustion chamber.

The top and bottom cones of the oxygen tank were covered with ½-in.-thick felt covered in turn with aluminum foil; these covers were not removed. The cylindrical part, however, was enclosed within two 1-in.-thick felt pieces covered with 0.008-in. aluminum foil and wired to two strips of perforated steel to facilitate pulling these coverings away.

For simplicity, an indicator to show when the oxygen-tank vent valve was closed and the light previously used to show when the gasoline valve was opened, were omitted.

The rocket was 11 ft long over all and weighed 33½ lb.

Test. In carrying out the test it was found that the pressure of oxygen in the gas-supply tank could not be raised over 200 psi, owing to a leak at the hose connection. When the pressure was shifted from the storage tank to the two liquid tanks, it fell to 75 psi. Nevertheless, the two felt pieces were pulled off, and the pressure then rose to 125 psi and remained there, owing to the evaporation of the oxygen. In fact, frost could be seen on the oxygen tank throughout the run.

Test of December 22, 1930:
Flight Test of Pressure Rocket

The purpose of this test was to obtain a flight with the rocket provided with a pressure-supply tank, tested December 10, as few changes as possible being made in preparing the rocket for flight.

The rocket frame, to which the three tanks and the combustion chamber were bolted by means of nickel strips, consisted of two ¾-in.-O.D. square 17 ST aluminum tubes, one on each side. Four guides having three rollers each were used to retain the rocket between the pair of vertical ½-in. pipe guides in the tower.

Four 0.020-in.-thick 17 ST aluminum-alloy stabilizing vanes were used at the bottom of the rocket; these were 11 in. wide and 18½ in. high, with the inner edge ¼ in. from the chamber and nozzle. Across the bottom the width from tip to tip was 24¾ in. The 6-ft-diameter pongee parachute was contained within a cylindrical box or receptacle, of 0.008-in. sheet aluminum, at the top of the rocket. It was arranged to be pulled out when the wind, coming from below at the first part of a vertical descent, lifted off an 8½-in.-diameter, 0.008-in. conical aluminum cover that extended over the edges of the box.

No casing was used to cover the tanks and chamber of the rocket, and there was no attempt at streamlining the various parts, except in the use of the conical cap on the parachute box.

Test. The carrying out of the flight test was as follows: First, two gas-generating tanks were charged with liquid oxygen, and 200 to 250 psi pressure from these was supplied to the pressure-storage tank on the rocket; the gasoline valve and the valve allowing pressure to pass to the liquid tanks were then opened; the hose from the two gas generators was removed; and finally, after the rocket had risen a distance of 2 in. as shown by the coinciding of two white lines on markers, at the same time lifting two 19-lb concrete weights, the rocket was released by the pulling of two pins from the vertical pipe guides in the tower.

In this particular test the rocket was accidentally pulled from between the two pipe guides and was thus prevented from leaving the tower.

Test of December 30, 1930:
Repeat of Flight Test

The preceding flight test was repeated after several minor changes had been made.

Changes. The recess for the hose connection was chamfered out at a 5-deg angle to prevent binding, and the four roller guides on the rocket were more securely braced. The rear quadrant to the rocket from top to bottom, with the exception of the oxygen tank, was painted with Chinese red in order to make visible any axial rotation during flight.

Additional braces were used between the angle irons of the tower and the two vertical pipe guides. Further, a shelter, similar to that already used 50 ft from the tower, was constructed 1000 ft from the tower.

Test. In carrying out the test the storage-tank pressure was raised to 200 psi, and the hose was disconnected. The igniter was then fired, the gasoline valve opened, the oxygen-tank vent closed, and the gas pressure valve opened between the storage and liquid tanks. The rocket was allowed to rise 2 in. as before, and the pressure to rise to 225 lb before it was released.

The rocket rose rapidly within the 60-ft tower, reaching a speed of 60 or 80 mph. It headed into the 10- or 12-mph southwest wind, showing a short white flame unaccompanied by smoke. It finally became horizontal, the flame disappearing a second or so afterward. The rocket then left a grayish smoke trail and made a whistling noise heard easily half a mile away.

From the recording telescope record, the greatest height was 2000 ft, reached 400 ft from the tower in 7 sec. The firing time was 8 to 8.5 sec. The rocket landed about 1000 ft from the tower; since the parachute was not released, the upper part was damaged. It rotated about half a turn during the ascent.

From this test it was concluded that the thrust from the chamber was substantially axial with respect to the chamber, that there was little if any torque due to the propelling flame, and that no irregular motion need be expected with an adequate arrangement of baffles or floats in the tanks.

Test of January 15, 1931:
Cylindrical Combustion Chamber

In this test, which was the first of a series on combustion chambers, the liquid oxygen was fed tangentially, and the gasoline was introduced as a spray at the vertex of the upper cone of the chamber.

Apparatus. The combustion chamber consisted of an $8\frac{1}{2}$-in.-diameter, $4\frac{1}{2}$-in.-long cylindrical part, with a 120-deg lower cone and a 10-in. nozzle, all of sheet nickel. A 120-deg steel upper cone was lined with a $\frac{1}{4}$-in.-thick Alundum form.

The two opposite oxygen orifices consisted of $\frac{3}{8}$-in.-O.D. steel tubes, with the ends flattened to slots $\frac{1}{64}$ in. wide. The gasoline orifice consisted of a spray head, this being a small cavity of $\frac{1}{2}$ in. I.D. with four No. 54 drill holes entering tangentially. The opening into the combustion chamber was a No. 24 hole. The spray, using water at 20 psi, was in the form of a thin conical sheet of about 100-deg angle, breaking up into fine drops at about $1\frac{3}{4}$ in. from the orifice and becoming 1 in. wide at a distance of 6 in.

The water flow at 20 psi was 5.07 oz/sec for the two oxygen orifices together, and 1.05 oz/sec for the gasoline orifice. A jacket containing about

10 lb of water was used around the nozzle and chamber, extending to within about 2 in. of the top of the cylindrical part of the chamber.

Test. In the test the pressure, produced by a gas-generating tank, varied between 75 and 150 psi, the variation possibly being due to the cooling within the oxygen tank. The flame was short, noisy, and intensely white. It lasted for 15 sec, accompanied by a small lift, at most 30 or 40 lb. A part of the exposed end of the chamber cylinder showed redness of varying intensity, becoming brighter 4 sec from the end of the run and finally burning through.

The amount of liquids used appeared to be small, the gasoline being not over 1 lb.

Test of March 20, 1931:
Spherical Chamber

In the next test the chamber consisted of two 9-in.-diameter nickel hemispheres, $\frac{1}{32}$ in. thick, welded together to form a sphere, with the oxygen entering tangentially and the gasoline entering as an axial spray as before.

Apparatus. The two tangential oxygen orifices were No. 29 holes in hemispherical ends of $\frac{3}{8}$-in.-I.D. steel tubes. These were located $\frac{5}{16}$ in. above the equator of the sphere and together gave 6.6 oz/sec of water at 20 lb pressure.

The gasoline orifice, a $\frac{3}{8}$-in.-I.D. steel tube at the top of the sphere, had a conical end and was provided with a rotator, or spray element, consisting of a $\frac{3}{32}$-in. steel disk placed $\frac{1}{4}$ in. from the end of the hole. This disk had eight saw cuts, 0.018 in. wide, at an angle of 29 deg with the turbine axis and sufficiently deep to give a flow of 1.3 oz/sec of water at 20 psi. This spray head produced a hollow cone of 90-deg angle, about 1 in. wide where it struck the sphere.

The upper part of the sphere was protected by a perforated steel cone $\frac{1}{32}$ in. thick, $7\frac{7}{8}$ in. in diameter at the base, and having a $1\frac{3}{4}$-in.-diameter hole at the top, where it was welded to the upper hemisphere. The edge of this cone was $1\frac{1}{8}$ in. above the junction of the two hemispheres and $\frac{1}{4}$ in. from the wall. It was covered with a thick coating inside, and a thin coating outside, of a refractory cement mixture consisting of equal parts Insalute No. 1 and Alundum cement No. 1019. The weight of the chamber complete was $3\frac{1}{2}$ lb.

The nozzle opening was 1 in. in diameter, the corner being rounded. A water jacket, extending high enough to cover the chamber completely, was provided.

Test. A gas igniter was used in order to provide a sustained flame. It consisted of an inner and an outer steel tube, in which acetylene gas and air, respectively, were supplied under pressure. The flame was started by means of a small powder flare, and the igniter was below the nozzle.

The pressure was maintained at 150 lb. Over the 25-sec period of strong lift, the average lift, from the lift-time curve, was 71 lb. The average velocity was estimated as 3050 ft/sec; and the total heat given to the water, 323,000 small calories. After the test two holes were found to have been burned in the refractory cone.

Test of April 2, 1931:
Spherical Chamber

This test was similar to the preceding, with a greater flow rate of gasoline. The main alteration was in the gasoline-spray head. This consisted of a ½-in.-I.D. steel orifice tube with a No. 8 hole in a conical end and a rotator disk of ⅜₂-in.-thick steel having eight saw cuts 0.024 in. wide, 0.09 in. deep, and at 70 deg with the tube axis. The flow of water at 200 psi was 2.45 oz/sec.

The perforated steel form for the refractory cement was covered on both sides with iron screening, wired on as a reinforcement for the refractory covering.

The period of strong lift was 25 sec, and the integral of the lift-time curve was 2339. The amount of liquids used was 16.7 lb of oxygen and 3.43 lb of gasoline, the ratio being 4.85. The mean velocity was calculated as 3820 ft/sec, and the flame was 16 to 18 in. long. The heat given to the jacket was estimated as 364,000 small calories, this being under 1 per cent of the total heat of combustion of the gasoline used.

Test of April 13, 1931:
Spherical Chamber

This test was a repetition of the preceding, with the gasoline increased so as to be more nearly in the proper proportion with oxygen for complete combustion. A new rotator for the ½-in.-I.D. steel tube was ⅛ in. thick and was provided with six saw cuts along the side at 80 deg with the axis, 0.024 in. wide and ⁵⁄₃₂ in. deep. The orifice hole was of No. 1 drill size, the rotator being located ⅜ in. from this hole.

The average angle of the hollow spray cone was 90 deg, and the flow, with water at 20 psi, 3.15 oz/sec.

The run lasted for 18.5 sec; the lift-time integral being 1759 and the calculated gas velocity 3290 ft/sec. The amount of liquid oxygen used was 13.6 lb, and of gasoline 3.5 lb, making the ratio 3.88.

The heat conducted to the water jacket was 83,500 small calories, the relatively small amount possibly being due to the considerable amount of oxygen that passed through the delivery tube to the chamber while the oxygen tank was being filled, or possibly being attributable to the tank's being warm initially.

Test of April 22, 1931:
Spherical-Chamber Repeat Test

The preceding test was repeated with a longer nozzle but without other essential changes, in order, if possible, to obtain a greater velocity by expansion.

The gasoline orifice of April 2 was employed, the flow of water at 20 psi being 2.35 oz/sec. Two new oxygen orifices were made, giving a total flow of water at 20 psi of 7.2 oz/sec. The steel cone serving as a support for the refractory cement was 8 in. in diameter at the base, which was 1¾₆ in. above the middle of the sphere. The nozzle was 26⅝ in. long, of 1 in. diameter at the small end and 5 in. at the large end.

A run of 10 sec was obtained, at 200 psi pressure, but the lift was low. It was found afterward that the nozzle had burned through just below the throat.

Test of May 1, 1931:
Repeat Test

An attempt was made to test the spherical chamber with a long nozzle again, but the chamber exploded shortly after the pressure was applied. This result appeared to have been due to oxygen spray, formed when the oxygen first entered the chamber, striking a protuberance of brass ½ in. long and ⅜ in. in diameter, extending inward from the equator of the chamber, where the two hemispheres had been brazed together. Or the cause may have been too quick an application of pressure.

Test of May 4, 1931:
Repeat Test

A further attempt was made to test the spherical chamber with a long nozzle. This time when the pressure, applied rather slowly, reached 100 psi, a cloud of steam was seen over the water jacket, and an examination showed that the nozzle had again burned through just below the throat.

Test of May 9, 1931:
Repeat Test

The preceding test was repeated except for the addition of a refractory liner extending part way down the nozzle. This refractory lining extended downward from the throat a distance of 9⅝ in. and was ⅛ in. thick. It consisted of equal parts of Insalute and Alundum cement coated over iron wire screening held by nickel strips.

When the pressure had risen to 200 psi in the test, a cloud of steam was again seen to rise from the water jacket. An examination showed that all the cement had been melted and also that a hole had been burned in the nickel wall of the nozzle, 3½ in. down from the throat. The run lasted 9 sec, with the lift reaching 100 lb. The velocity appeared to have been rather high, being 3200 ft/sec, assuming the mass of liquids to have been 5.6 lb; or 4500 ft/sec, assuming the mass to have been 4 lb.

Test of May 19, 1931:
Cylindrical Chamber with Oxygen in Excess

One further test was made using oxygen in excess, but this time with a cylindrical chamber.

Chamber. The cylindrical part was 5 in. in diameter and 10 in. long. The upper and lower cones were of 90 deg, and were lined inside with Insalute-Alundum cement mixture, ⅛ in. thick, over iron wire screening, the lining in the lower cone extending to within ¼ in. of the throat.

The gasoline orifice was the same as that used in the test of April 22, and the two oxygen orifices were the same as in the preceding test.

The conical nozzle was 24⅜ in. long, increasing from 1 to 5 in. in diameter. Together with the throat, it was water-cooled by introducing water through a ¹⁄₃₂-in.-wide slot ¼ in. above the throat along the lower chamber cone, whose upper edge, forming the slot, was ¹⁄₃₂ in. less in radius than the lower part. This overhang of the upper part served to prevent gases from passing into this slot as they approached the throat. The water entered the slot from an outside cylindrical space supplied with water tangentially through a No. 50 hole, the flow at 20 psi water pressure being 0.97 oz/sec. In addition, a water jacket was used around the nozzle.

Test. During the test the pressure remained at 200 psi. The lift rose to 100 lb during the 17.5-sec run, the lift-time integral being 1417 and the average velocity 3020 ft/sec. The estimated weight of oxygen was 12.8 lb, and of gasoline 3 lb, making the ratio 4.27.

The tangential water flow in the nozzle was 3 oz/sec under full tank pressure. This internal water-cooling of the nozzle, although preventing burning or melting, nevertheless allowed 470,000 small calories to pass to the outside water jacket. The rather long nozzle apparently produced gas shock and overexpansion, as suggested by the appearance of the flame, which was 2 ft long, and intensely white, with irregular edges.

Test of May 23, 1931:
Large Cylindrical Chamber

Because of the apparent lack of advantage of tangential circulation of oxygen over gasoline, a return was made to a chamber cooled by the latter type of circulation, this chamber being sufficiently large to produce about double the previous lift.

Chamber and auxiliaries. The cylindrical part of the sheet-nickel chamber used was 5⅝ in. in diameter and 11 in. long. The upper 120-deg cone was lined with $\frac{1}{8}$-in.-thick Insalute-Alundum cement, applied over iron wire screening. The lower cone was also of 120 deg, and the nozzle was 14 in. long, with a $1^{13}\!/_{32}$-in. throat and a $3\frac{1}{2}$-in. end diameter.

The oxygen orifice consisted of an $^{11}\!/_{16}$-in.-I.D. steel tube having a hemispherical end containing a No. 7 hole. The spray was produced by a rotator of $\frac{1}{32}$-in.-thick sheet nickel having eight blades, each formed by a radial cut to a $\frac{3}{16}$-in.-diameter circle. These blades were bent to an angle of 20 deg with a plane at right angles to the axis. This rotator was brazed at the edges into a groove at the top of the inside of the orifice. The flow of water at 20 psi was 6.4 oz/sec.

The two tangential gasoline orifices were $\frac{1}{32}$-in.-wide slots, each in the pinched-together ends of a $\frac{1}{2}$-in.-O.D., $\frac{1}{32}$-in.-wall nickel tube. The total flow of water at 20 psi, for both, was 11.23 oz/sec. The total weight of the chamber was 5 lb.

A copper-tube jacket for producing pressure was used around the nozzle. This consisted of twenty-six $\frac{3}{16}$-in.-O.D. by $\frac{1}{64}$-in.-wall copper tubes, extending lengthwise from a $\frac{1}{2}$-in.-O.D. ring-shaped steel tube $\frac{5}{8}$ in. above the bottom of the nozzle to a similar ring-shaped steel tube at the top of the lower cone of the combustion chamber.

Iron wires, 0.028 in. in diameter and coiled into $\frac{1}{8}$-in.-O.D. spirals, were placed in these copper tubes for the purpose of breaking up drops of liquid oxygen. Two $\frac{1}{2}$-in.-O.D. steel tubes conveyed liquid oxygen from a pressure-regulator valve at the bottom of the oxygen tank to points on the opposite sides of the lower steel ring of the jacket, and two similar tubes led the evaporated gas up through a $\frac{5}{8}$-in.-O.D. steel tube to the pressure system of the rocket. The weight of the jacket was 2 lb.

The pressure-regulator valve was controlled by a metal bellows at the top of the oxygen tank, as before, but was modified so that, on rise of pressure, the first $\frac{1}{8}$ in. of upward motion caused the $\frac{3}{8}$-in.-diameter valve at the bottom of the tank to close, thus shutting off the flow to the nozzle jacket. The next $\frac{1}{16}$ in. of motion merely extended a safety tension spring placed in the rod between the bellows at the top of the tank and the valve opening at the bottom. During the last $\frac{1}{16}$ in. of possible travel, the top end of the rod pressed against the stem of a bicycle-tire valve, which served as a safety valve. This regulator was held by a toggle-joint linkage so as to keep the valve closed before the run.

A small sheet-iron tank containing carbon dioxide under 125 psi pressure was clamped to the tower and at the end of a run was opened to the gasoline tank, to dilute any explosive mixture.

Test. During the run the pressure fell from 175 to 150 psi, the rocket at the same time becoming somewhat tilted in the tower. The rocket was in good condition after the test, except for the lower edge of the refractory liner in the upper cone. The masses of oxygen and gasoline were, respectively, 12.8 and 14.5 lb, making the ratio 0.882. The integral of the lift-time curve was 2497, in pounds per second, and the calculated gas velocity was 3200 ft/sec. The lift, from 7 to 20½ sec after the start, averaged 143 lb.

Test of May 28, 1931:
Repeat Test

The object of this test was to repeat the preceding test with the rocket kept plumb in the tower.

The pressure was maintained automatically at 200 psi after being raised to this amount by the pressure-generating tank, except twice when pressure from the gas-generating tank was required. The amount of oxygen used was estimated to be 12.7 lb and the gasoline to be 17 lb, making the ratio 0.75. The integral of the lift-time curve was 2807, and the jet velocity 3200 ft/sec. The lift averaged 170 lb during most of the 19-sec run. Frost appeared on the copper-tube nozzle jacket for 3 in. up one side.

When the chamber was dismantled after the run, it was found that some of the refractory lining had dropped from the bottom edge of the upper cone, and also that one of the gasoline orifices had become widened under pressure, becoming nearly ⅟₁₆ in. wide at the middle of the slot.

Test of September 29, 1931:
Flight Test

The purpose of this test was to obtain a flight with a remotely controlled rocket of about 180 lb lift, with a copper-tube jacket, pressure regulator, and streamline casing.

Chamber. The construction of the chamber was the same as for the preceding test, except for a few minor changes. The oxygen orifice was provided with a No. 5 hole and gave a flow of water of 6.25 oz/sec at 20 psi. Together, the gasoline orifices gave 11.40 oz/sec.

The nozzle jacket was the same as before except that the copper tubes extended 3½ in. above the top of the lower cone, being in close contact with both this cone and the nozzle. It consisted of two halves, to facilitate installation around the chamber.

Tanks. The gasoline tank, a 9⅜-in.-O.D., 10-in.-long cylinder with hemispherical ends, weighed 9½ lb. The cylindrical part of the liquid-oxygen tank was 2⅝ in. long and 9⅜ in. in diameter with hemispherical ends; this tank weighed 5¾ lb.

The oxygen tank was supported above the chamber by three 1-in.-diameter, 0.018-in.-wall nickel tubes, each 14 in. long, and the gasoline tank was supported above the oxygen tank by similar tubes, each 10 in. long. All these tubes were connected to the pressure line by ⅛-in.-O.D. copper tubing. Those in contact with the liquid-oxygen tank were wrapped with felt to a distance of 3 in. from the tank. Both tanks were provided with baffles of 0.004-in. aluminum sheet at every 2 in. of height.

Other equipment. The pressure-regulator bellows was of ⅝ in. O.D. instead of 1⅛ in. as previously used. Two regulator springs extended along each side, so adjusted that an internal pressure of 130 psi caused the top of the bellows to start to rise; 210 psi produced a rise of ¼ in., and 230 psi one of ⅜ in. For falling pressure the corresponding distances and pressures were, respectively, ¼ in. at 190 lb and zero for 120 lb.

The streamline casing, of 0.020-in. duralumin sheet, consisted of a conical cap, 8½ in. in diameter and 24 in. high, on the top of the gasoline tank; a cylindrical part between the gasoline and liquid-oxygen tanks, of the same diameter as these tanks, with a door for the detachable pressure and control lines; and a jacket around the chamber and nozzle consisting of a short cylindrical part, with a conical part below tapering to the outlet opening of the nozzle. Two felt pieces were pulled from the side of the oxygen tank just before the rocket was released.

Four air vanes of 15¼ in. total width were provided at the rear of the rocket, having vertical outer edges 12¾ in. high, tapering to 18¼ in. where the tops of the vanes joined the jacket. The delivery tubes passed outside the tanks and casing, and were enclosed within two duralumin channel pieces each 5 ft 9 in. long.

The rolled parachute was fastened to one of the three steel support tubes between the gasoline and oxygen tanks. Release of the parachute was by a timed contact constructed from the works of a small watch. When contact was made, a half of the casing between the above two tanks was freed by an explosive pin containing a black-powder composition, the charge being fired by the aid of two small pencil-size dry batteries. The door that covered the parachute was forced outward by a spring.

The total length of the rocket was 9 ft 11 in.; the weight empty, 37 lb; and the estimated loaded weight, 87.2 lb.

Test. In operating the rocket by remote control, the procedure was as follows: pressure was applied, hoses and controls were removed, and releases were operated—all by falling weights freed by "exploders," or short aluminum tubes or links. Each exploder contained a blasting cap and was enclosed in a short length of 1½-in. pipe acting as a shield. Timing was accomplished by a weight in a dashpot containing kerosene, this weight being released by a similar means. The rocket was freed when the pressure rose to 190 psi, this pressure serving to release the hose and controls and to start the gyro timer, the arm used for this purpose releasing the lever holding the rocket.

In the flight test the rocket rose rather rapidly out of the tower and then appeared to lose thrust, rising to under 200 ft and then descending to the ground and passing along it, the gasoline tank finally exploding. The rocket was in the air for 9.6 sec, and the firing took place for 13 sec.

Test of October 13, 1931:
Flight Test

A further flight test was made with a rocket of the same general construction but having alterations of the chamber, parachute-releasing device, and rocket releases. Also, the rate of flow of gasoline was decreased in order to avoid low nozzle-jacket temperature and thus possibly to avoid a decrease of pressure during flight.

Fuel injection. Each of the two gasoline orifices in the chamber consisted of a small steel cup, or closed-end tube, of ½ in. I.D., a hole of rectangular section extending from the bottom at right angles to the axis, through a short lug. This hole was ¼ in. long, 0.081 in. wide, and ⅛ in. deep at the narrowest part of the lug. These cups were of advantage in permitting the ½-in. steel tubes leading gasoline to the chamber to be entirely within the tapered streamline casing at the rear of the rocket. The flow of water at 20 psi through both orifices together was 9.05 oz/sec.

The oxygen spray was produced by a deflector disk instead of by a spray head. This disk, of steel, was mounted on a 0.148-in.-diameter rod held centrally in the oxygen orifice, which consisted of a No. 2 drill hole in the rounded end of an otherwise closed steel tube. The deflector was ⁵⁄₁₆ in. in diameter, the upper edge being beveled to an angle of 62 deg with the horizontal. The oxygen leaving this edge formed a hollow spray cone that was everywhere ½ in. from the refractory cement lining of the upper cone. The water flow, at 20 psi, was 6.25 oz/sec.

Tanks and regulator. The same oxygen tank was used, but a new gasoline tank was made, having a 10½-in.-long cylindrical part, 9½ in. in diameter, with conical ends. Three 1-in.-O.D. nickel tubes and three 1-in.-O.D. steel tubes were used between the chamber and oxygen tank, and between the oxygen and gasoline tanks, respectively, as before, but none of these tubes was internally pressurized.

The same pressure regulator was used, having as before a ⅜-in. total motion, the valve in the bottom of the oxygen tank beginning to close at 165 psi and closing fully at 200 psi, and the valve rod reaching the upper limit of travel at 215 psi. These operations were the same for rising and for falling pressures.

Parachute and jacket. The parachute was enclosed in a cylindrical box of sheet tin, 11 in. long and 2½ in. in diameter, having a flat spring on the bottom. A door, on being released, allowed the parachute to be ejected by this spring. The same clockwork timer was used, set to eject the parachute 25 sec after the start.

The streamline jacket was similar to that of the preceding test, except that the bottom cone extended up to the oxygen tank, and the upper end of the casing consisted of a 120-deg cone on a long conical frustum. The various delivery tubes extended beyond the 9-in. cross section of the rocket only along the sides of the tanks, a dummy ½-in. aluminum tube being used opposite the ½-in. pressure tube, along the side of the gasoline tank, to equalize air resistance.

The length of the rocket was 7 ft 9 in., and the weight empty, 40 lb, the center of gravity being 1½ in. below the cylindrical part of the liquid-oxygen tank.

Test. In the test the pressure began to rise 5 sec after the start key was pressed, and reached 190 psi in 7 sec more, at which pressure the rocket was released. It rose rapidly through the tower and increased in speed thereafter, finally moving horizontally. During the last 2 or 3 of the 13 sec of firing, it moved from side to side, possibly owing to uneven feeding of oxygen. Two or three seconds thereafter, while traveling nearly horizontally, the gasoline tank exploded. The flame during the thrust period was bright yellow, about 10 ft long, indicating a considerable excess of gasoline.

Test of October 27, 1931:
Repeat Flight Test

This test was a repetition of the preceding except for decreasing the rate of flow of gasoline in order to increase the tank pressure, and for the installation of a valve device for shutting off the gasoline on a sufficient fall of supply pressure in order to avoid explosion of the gasoline tank.

Chamber and evaporator. The chamber was the same as in the preceding test except that the rectangular slots for the gasoline were 0.076 in. wide instead of 0.081 in. The lower end of the copper-tube jacket was raised 3 in. above the open end of the nozzle in order to provide space for steering vanes, to be added later. The upper end was also raised, to 2½ in. from the upper cone, in order to provide more tube area for evaporation. These changes brought the copper tubes into contact with two-thirds of the cylindrical part of the chamber, the lower cone, and part of the nozzle.

A cork float, bearing a valve seat at the bottom, was used for closing the flow in each tank as before. In the gasoline tank a spring that forcibly closed this valve device was released when the tank pressure fell to 100 psi. This was accomplished by a 1⅛-in.-O.D. bellows, kept collapsed by two springs on opposite sides until extended by pressure. This extension was an idling stroke, the return stroke pulling a pin which extended through packing and which released an axially located rod in the gasoline tank, this rod serving to push the cork float downward by a compression spring.

A pressure-time recorder was used on the rocket, consisting of a 5-in.-diameter disk rotating at one turn per minute by the works of an Ingersoll watch, together with a pressure element consisting of a 7/16-in. bellows, held movably collapsed by two opposite springs and bearing a pencil. A trace of $7/32$ in. was produced by an increase in pressure from 115 to 200 psi.

Test. In the test the pressure began to rise 2 sec after the starting key was pressed and reached 190 psi after 10 sec more. The rocket rose rapidly after leaving the tower but soon decreased in speed and also moved away from the vertical. After 8.6 sec of flight, black smoke appeared from the chamber, and the gasoline tank exploded a second or so afterward, when the rocket was at a height of 1330 ft.

The pressure-time record showed that the pressure dropped from 190 psi on leaving the tower to 115 psi after 7 sec, remaining at 115 for 3 sec more. Possibly the explosion was due to the operation of the gasoline cutoff device while the rocket was still firing, without closing the gasoline-tank valve completely.

Test of November 18, 1931:
Flight Test with Nitrogen-Gas Pressure

The object of this test was to obtain a flight with a rocket using an inert gas, nitrogen, for producing the tank pressure. Several minor modifications were also made, including a reduction in the flow of the gasoline.

Nitrogen system. A liquid-nitrogen tank was used for supplying pressure during the flight. It was located just above the combustion chamber and consisted of a 5-in.-diameter, 9-in.-long cylindrical part with 90-deg conical ends, all being covered with $1/2$-in.-thick felt and aluminum foil.

The liquid nitrogen was supplied to the jacket around the chamber and nozzle through two $1/2$-in. valves at the bottom of the nitrogen tank. One of these was used to give a large continuous supply, and the other was connected by a rod to a control bellows at the top of the tank, this being used to make up the difference in the total flow required. Three thin aluminum baffles were used in this tank. Check valves were used in the $1/2$-in.-tube nitrogen-gas lines to the gasoline and oxygen tanks in order to prevent any mixing of the vapors from these tubes in the nitrogen tank.

The copper-tube jacket around the chamber was modified in such a manner that twice as many tubes could be used as before. This modification consisted in using $5/8$-in.-O.D. square steel semicircular tubes, instead of $1/2$-in.-O.D. round steel tubes, for the manifolds at the ends of the copper tubes. The wire spirals, serving as baffles, were No. 20 instead of No. 22.

Other modifications. The chamber gasoline slots were reduced in width to 0.067 in., the total flow being 7.6 oz/sec for water at 20 psi.

The gasoline-cutoff valve-rod release was simplified by the use of a horizontal bellows for the pin releasing this rod, instead of a vertical bellows as used previously. The rod on this bellows was also used to free the clockwork timer for the parachute, the explosive catch or lock of the release being fired 6 sec after the pressure in the gasoline tank fell to 75 psi, thus operating the cutoff. In this way the uncertainty due to variation of the propulsion period was avoided.

The pressure-recorder pencil slid on a rod, moved by a yoke on the top of the nitrogen-pressure regulator, this arrangement of indirect connection preventing vibration of the recording pencil.

The streamline casing consisted of a 0.020-in. duralumin shell of 12 in. diameter, the tanks and chamber being attached to two ¾-in.-square duralumin tubes, as in the rocket tested December 30, 1930. The felt and aluminum-foil covering of the oxygen tank was not removed. The cap was an ogival aluminum spinning, and the lower end of the casing was a conical frustum 26½ in. high, on which were four vanes, 6 in. wide and 18 in. high, tapering above this height, at 45 deg, to the surface of the conical frustum.

Test. When the starting key was pressed, the gasoline appeared to have been turned on, but no further action took place. Two or three minutes later, however, one of the explosive links operated, and an explosion in the combustion chamber followed. It appeared, first, that the igniter did not fire, possibly because it was too cold from the liquid oxygen which passed through the chamber during filling; and second, that the explosive link which shut off the gasoline, when the stop key was pressed, produced entanglement of the armored cables, thus closing a circuit.

Test of November 23, 1931:
Static Test, Modified Oxygen Injection

The object of this test was to determine the effect of a different method of introducing the liquid-oxygen spray into the combustion chamber, using, for simplicity, the rocket tested May 28, 1931, with no pressure regulator and hence no copper-tube jacket.

Chamber. The chamber and nozzle walls were of 0.031-in. sheet nickel, the chamber having a cylindrical part 12 in. long and 5¾ in. in diameter, with a 90-deg upper and a 120-deg lower cone. The nozzle was 14 in. long, with a 1¹³⁄₃₂-in. throat and a 3½-in. open-end diameter.

The oxygen orifice was located 2⅜ in. below the level of the top of the cylindrical part of the chamber, and the deflector, on the 0.148-in.-diameter rod passing through the No. 2 hole orifice, was ⁷⁄₁₆ in. below this hole and deflected the oxygen upward and outward in the form of a hollow cone, striking the chamber wall ⅝ in. below the top of the cylindrical part.

The deflector producing this spray cone was ½ in. wide and ⅛ in. thick; the inner part of its top surface was tangent to the 0.0148-in. supporting rod; and the outer edge was curved, being raised ¹⁄₁₆ in. below the lowest part of this upper surface, and thus directed the oxygen upwardly.

The top of the cylindrical part of the chamber was provided with a nickel ring that projected $3/16$ in. inside and $1/4$ in. outside the chamber wall. An Insalute-Alundum cement surface, on perforated steel covered with iron screening, had the form of a flat ring extending inward $3/8$ in. from the nickel ring, with a 45-deg cone extending downward to the bottom of the $3/4$-in.-I.D. oxygen entrance tube. This refractory wall was $1/8$-in. thick. Four $1/4$-in.-diameter holes on the inverted cone allowed the pressure to equalize on the two sides. The water flow at 20 psi, through the oxygen orifice, was 6.4 oz/sec.

The two gasoline orifices were the same as those used in the test of October 27, 1931.

Static-test tower. The 20-ft static tower was remodeled so that large as well as small rockets could be tested. A 1-in. iron rod extended downward from a plate on the top of a very strong coil spring at the top of the tower, this rod bearing an angle-iron cross, from the arms of which four 55-gal steel drums were suspended. With water in these drums, the total load on the spring could be raised to about 2000 lb, thus permitting the testing of rockets having nearly this amount of lift. The rocket was attached to this cross, and an improved lift-time recorder was attached to the 1-in. rod.

The rinsing of the gasoline tank with carbon dioxide, after the run, was accomplished by opening the valve of a commercial carbon dioxide cylinder, in which was a pressure of 150 psi, and letting this gas escape through the gasoline tank.

Test. In the test the pressure was maintained at 200 psi, the run lasting for 24 sec. The flame was noisier than usual and was about 2 ft long, pointed, and intensely white near the nozzle. The refractory cone became cracked but was not melted or broken.

The maximum lift was 270 lb, the lift-time integral being 4769. Assuming the total mass of liquids used as 30 lb and allowing for the losses at the beginning and end of the test, the gas velocity was 5088 ft/sec, the ratio of oxygen to gasoline thus being 0.578.

Test of December 23, 1931:
Static Test, Nitrogen Evaporation Apparatus

In this test, in the static tower or proving stand, an attempt was made to obtain nitrogen-gas pressure by having liquid nitrogen flow through the system partly by gravity and partly by a thermal pulsometer pump. Several further modifications were made, including a liquid-nitrogen tank placed within the liquid-oxygen tank, and a jacket wall, around the chamber and nozzle, held spaced from the chamber and nozzle by closely spaced short columns.

Pulsometer. The pulsometer device consisted of a space in the top of the combustion chamber, in which the pressure could be dropped slightly at frequent intervals, permitting periodic surges of liquid nitrogen to enter from the liquid-nitrogen tank and thus produce frequent bursts of pressure by rapid evaporation, this pressure serving to force the nitrogen through the jacket around the chamber and nozzle at an accelerated rate.

The space for evaporation, in the top of the combustion chamber, consisted of the upper 90-deg chamber cone, and a lower 45-deg cone, of the same shape and general position as the refractory-lined cone used in the preceding test, on a 1-in.-wide sheet-nickel ring located at the top of the cylindrical part of the chamber. No other change was made in the chamber from that used in the preceding test.

The drops in gas pressure in this double cone space were produced by a pneumatically-balanced valve having a steel valve rod of $\frac{1}{4}$-in. diameter and $\frac{1}{4}$-in. stroke, moved so as to open for a short time at intervals of 1 sec by the clockwork of an Omnigraph telegrapher's learning instrument. These openings were such as to drop the pressure in the double cone space by about 15 psi at 200 psi, thus facilitating the flow of liquid nitrogen from the liquid-nitrogen tank, which flow entered the space tangentially and hence did not come into contact with the heated part of the surface immediately.

A check valve, spring-loaded so as to open for small pressures, was used to prevent backflow into the liquid-nitrogen tank, and a similar check valve was used to prevent backflow from the jacket space around the chamber into this pulsometer space. A silk cloth strainer, held in 3-in.-diameter perforated steel supporting disks, was used between the pulsometer space and the mechanically operated valve. The exhaust tube from this valve passed to the pressure regulator, so that the pulsometer device functioned only when required to maintain the pressure.

Nitrogen tank. The nitrogen tank, inside the liquid-oxygen tank, was of 0.018-in. sheet nickel, having a cylindrical part 5 in. in diameter and 12 in. long, with 90-deg conical ends. It was covered with asbestos, outside of which was 0.010-in. sheet copper, soldered liquid-tight. This covering served to keep the liquid oxygen out of direct contact with the wall of the nitrogen tank and permitted the pressures within the two tanks to be considerably different. The complete nitrogen tank weighed 3 lb 9 oz, and the oxygen and nitrogen tanks, together, $8\frac{1}{2}$ lb.

The filler tube for the nitrogen tank extended up through the oxygen tank, as did also the tube, jointed in the middle with a spring to make it extensible, serving as the regulating valve rod, and held up as long as the nitrogen-tank vent valve was to be open.

Other modifications. The regulating valve member, at the bottom of the nitrogen tank, was flat, 1 in. wide, and covered a $\frac{1}{2}$-in. valve hole, the disk being faced with kangaroo leather, which was found to be soft and yielding at liquid- oxygen temperature. The spring-loaded check valve between the nitrogen tank and the pulsometer was located between the bottoms of the nitrogen and oxygen tanks, in order to be cooled before the test.

A liquid-nitrogen separator was used in the gas-delivery tube between the chamber jacket and the two liquid tanks. It consisted of two sheet-nickel cones of 120 deg, joined base to base, with the tube from the jacket entering tangentially at the common base, and a tube leading out, on the opposite side, to the gasoline tank. The tube to the oxygen tank passed out of the apex of the upper cone. By means of this device, any liquid-nitrogen drops were separated by centrifugal force and carried to the gasoline tank, where they became evaporated and furnished pressure.

Arrangements were made by which the hose from the two gas-generator tanks could be removed and the pressure producd by the rocket system could be observed by a pressure gauge on the rocket. A hand vent valve was also provided, as well as a safety valve set for 220 psi.

The jacket around the nozzle and the lower two-thirds of the chamber consisted of a wall of 0.018-in. sheet nickel, spaced $1/4$ in. from the chamber and nozzle walls. This jacket was supported on flathead $1/4$-in.-32 screws, the heads being brazed to the chamber and nozzle in rows $5/8$ in. apart. The jacket was fastened to the free ends of the screws after being rolled, by being brazed to one of the rows of screws, and then unrolled as row after row was brazed. The whole job required 51 dozen screws and ten $1/16$-in. brazing rods, and weighed 6 lb complete.

Test. In the test 200 psi was first produced by the two gas-generating tanks. Then, when the connecting hose was pulled off, the pressure became steady at 125 psi. The run was continued until the gasoline tank was completely empty, the automatic gasoline shutoff not being used. The maximum lift was 210 lb but averaged 125 lb for a large part of the 31-sec run. The lift-time integral of 3240 gave, for an estimated total mass of 34 lb, a velocity of 3040 ft/sec.

No frost was observed on the jacket around the chamber, although after the run the upper half of the jacket was found to be warmer than the lower part.

An examination showed that the lower cone of the double cone space in the chamber had been collapsed and cracked by the chamber pressure, the nitrogen tank also having collapsed, probably when the gasoline tank became empty and the nitrogen-gas pressure fell. It appeared likely that most of the nitrogen pressure was produced by gravity, since otherwise the pressure would have tended to rise to 200 psi, and also to have been less steady.

Test of January 14, 1932:
Attempted Static Tests, Nitrogen Apparatus

An attempt was made to use gravity for feeding liquid nitrogen to the chamber jacket, using a regulator valve and delivery tubes of large area.

Chamber. The chamber was of the same inverted refractory-cone construction as tested on November 23, 1931, the gasoline orifices giving a total flow of 8.2 oz/sec at 20 psi pressure, and the entire chamber weighing 5¼ lb.

The copper-tube jacket, of two longitudinal halves as before, had 52 tubes around the cylindrical part of the chamber and 26 around the nozzle. The square semicircular tubes used at the top and bottom of the cylindrical part of the chamber were ⅝ in. O.D., and the two square semicircular tubes used at the bottom of the nozzle were ½ in. O.D. Each half jacket weighed 2 lb 3 oz, and the entire chamber and jacket assembly weighed 11½ lb.

The valve opening, from a nitrogen tank of the same size as before, was 1⅞ in. in diameter, and the valve disk was of brass, 2⅜ in. in diameter and ⅛ in. thick, this disk being dished out so that a band only ¹⁄₁₆ in. wide made contact with the valve seat. This seat was provided with steel flanges, from which two ½-in.-O.D. tubes extended down to the copper-tube jacket. The valve flange was joined to the valve seat by a thin part, to prevent distortion of the seat by stress at the flanges.

Gas generator. A new gas-generating tank was constructed which would have a smaller rate of evaporation of nitrogen than that previously used. The nitrogen was contained in a paper cylinder, lined with 0.001-in.-thick sheet brass, inside the nitrogen tank used in the test of November 18, 1931, but without the baffles. The nitrogen container was surrounded by a jacket having a space ½ in. wide for liquid oxygen, at atmospheric pressure. It was mounted over a tank consisting of an iron pipe containing 16 lb of galvanized iron nails. The generator was operated by opening a 1-in.-diameter valve in the bottom of the liquid-nitrogen container. In a test in which the delivery hose was open to the air, a steady pressure of 200 psi was easily produced by this new gas-generating tank.

Tests. Two tests were attempted, one on January 14, in which the igniter did not fire because of weak batteries, and one on January 23, in which gasoline was found to have entered the oxygen tank, making a run inadvisable. No further attempts were made with this unit, because shop tests in the meantime had indicated the possibility of obtaining a positive and controllable rate of liquid-nitrogen feed flow to the chamber jacket.

Test of January 26, 1932:
Static Test, Nitrogen Pump Apparatus

The object of this test was to investigate the possibility of supplying nitrogen pressure on a rocket by means of positive pumping action into a copper-tube chamber jacket, using a bellows pump and a bellows engine.

Chamber and tanks. The chamber and jacket were those used in the preceding test.

The liquid-nitrogen tank, inside the oxygen tank as before, was 6 in. in diameter and 12 in. long, with 120-deg conical ends, being covered completely with asbestos and 0.010-in. sheet copper. No shutoff device was used in the gasoline tank, but a drain plug was installed just above the gasoline on-and-off valve, so that the tank and delivery line could be emptied completely if it was necessary to stop a test and remove the rocket from the tower. Check valves were used in the pressure lines to the oxygen and gasoline tanks, to avoid an explosive gas mixture.

Nitrogen bellows pump. The nitrogen pump consisted of a 4-in.-O.D., No. 1000-18 Sylphon metal bellows, of $3\frac{1}{8}$-in. extended length, used with a 1-in. stroke. Steel disks, $\frac{1}{8}$ in. thick, were soldered on the ends of this bellows. The operative volume inside the bellows was reduced to as small an amount as possible, on the upward or compression stroke, by having a $2\frac{7}{8}$-in. diameter, 2 in. long, steel cylinder brazed to the lower disk, this cylinder having at the top a $\frac{1}{8}$-in.-thick disk, on which was the intake valve. The intake-valve seat was $1\frac{3}{8}$ in. in diameter, $\frac{1}{32}$ in. wide, and had an angle of 45 deg. The valve surfaces, of steel, were ground in position (Fig. 3).

The outlet valve was 1 in. in diameter and was located in a cylindrical recess or box on the upper bellows disk, in such a way as to make the bottom face of the valve disk flush with the bottom face of the upper bellows disk. A coil spring kept the outlet valve normally closed.

Two steel tubes, on opposite sides of the lower bellows disk, served as pull rods, and when pulled upward caused nitrogen to be forced out of the pump, the upper bellows disk being held stationary by two other tubes connected to a single axial tube at the bottom of the nitrogen tank. All four vertical rods were guided by steel-tube sleeves.

Two coil springs served to keep the lower disk pulled normally downward, and a friction sleeve on the inlet-valve rod served to cause this valve to open fully on the suction, or return, stroke and to close at the beginning of the pumping stroke.

Bellows engine. Although the bellows pump was required to operate at only a small pressure differential, namely, the excess of pressure necessary to force the nitrogen through the copper-tube jacket, the bellows engine, located at the top of the oxgyen tank, was required to operate between full tank and atmospheric pressure.

This engine consisted of four $1\frac{1}{2}$-in.-diameter, 2 in. long, No. 90224-12 two-ply Sylphon bellows, soldered together in line.The four bellows were needed in order to give a stroke as long as 1 in. This row of bellows was fastened at the top to the upper end of a $1\frac{5}{8}$-in.-O.D. steel tube or sleeve, in which they moved, this tube being joined at the lower end to a $\frac{3}{4}$-in.-diameter steel tube extending down through the oxygen tank to the liquid-nitrogen tank. The pump rod, consisting of a $\frac{3}{8}$-in. steel tube, extended down through this $\frac{3}{4}$-in. tube.

The volume inside the row of bellows was reduced to as small an amount as possible at the end of the return, or idle, stroke, just as with the pump, by using a $\frac{7}{8}$-in.-O.D. steel tube closed at the top, from which the $\frac{3}{8}$-in.-O.D. steel pump-rod tube passed down to the movable part of the pump. This $\frac{7}{8}$-in. steel tube was guided in a perforated steel tube or sleeve, attached to the upper end plate of the engine tube, thus avoiding contact with the bellows.

The fixed part of the engine valve was fastened to the upper end plate of the engine. This part consisted of two small coaxial chambers, the lower being connected to the pressure supply and the upper to the outside air. Extending through both chambers was a stationary steel tube, $4\frac{1}{2}$ in. long and $\frac{9}{16}$ in. O.D., having 12 holes leading into each chamber or compartment. A steel-tube valve sleeve, sliding inside this perforated tube, had corresponding holes, so that at the upward position of the valve sleeve the engine exhausted to the outside air. At the lower position of the valve sleeve the engine performed the power stroke, which compressed two strong springs, on the sides of the pump, sufficiently to produce the return stroke when the valve was shifted. The distance of travel of the valve sleeve was $\frac{5}{16}$ in., and a spring-and-trip device was used to throw the valve from one position to the other just before the bellows engine reached either end of the stroke.

Auxiliary equipment. The exhaust tube of the bellows engine was connected to the pressure regulator, a needle valve being used between the engine and the pressure regulator in order to prevent the engine from running too rapidly. The pressure regulator, of large capacity as used in the test of December 23, 1931, was covered by a tin box, on which was a spring-loaded 6-in.-diameter aluminum-foil disk that served as an indicator to show engine operation.

There was also an igniter indicator, consisting of a weight on a thread extending up through the nozzle and chamber to the top of the igniter, the dropping of this weight giving visual evidence that the igniter operated.

The gas-generating tank, having an oxygen-jacketed nitrogen pressure tank, as used in the preceding test, was again employed, and this, together with the gasoline and oxgen tanks, was blown out with gaseous nitrogen before the run.

Test. In starting the test, the cord to the hose pull-off broke, so that the gas-generating tank could not be disconnected from the rocket during the entire run. This condition caused the pressure to rise to 250 lb and probably kept the bellows engine from working, although lack of operation could not be determined with certainty owing to vibration of the engine indicator.

The maximum lift was 230 lb; the time of the test 19 sec; the integral of the lift-time curve 3449; and the estimated jet velocity 3650 ft/sec. The flame was 6 in. or so long, and was pointed. A secondary, yellowish flame appeared in the concrete gas deflector, below the rocket.

The rocket was in good condition after the run except that some of the cement on the inverted refractory cone in the chamber had broken off, and the engine bellows had contracted to such an extent that stronger springs were required to produce the return stroke of the engine.

Test of February 4, 1932:
Repeat Test

The object of this test was to repeat, in a satisfactory manner, the preceding test, in which nitrogen pressure was produced by a bellows pump and engine combination.

Changes. No changes were made except to use a stronger compression spring on the pump rod, or tube, in order to ensure that the engine would complete the return stroke. An engine indicator of low inertia, consisting of a bundle of eight white strings each 4 in. long, was placed at a point just over the $\frac{1}{2}$-in. hole that served as outlet in the box surrounding the pressure regulator. The exhaust served to blow the strings out horizontally.

In a shop test, using nitrogen gas for power, the engine made three strokes per second at 200 psi and one per second at 125 psi, stopping when the pressure fell to 100 psi. A needle valve was used, as before, to regulate the speed of the engine.

Test. In carrying out the test the pressure from the gas-generating tank rose to 200 psi, at which time the connecting hose was disconnected. The pressure then fell to about 100 psi but soon rose to 150 psi, where it remained until just before the oxygen tank became empty, when it fell to 100 psi. After the run considerable liquid nitrogen remained in the tank on the rocket but none in the gas-generating tank.

The entire run lasted 32 sec, the maximum lift being 178 lb; the lift-time integral 3430; and the estimated jet velocity 3230 ft/sec. The engine indicator showed operation at about one stroke per second during the 150-psi period. During the test there was no frost on the jacket around the chamber and nozzle or on the piping.

The slowness of engine operation indicated that the exhaust stroke occupied too long a time.

Test of February 11, 1932:
Repeat Test, with Faster Engine Operation

The object of this test was to repeat the preceding test with more rapid engine operation and a reduction in the proportion of gasoline to oxygen.

Changes. New gasoline orifices were used in the chamber, giving 3 oz/sec each instead of 4.1 oz/sec each.

An increase in engine speed was made possible by a larger-capacity regulating valve having a movable $\frac{7}{16}$-in.-O.D., steel sleeve, with three rows of eight $\frac{1}{16}$-in.-diameter holes. This tube slid in a $\frac{1}{16}$-in. stationary tube having corresponding holes through which the engine exhaust passed from a chamber or compartment around the fixed perforated tube. The needle valve was included for adjustment of engine speed. A more sensitive engine indicator was used, consisting of a strip of thin silk about 4 in. long placed over the exhaust opening. The ignition-indicator thread was replaced by a 0.010-in. tinned iron wire.

Test. In the test the valve of the gas generator was held open for about 4 sec in order to reach 200 psi as rapidly as possible. After the hose was pulled off, the rocket pressure fell to about 125 psi but rose rapidly to 175 psi, and then, after about 4 sec, to 200 psi, at which it remained until the end of the test.

The silk engine indicator stood out practically horizontally during the entire run, indicating rapid and probably continuous running of the engine. No frost was observed on the jacket or nitrogen piping.

The maximum lift was 193 lb; the period 20 sec; the lift-time integral 3570; and the estimated jet velocity 4475 ft/sec. The flame was very steady and bright, longer than in the two preceding tests. It consisted of an intensely bright pointed flame, 8 or 10 in. long, surrounded by a less intense flame extending down into the concrete gas deflector.

The engine speed appeared to be about right for maintaining 200 psi, inasmuch as the exhaust valve did not appear to become closed for any appreciable time. Possibly the proportion of gasoline could be reduced still further, to give greater jet velocities without serious heating of the chamber, nozzle, or jacket.

Test of April 19, 1932:
Flight Test, with Nitrogen Pressure, Flight Stabilization

This test was made with the object of securing a flight with a rocket in which pressure was developed by means of a bellows pump and engine, and in which flight stabilization was secured by the use of air and blast vanes controlled by a pilot gyroscope.

The combustion chamber, jacket, pump, engine, and pressure regulator were all the same as in the preceding test. In addition to the oxygen, nitrogen, and gasoline tanks, three small tanks were used to act as reservoirs of 55-psi nitrogen-gas pressure, for operating the directing vanes.

Vanes. Four blast vanes and four air vanes were used, each air and corresponding blast vane being connected. The blast vanes, 1 in. wide, were hinged at the nozzle, and extended rearward a distance of 2⅛ in. and thence inward at 38 deg for a distance of 1 in. The inner, or blast, surfaces were covered with Insalute-Alundum cement, ⅛ in. thick, on iron screening. These vanes were arranged to swing both inward and outward.

The air vanes, 1 in. wide and 2¼ in. long, were fastened to the outer sides of the blast vanes by narrow welded steel webs, these being in planes containing the axis of the nozzle.

The double vanes just described were operated in pairs, the blast vane of one pair acting on the jet from the nozzle while the air vane of the opposite pair acted upon the slip stream. The vane displacement was obtained by the use of two rings of $\frac{3}{16}$-in.-O.D. steel tubing, to which the blast vanes were movably fastened near the upper, or hinged, ends. Four rods served to push these rings in such a way as to cause opposite vane pairs to become operative, these rods being pushed down by 55 psi pressure applied to the inside of four rubber cylinders (in $\frac{9}{16}$-in.-O.D. steel tubes), closed at one end, obtained from automobile-tire pressure gauges.

Gyroscope. The pilot gyroscope, located between the liquid oxygen tank and the chamber, consisted of a 4-in.-diameter rotor or disk, with a rim $\frac{7}{16}$ in. wide and $1\frac{7}{32}$ in. thick. This rotor was on a steel spindle, on each side of which were two thin brass spools which made possible the spinning of the gyro, by means of four 23-lb-test fishlines, each 3 ft 8 in. long and so wound that there was no moment of force during the spinning. A 5-lb weight was used on each line (Fig. 4).

The gyro was balanced by two small aluminum cylinders, one placed on the inner and the other on the outer gimbal. The effect of the copper brushes against the commutators was found to be practically negligible. The four gyro weights were found to be sufficient to cause the gyro to rotate, without appreciable change of level, for 6 or 7 min. The gyro rotor, together with the spindle and brass spools, weighed 1.04 lb.

The gyro was mounted in 17 ST aluminum gimbals using hardened pivots in hardened steel bearings. The gimbal shafts were sufficiently long to provide space for commutator parts, consisting of fiber disks $\frac{1}{8}$ in. thick, some having thin brass rings around the entire edge, and others having semicircular brass rings, of the same radius as the remaining fiber part so that the diameter was everywhere the same.

These commutator disks were of $\frac{3}{8}$ in. diameter except where wires passed through them from inner $\frac{3}{8}$-in. disks, requiring the diameter to be $\frac{1}{2}$ in. Current from the inner gimbal passed to the outer gimbal through the commutator disks with full brass rings. The commutator disks having the semicircular brass rings were turned until contact was made with copper brushes, when the rocket axis was inclined 13 deg from the vertical, the disks then being locked in place by means of a nut.

Before the start the gyro was prevented from rotating by an arm having a felt pad bearing against the rotor, and was prevented from turning by another arm having a V-shaped slot that held the top of the inner gimbal stationary.

Servomechanism. The currents, controlled by the gyro commutator, were supplied by eight pencil-type dry batteries, each containing two small cells, these batteries consisting of two parallel groups of four each, in series. They energized one or more of four bell magnets, the armatures of which moved ⅛-in.-diameter valve rods, return motion taking place by means of small coil springs. The magnet poles were covered with paper to prevent the armatures from sticking.

These valves were supplied with 55 psi pressure and were pneumatically balanced. For this balancing each ⅛-in.-diameter valve rod had a groove at the middle, and slid, with ⅛-in. stroke, in valve blocks that in turn had grooves in the ⅛-in. holes in which the valve rods slid, these grooves communicating, at the ends of the stroke, with the grooves on the valve rods. Holes on opposite sides of the valve block served to allow the gas under pressure to flow to one of the inner grooves, and thence to one of the closed-end rubber cylinders, or tubes, that moved one pair of vanes in one direction. Two holes to the other inner groove served to vent this pressure from the rubber cylinder to the atmosphere and thus to allow the pair of vanes to return to the idling position.

Pressure for the vane operation was supplied from the high-pressure nitrogen system through a reducing valve, consisting essentially of an automobile-tire valve and a single-ply 1⅛-in. Sylphon bellows. The three small storage or ballast tanks, for maintaining the control pressure sufficiently constant, were of 0.018-in. sheet nickel; each was 3 in. in diameter and 6 in. long, with 120-deg conical ends.

Another automobile-tire valve was used in the 200-psi pressure line to the 55-psi reducing valve, in order to prevent backflow of vane-control pressure after oxygen-, nitrogen-, and gasoline-tank pressures had dropped to atmospheric, thus permitting steering after propulsion had ceased. Further, a silk strainer in a 1-in.-diameter tube was used in the 55-psi pressure line, to avoid dust and dirt in the vane-control valves, for the reason that these valves were used dry, with leaking reduced by lapping out the valve blocks to as small a clearance as possible.

Parachute and other equipment. The parachute, which was projected from a box as in the test of November 18, 1931, was released just under the peak of the ascent by means of special commutators and brushes on the gyro gimbals. For this purpose four commutator disks having semicircles of brass strip on the edge were used, contact with these brass strips being made when the rocket tipped to 130 deg from the vertical in any direction. Since the center of air resistance of the rocket was necessarily below or rearward of the center of gravity, in order for the flight to be stable, the rocket would head downward after attaining maximum height, regardless of the direction and speed.

The clockwork of the pressure-time recorder was the same as that used in the test of November 18, 1931, the trace being made on paper on a drum ¾ in. in diameter and ¾ in. long. The pressure element consisted of metal bellows held normally contracted by two springs on the sides, a piece of flat spring steel pressing a pencil on the recording drum.

The casing consisted of sheets of 0.020-in. 17 ST aluminum alloy, bent into 12-in.-diameter cylinders and held to ⅜₆-in.-O.D. steel-tube rings fastened to the two ¾-in.-O.D. square steel tubes constituting the frame on which the rocket chamber and tanks were supported. The four rollers, running in the pipe guides in the tower, were pushed off by compression springs as the rocket rose from the tower.

The finished rocket weighed 91½ lb, and was 10 ft 9½ in. long. The center of gravity, empty, was 4 ft 11 in. from the rear end.

Releasing sequence. Regarding the controls, pressing the first key freed the gyro for spinning. When one of the 5-lb weights for spinning the gyro finally dropped, it struck a platform that closed a switch, thus firing the igniter. The heat of the igniter melted a 0.010-in. iron wire, which allowed a weight to drop and close a switch, thus freeing a kerosene dashpot weight, which turned on the gasoline. The final motion of this dashpot weight freed a lever that operated the gas-generating tank, at the same time closing the vent valves on the oxygen and nitrogen tanks, together with a safety valve on the gas-generating tank, which had previously been held open.

Rise of pressure to 205 psi closed an electrical circuit that freed the main releasing lever. This lever served to pull off the pressure hose to the rocket, freed the gyro for turning, removed the control cord to the gasoline valve by which the latter could be shut off in case of a poor start, allowed the doors in the casing to close, and freed the clock of the pressure-time recorder. It also freed a clockwork timer on the tower, which fired the two explosive links that held the rocket, after a delay of 3.5 sec, the time required for the pump and engine to restore the pressure to 200 psi after the pressure hose had been removed.

Test. In the test the pressure reached 200 psi 20.5 sec after the first key was pressed, this being the total time required for the gyro weights to fall, the igniter to fire, the gasoline to be turned on, and the gas-generator tank to operate. The rocket started to rise 25 sec after this key was pressed, the time beyond 20.5 sec being that required for the main release lever to be moved and for the 3.5-sec delay. The rocket landed about 5 sec later (Fig. 5).

After leaving the tower, the rocket rose slowly, although in a straight line, emitting a rather bushy yellowish flame. It became inclined toward the south soon afterward, however, and descended, apparently without reduction of thrust, striking the ground on one side. The rocket was considerably damaged except for the tanks, which probably were saved because of the high internal pressure.

There were two reasons for believing that the directing vanes had operated: first, two vanes were warmer than the others after the test; and second, the initial inclination of the rocket from the vertical appeared to take place more slowly than in preceding flight tests. Apparently, the directing vanes were so close to the nozzle opening that the gases from it were obstructed, since excessive chamber pressure was found to have rounded the upper or forward cone considerably.

Test of May 20, 1932:
Repeat Flight Test

The object of this test was to repeat the preceding test, using larger directing vanes placed at a greater distance from the open end of the nozzle.

Changes. Additional changes were the supporting of the tanks and chamber by thin sheet-nickel necks extending between them, and under internal pressure, and the reducing of the length of the rocket as much as possible by enclosing the bellows engine in the gasoline tank.

The chamber, chamber jacket, tanks, bellows pump and engine, and pressure regulator were essentially the same as for the preceding test. The pressure regulator was adjusted to start closing at 190 psi and to be completely closed at 205 psi.

The oxygen and gasoline tanks had 9-in. hemispherical ends. The chamber was fastened to the oxygen tank by a 55-psi pressurized sleeve or neck of 0.031-in. sheet nickel, 4 in. in diameter and 5 in. long, a hole in the apex of the upper cone of the chamber making the pressure in the sleeve equal to that in the chamber. Asbestos paper and flake asbestos, held in place by wire screening, were used for insulation inside this sleeve in contact with the bottom of the liquid-oxygen tank.

The pressurized neck between the oxygen and the gasoline tanks was 4 in. in diameter and 8½ in. long, and constituted the pressure-storage tank for the directing vanes. Because of the lack of axial space between chamber and tanks, the gyro was located over the gasoline tank, being held in a ¾-in.-O.D. 17 ST square-tubing support frame.

The ¾-in. O.D. square steel tubes holding the detachable roller guides were brazed airtight in the two pressurized sleeves, the lower square tube extending straight across the sleeve and the upper being in two 1½-in.-long sections, in order to avoid interference with the axial tube between pump and engine.

Piping. The tanks were piped as follows: the liquid-oxygen delivery tube passed from an open end just below the nitrogen tank, then around the latter, and thence out of the bottom of the oxygen tank. It then passed to the lower pressurized connecting sleeve, entering at the lower edge and passing to the axial orifice in the combustion chamber.

The liquid-nitrogen tube passed up inside the nitrogen tank, from the bellows pump at the bottom, and down the outside of this tank but inside the oxygen tank, where it was covered with asbestos and thin sheet copper. After passing out of the bottom of the oxygen tank, it branched to two tubes, one joining the bottom of each half copper-tube jacket at the nozzle end.

The nitrogen-gas pressure line began with two tubes, one from the top of each half copper jacket, and thence passed along the sides of the tanks to the top of the gasoline tank. Just below the liquid-oxygen tank, where the line curved outward sharply, a tube on the inside of the curved portion was joined to it at right angles. This arrangement constituted a liquid-nitrogen separator, one branch of the cross tube passing to the oxygen tank and the other to the nitrogen tank, any drops of liquid nitrogen being carried toward the gasoline tank by centrifugal force.

The pressure line to the engine led from the nitrogen-gas pressure tube, just below the check valve for the gasoline tank. The exhaust tube from the engine passed from the top of the gasoline tank down to the brass needle valve for adjusting the outflow, and thence to the sleeve valve on the pressure regulator.

Vanes. The four 20-gauge stainless-steel directing vanes, designed to operate against the rocket blast, were 3 in. wide and 6 in. long, with the outer lengthwise edges bent over at right angles to provide extra stiffness. The upper edges of the vanes were hinged on an eight-sided ring of steel tubing, 12-in.-O.D., and were held 5 in. below the end of the nozzle by four steel tubes.

A steel rod was bolted to the inside surface of each vane, near the top, this serving to pull the vane inward; these rods were located just inside the four steel support tubes for the vane system. Each rod could be drawn upward or forward by a 1½-in.-O.D. single-ply Sylphon bellows, enclosed in a steel tube, a yoke serving to joint the upper end of the bellows with the pull rod beneath. The complete vane-and-bellows assembly weighed 5½ lb, and a 50-lb bellows pressure produced a 6-lb force on the rear edge of a vane.

Gyro and controls. The gyro rotor and arbor were somewhat heavier than before, weighing 1.42 lb, as compared with the 1.04-lb gyro and arbor used in the preceding test. For reasons of space, the gyro was located at the top, or forward end, of the rocket, as already explained. Because of this, the rod which prevented the gyro from turning prematurely, by engaging the top of the inner gimbal, moved upward, when freed by a spring, into a tube or sleeve at the top of the frame supporting the gyro. The gyro was prevented from rotating until released by a lever having a felt pad on the end, as in the preceding test. Both of these arrangements were, however, within the ogival cap.

The lines for spinning the gyro passed out of a ring-shaped space near the top of the ogival head, which was closed after the start by a ring pulled downward by two springs inside the cap. The arrangement for holding this ring in the raised position consisted of a rod extending above the top of the ogival cap and supporting two wires that held the ring until it was released.

The thin copper-strip brushes engaging the gyro commutators were improved by being held in red fiber blocks with a screw for adjusting the tension against the commutator strip in an offset on one of the blocks. The magnet valves were mounted on ⅟₁₆-in.-thick 17 ST aluminum strips and were provided with adjusting screws to limit the travel of the valve rods. The current capacity of the battery was increased by using seven sets of pencil batteries in parallel in each of the two sets.

Other equipment. The pressure recorder was reduced in size and weight by using a 250-lb steam gauge bearing a flat steel spring and pencil, and an aluminum disk on an alarm clock mechanism without the escapement.

The casing was of 0.020-in. sheet aluminum, as before, fastened to four 12-in. diameter rings of steel tubing. The liquid- and gas-delivery tubes were brought inward, close to the two pressurized sleeves, in order to provide as much space as possible for the various operating devices. The parachute was released by freeing a portion of the casing, as before.

The length of the rocket was 11 ft 2 in., and the weight 74 lb.

Arrangements at the tower were modified by having the ring at the bottom of the nozzle rest on a steel thimble, so that space above the 3-ft square sheet-iron plate on which the rocket had previously rested was provided for the directing vanes. Further, since the gyro was located much higher in the tower than before, two 12-in.-diameter galvanized-iron tubes were installed as windshields for the descending weights.

Test. In the test, although the starting controls operated satisfactorily, a flame appeared momentarily at the top of the combustion chamber before the rocket could be released. On examination it was found that the top of the chamber had been burned through in two places, the parachute had become released, and the gyro had tilted considerably.

Before a further test could be made, the first of the periods available for this series of tests had terminated. The further 2 years' work, which had been provisionally decided upon, was voted by the advisory committee; but owing to the death of Mr. Daniel Guggenheim, together with the economic depression, the research could not be continued immediately.

3

Work on Rocket Problems at Clark University

September, 1932 — July, 1934

Unable for the time being to continue the work in New Mexico, Dr. Goddard returned to his teaching position at Clark University, at Worcester, Mass., and took up a variety of general problems relating to rockets, the solution of which would be helpful when field experimental work again could be resumed on an adequate scale.

Much of this work was carried out with the assistance of a grant made in September, 1932, by the Smithsonian Institution.

"In order to do as much as time and funds would allow," wrote Goddard concerning this period, "it was planned to develop new methods and new techniques in as many different lines as possible, not so much for the purpose of making specific devices that could be used at once on a large rocket, as to find what lines of development, and what methods, would appear most desirable in accelerating further progress."

Among the investigations that followed were comparisons of various heat insulators, an exploration of better ways to make strong bolted joints, studies of methods of making welded joints without affecting the strength of heat-treated metal, methods of balancing gyroscopes, improvements in bellows-type pumps, preliminary investigation of centrifugal and other pumps for rocket propellants and engines for driving them, and the experiments described in this section.—Editors

Rocket Chambers Utilizing Atmospheric Air

A rocket chamber utilizing atmospheric air for combustion instead of liquid oxygen would be of advantage in avoiding the weight of the liquid oxygen and the liquid-oxygen containers, although operation would not be possible in extremely thin air.

A United States patent for a device for accomplishing this purpose was applied for in 1931 (No. 1980266). In this device air is compressed by the motion of the vehicle, and successive explosions are employed, this action making compression by a resonance effect possible. It is desirable, for the sake of efficiency, to have as high a compression as possible just as the explosion takes place, and the compression should require a minimum of speed, in order to avoid excessive air resistance. Discharge could take place directly into the air at high vehicle speeds, or against the blades of a turbine at low vehicle speeds.

The use of such chambers on the ends of a propeller is not desirable, even if atmospheric air is used, for the reason that all the fuel expelled must be given the forward speed of the propeller before being ejected, and also because the highest practicable propeller speed, 1000 ft per second, is much too small to permit securing a high efficiency from the combustion.

In order to learn the conditions governing combustion in a rocket chamber using atmospheric air, the following experiments were carried out.

Test of Fixed Chamber, with Fuel Spray and Air Blast

The first test performed with a fixed chamber, similar to the Karavodine-type chamber, was performed on November 11, 1932. The chamber was short, and the flame produced was either continuous or consisted of explosions following each other in rapid succession.

The arrangement differed from that used with the Karavodine chamber in that a spray of gasoline was produced close to the intake valve. The spray device employed was the result of a number of tests. The gasoline passed from a No. 80 hole under a pressure of 2 to 5 lb and impinged upon the end of a rod, which was flat except for a very narrow rim. The spray, in the form of a cone, was directed toward the inflowing air.

Tests of December 2 and 3, 1932, gave no ignition, even when a blast of air at 60-lb pressure was admitted through the pipe. It was found that the wall of the steel tube containing the spray-producing device was wet with gasoline for some distance around this device, and it was concluded that more complete atomization was desirable.

Accordingly, a new spray device was designed, consisting of two tubes having No. 80 holes at the ends and held at an angle of about 90 deg with each other. Through one tube gasoline at 5 lb pressure was passed, and through the other, air at 10 lb pressure. This device gave a very fine spray distributed evenly throughout a rather narrow cone, but did not suffice to make ignition possible.

Tests of Chamber, Rotating and Fixed, with Fuel Spray and Air Blast

A different arrangement was then used, in order to obtain combustion if possible. A light chamber, nozzle, and mixing chamber were made and mounted on a bicycle wheel, provided with a drum of large radius around which a rope could be wound. Pulling this rope caused the chamber to rotate and introduced air. Such motion of a chamber through the air is the method of compressing the air that would be used in an atmospheric-air rocket. Further, if several chambers were used end to end, forming a kind of torous ring, with projecting cowls to catch the air, they could be used around a four-bladed propeller, although the efficiency of such a device is limited, as already explained.

In order to eliminate the effect of centrifugal force, which would cause friction on the valve rod, hinged valves were used. The axis of each hinge was in the direction of a radius of the bicycle wheel. An arm bearing pivots was used on each half of the valve, these pivots engaging adjustable brackets on the outside of the combustion chamber. The arrangement permitted the two halves of the valve to swing into the combustion chamber and was of advantage in placing the pivots and brackets where there was no flame.

The spray device consisted of a jet of air and gasoline, as already described.

Four containers were mounted on the bicycle wheel, three to supply air at 10 lb pressure and one to supply 2 to 5 lb pressure of carbon dioxide gas to the gasoline tank. Levers operated by the rotation of the bicycle wheel opened cocks to supply these pressures. The spark coil was permitted to run continuously.

In tests with the chamber rotating, January 31 and February 1, 1933, the gasoline burned rather steadily and, apparently, was not well mixed with the air. It was decided, accordingly, to test the chamber while fastened permanently in position, so that conditions would be more under control.

A test was made on February 11, using air at 10 lb and ether under carbon dioxide pressure of 3 lb for the spray, together with a blast of air at 10 lb pressure, delivered into the mixing chamber from a small tube. Loud pops occurred at intervals of 5 or 6 sec, with backfiring at each pop. This, apparently, was the time required to fill the combustion and mixing chambers with air and vapor.

Test of Fixed Chamber
with Displacement of Charge

It appeared desirable to make the displacement of air into the combustion chamber positive, and to this end a sleeve, bearing a valve consisting of a round disk hinged at the top, was used in the combustion chamber. The stroke of this sleeve toward the nozzle was made by pulling a cord, and the sleeve was returned to the valve end of the chamber by a coil tension spring.

On February 21 several explosions were produced by this arrangement, but there was frequent backfiring.

An examination of the hinged valves, after a further test on February 22, in which the sleeve was moved back and forth by an electric motor, showed that there was possible leakage past the valve seats.

This difficulty was remedied in a test performed March 2, in which a circular disk valve, with a valve rod, was used, the valve being carefully ground to the seat. The backfiring was nearly eliminated in this test. The spark was arranged to occur only when the sleeve had reached the nozzle end and had started to return. The pressure on the ether was made 3 lb at the start and 2 lb after the engine had run for a while. It was noticed that the explosions, occurring every other stroke, were loud and sharp at first but became softer and softer, finally producing backfiring.

In a further test, on March 9, the pressure on the ether was 5 lb. Firing took place with a loud pop on each alternate stroke. If one alternate stroke was missed, the next explosion was especially loud. There was a considerable force on a piece of tin held over the nozzle when the explosions occurred. After a number of explosions the sound was less intense, apparently because of too rich a mixture, as in the preceding test. When the spark was made to take place after the sleeve had moved only halfway from the valve to the nozzle, backfiring occurred with each explosion.

Test of Fixed Chamber
with Positive Charge Displacement

In view of the gradually changing mixture, which reduced the force of the explosions, it was decided to use a similar chamber but with a sleeve or piston giving a positive displacement of the air and vapor, and to have this motion take place in a separate chamber, between the mixing chamber and the combustion chamber (Fig. 6).

The valve at the entrance to the combustion chamber consisted of a valve plate, movable inwardly, and normally pressed against the seat by a coil tension spring. The valve was mounted in a short sleeve of the same diameter as the combustion chamber. One end of this sleeve was screwed to the outside of the combustion chamber. The sleeve was further fixed to the chamber by long bolts that passed through flanges on the sleeve and on the chamber.

The valve on the moving piston consisted of a valve plate bearing a closed valve stem that slid in a tube integral with the valve seat. Rods served as stops to limit the travel of the valve, and two coil tension springs served to keep the valve normally closed. Tightness of fit of this piston in the tube was secured by an oiled leather pump packing.

A third valve, between the mixing chamber and the second chamber, was opened by forward motion of the piston rod and closed by a rearward motion of the same rod. The valve plate was attached by rods to a sleeve on the piston rod. This sleeve contained adjustable friction packing, so that the valve plate could slide positively back and forth with the motion of the piston rod. The valve seat was fastened in the end of the chamber. All three valves were carefully ground against their respective valve seats.

This device was found, April 17, 1933, to have a very rich mixture even under conditions that gave repeated explosions, namely, at 10 lb air pressure and 1½ to 3 lb pressure on the ether. The flames from the nozzle were soft puffs rather than explosions, and there was occasional backfiring, due apparently to the flame in the combustion chamber continuing to burn while a fresh charge was being introduced from the connecting chamber.

Test of Fixed Chamber with Explosions
Automatically Controlled by Valve Movement

A final form of chamber was made and tested for the purpose of obtaining, if possible, automatic firing by utilizing the motion of the valve rod, which operated the spray devices and also made contact for the ignition. Such a form of chamber, incidentally, would be the simplest that could operate by pressure surges produced by very rapid motion of the device through the air (Fig. 7).

Suction to produce an intake of the explosive charge was obtained by using a long nozzle, this being a ⅝-in. pipe, 9 ft long, like that used in the Karavodine turbine referred to previously. A plug was used on the end of the valve rod, nearly closing the opening into the nozzle, to prevent the explosive charge from entering the nozzle.

For automatic operation of the chamber, it was found necessary to have the return of the valve to the seat take place slowly enough to allow a sufficient explosive charge to be admitted. This delay was accomplished by using a tin disk having notches cut in the periphery, and vanes along the side, immersed in a tank of water.

At each explosion the lower end of a ½ in.-diameter steel tube, turning on a fixed tube near the lower end and pinned loosely to the valve rod, was moved toward the chamber. The upper end was therefore jerked away from the chamber. In this way a catch on the end of the spring at the upper end of the ½-in.-diameter tube engaged one of the notches in the tin disk and turned the latter slowly. This method provided a sufficient delay of the valve in returning to its initial position.

In the final test, made June 17, 1933, the engine operated automatically at the rate of about 120 explosions per minute. Each explosion was sharp and of sufficient force to produce a hard blow on a piece of tin held close to the open end of the nozzle.

The air pressure for the atomizers was 17 psi. An auxiliary stream of air was turned on, after the engine had started, to keep the mixture from becoming too rich.

The most satisfactory of the various spray devices that were developed consisted of three tubes supplying air under 10 to 15 lb pressure from No. 80 holes, the three air jets being directed against a jet of water issuing from a single No. 80 hole, at 25 lb pressure, in the end of a tube. This device was tested on January 11, 1933.

The conclusion to be drawn from the last series of combustion-chamber tests is that a rocket can be made, using compression due to motion through the air, with a nozzle sufficiently long to produce considerable suction. The force of the suction is sufficient to operate a valve for the fuel and to make contact for the igniting spark.

The open end of the chamber could face forward, in the direction of motion of the airplane; or it could face in the reverse direction, if deflectors were used to reverse the direction of the air and cause it to be deflected forward, into the chamber.

At high airplane speeds, and with pressure produced by resonance, that is, by the alternate admission and blocking of the air stream into the combustion chamber, it should be possible to use a relatively short nozzle and at the same time to obtain a very considerable compression. For moderate vehicle speeds, greatest efficiency would be obtained if the blast were used to operate a turbine propeller.

PRESSURE CONTROL OF COMBUSTION CHAMBER

Pressure-controlled Valves

Experiments were carried out in the fall of 1933 for the purpose of developing valves for liquid oxygen and gasoline that could be opened and closed quickly, with no appreciable leakage while the valves were closed, even though the liquid held by the valve exerted 200 lb or more pressure.

After a number of trials, a satisfactory valve for gasoline was developed. It consisted of a pin having a conical hardened steel point, in a tube, seating against an opening at the end. The seat was of copper, having a taper 10 deg wider than the taper of the end of the pin, the seat being "formed" by the steel pin before the valve was used. A compression spring tended to keep the valve closed, and when the liquid was under pressure the valve was kept closed by 200-lb gas pressure in a metal bellows located on the end of the valve rod. Relieving this pressure caused the valve to open.

A valve for use with liquid oxygen was also developed. In this case the valve rod projected through the hole in the end of the supply tube containing the liquid oxygen, and was provided on the end with a button that closed the opening when the rod was drawn inward. The orifice was a copper seat. A spring tended to keep the opening closed. Gas pressure in a metallic bellows kept the valve closed when the liquid was being supplied under pressure, and the relief of this gas pressure caused the valve to open.

Pressure-controlled Igniter

An igniter was also designed and tested which could produce an intense pilot flame in a combustion chamber almost instantly and which could cause the flame to disappear equally rapidly, as often and in as rapid succession as possible.

The satisfactory form of this device consisted of a small chamber through which passed a fine stream of gasoline or other liquid fuel. Oxygen gas was also admitted to the chamber, the gas being directed against a baffle plate. Both could be admitted simultaneously, for as long as desired, by a bellows supplied by gas pressure for each valve, as described above.

A spark passed between terminals on opposite sides of, and close to, the stream of liquid fuel, and served to ignite the fuel. A side tube, or bleeder pipe, conveyed oxygen gas from a point just behind the baffle plate to the place where the stream entered the main combustion chamber, directing it obliquely into the stream.

The operation of the device was positive, and there was very little heating of the small chamber where the stream of fuel was ignited.

Lever Operation of Controls

The operation of the valves and the igniter described above should be positive and in the proper sequence, on starting and stopping the combustion in the rocket chamber. A system whereby starting and stopping could be performed easily by the motion of a single lever was constructed.

This system consisted of a lever that moved a horizontal bar provided with cam surfaces. These surfaces engaged valves which while not in operative position supplied 200 lb of gas pressure to the rocket valves and maintained them closed, but which when put in operative positions relieved this pressure. A similar valve operated the igniter, but only at the starting of the pilot flame.

Packingless Pumps

Rocket fuel pumps must be very light and must be used without packing. These requirements limit them to a few special types.

Pulsometer Pump

This pump consisted of a metallic bellows, fastened at the upper edge to a pump head, and at the lower edge to a piston consisting of a hollow lens-shaped metal piece. Outside of the bellows was a casing, fastened at the upper end to the pump head and provided on the bottom with an inlet and outlet valve, for the liquid to be pumped.

In the lightest form the casing consisted of a cylinder of thin steel with a spherical segment on the bottom. The pump head consisted of a spherical segment, convex upward, strengthened on the upper side with radial ribs. This thin, convex metal construction was helpful because it made the pump both strong and light.

Power for operating the pump was supplied by gas pressure equal to the liquid pressure supplied by the pump, introduced between the pump head and the top of the piston, inside the bellows. A gas-pressure valve was mounted on the pump head, its operation being controlled by the motion of the piston.

A preliminary test, with a pump using a $2\frac{1}{4}$-in. metallic bellows, gave a pressure of 200 psi and showed that the method was practical.

Accordingly, a large pump having a $4\frac{5}{8}$-in.-diameter metallic bellows was constructed. Owing to the thinness of the metal of the pump, it was found that holding the pump head and casing together by flanges was not so satisfactory as making the ends concentric cylinders fastened together with radially arranged bolts and soldering the two edges together.

Even with this precaution against pump distortion or "breathing," the piston chattered violently on the downward, or power, stroke. Attempts were made to eliminate this chattering by the use of several devices: a valve in the air supply line, to check sudden flow of air into the pump; a valve closed when the water pressure in the delivery pipe exceeded the normal working pressure; and a dashpot on the axis of the pump, at the bottom of the pump casing.

None of these devices was successful. The chattering was eliminated, however, by the use of a thin steel sleeve, or cylinder, slightly wider than the bellows and soldered to the bottom of it. In a test at 200-lb delivery pressure and 30-lb suction pressure, 34 cu in. of water per second was pumped, or 7.5 gal per minute, at a delivery of 0.87 hp.

Centrifugal Pump

In the spring of 1934 it was decided to construct and test a centrifugal pump having a closed impeller of $2\frac{1}{2}$-in. diameter, rotating at very high speed, both sides of the impeller having radial vanes to prevent leakage, these vanes carrying the liquid around without radial flow, and producing a centrifugal force greater than that produced by the blades in the impeller.

The centrifugal pumps were operated by small turbines driven by compressed air from a storage tank.

In the first tests a two-stage turbine was used, each disk having an outside diameter of 4 in., but better efficiency was later obtained with a single-stage De Laval-type turbine of 5⅜ in. O.D. Two tapered nozzles were used, at diametrically opposite sides of the turbine disk.

A pump with an internal width of impeller of ¼ in., running inside a volute chamber, gave 200 lb delivery water pressure for 30 lb suction pressure and 200 lb air pressure for the turbine, with a leakage at full speed about half the leakage when the pump was not running. The speed was 30,720 rpm.

An attempt was made to reduce the leakage by employing an additional liquid seal around the shaft. This consisted of a housing on the pump casing, in which a disk fastened to the shaft rotated. This disk was provided with radial vanes on the side away from the pump, and the pump housing was provided with fixed radial vanes close to the other, or inner, surface of the disk. Pressure toward the pump was accordingly produced by centrifugal force.

When the clearance between the walls, disks, and radial vanes was made sufficiently small, the leakage was reduced to zero except when the delivery pipe was nearly closed. The power required was much greater, however, than when the extra liquid seal was not used. With the seal 150 lb air pressure gave only 75 lb water pressure, whereas without the extra seal 150 lb air pressure gave 200 lb pressure for a flow of water through the pump and 225 lb for the delivery pipe closed.

An attempt was made to reduce the energy required by the extra liquid seal by using curved blades on the disk of the seal and by beveling these blades on the "following" side. The frictional loss was reduced, but the leakage was increased.

Test with water. An impeller was then constructed tapering from an internal width of ¼ in. to ³⁄₃₂ in. at the edge. The delivery water pressure was 200 lb, and the suction pressure 30 lb with an air pressure, to the turbine, of 145 lb, at 30,720 rpm. The flow was 71 cu in. per second or 19 gal per minute, the horsepower being 2.12. There was no leakage.

Test with gasoline. Gasoline was tested in this pump, for a rate of pumping of about 1.5 lb per second or 10.8 gal per minute. A continuous-flow method was used, the gasoline being pumped at high pressure into a tank, from which it was led at low pressure into the suction pipe of the pump. This avoided exposing the gasoline liquid and vapor to the air. The gasoline-delivery pressure was 200 lb for 140 lb air pressure, at 38,400 rpm. There was a continuous leakage of ⅛ oz per second. From the behavior of the pump with water, the leakage should be zero for a slightly larger volume per second.

An impeller similar to that just described, but of ³⁄₆₄ in. internal width at the rim, gave greater pressures for both water and gasoline at low air pressure and less water pressure at high air pressure. It was found that a slinger, or disk provided with vanes, close to the casing and surrounded by a housing provided with a drain pipe, served to lead away all the leakage incident to starting the pump.

Test with liquid oxygen. A test was made with the ³⁄₃₂-in.-edge impeller pump using liquid oxygen, the pump being jacketed on the sides with liquid oxygen. A pressure of 100 lb was produced at a rate of 11.6 gal per minute, measured from the fall of level of the supply tank. This test indicated that liquid oxygen could be handled by a small high-speed packingless centrifugal pump and that, with the pump completely cooled, any desired pressure could be produced.

4

Tests Resumed in New Mexico, with Simple Pressure Fuel Feed, Flight Control and Parachute

A Series, September, 1934 — October 29, 1935

In the summer of 1934 a generous grant of funds from The Daniel and Florence Guggenheim Foundation made it possible for Dr. Goddard to resume the tests in New Mexico. The Foundation, in making this grant, carried on the work that had so much interested Daniel Guggenheim, its founder.

The president of the Foundation, Harry F. Guggenheim, whose contributions toward the development of commercial aviation and other industrial and civic interests were already well known, not only made funds of the Foundation available, but followed the progress of the experiments personally, helping materially in overcoming many obstacles and in calling the work to official attention in Washington and elsewhere.—Editors.

When the work was resumed in New Mexico in September, 1934, rockets using a simple fuel-feed system, even if not especially light, appeared best for developing satisfactory flight control and parachute release. This conclusion was reached on considering the number of problems involved in a liquid-nitrogen pressure system as developed during the previous work.

Test of January 15, 1935 (A-1)*:
Attempted Flight Test, Simple Pressure Rocket

The pressure system of the rocket constructed for the first test of the new series accordingly consisted of a nitrogen-gas storage tank, which, together with the oxygen and gasoline tanks, was of 0.030-in. sheet nickel with hemispherical ends. The pressure tank was reinforced in the middle

---

* Dr. Goddard in his records referred to this group of tests as the A series and numbered them consecutively. This numbering system is retained here in parentheses.

by several turns of strong iron wire. Tube supports were used between the tanks and combustion chamber, the supports above and below the oxygen tank having heat-insulating fiber bushings located close to the tank.

The main nitrogen valve on the pressure-storage tank opened in two steps, the pulling of one pin opening it slightly, and the pulling of a second pin opening it fully. A dangerously rapid rise of pressure in the chamber was thus avoided. A third pin was pulled by a bellows operator on the rocket when the storage tank pressure fell to 40 psi, in order to retain sufficient pressure in the storage tank to operate the steering devices after propulsion had ceased.

The operating pressure for the steering vanes, and also for spinning the gyroscope continuously during flight, was 35 psi, obtained from the storage tank by a reducing valve.

Gyroscope. The pilot gyroscope was considerably lighter than that used in the 1930-1932 tests, and was spun by a gas stream striking a milled edge. It was obtained from a Pioneer Instrument Company turn-and-bank indicator, was $1\frac{7}{8}$ in. in diameter, and with the mounting weighed 18 oz. The original bearings from the instrument were used, but the two gimbals were specially made, from 17 ST aluminum stock. The whole was mounted in a small square frame of 17 ST square tubing. The contact brushes rested in grooves in the fiber commutator sleeve, and the elements of this sleeve were held by a lock nut independent of the lock nut on the conical-ended screws that engaged the ball bearings. Contact for steering was adjusted to take place for an inclination of 10 deg from the vertical.

The magnet valves consisted of the pneumatically-balanced valves as previously used, operated by single-coil bell magnets and retracted by springs, also as before. The armatures turned on pivots, thus reducing side play, and each was prevented from making direct contact with the pole piece by a short copper stud driven in a hole in the center of the pole piece. The extent of motion of the valve rod in opening the exhaust port was adjusted by a screw held by a lock nut and engaging the free end of the rod. The magnets were actuated by four sets of three flashlight batteries in series, placed in cardboard tubes around the nozzle. The four magnet valves were placed at convenient locations around the cylindrical part of the chamber.

Vanes. The four guiding vanes consisted of curved strips, $1\frac{1}{2}$ in. wide, of 16-gauge stainless steel, which served to deflect the gases in the outer part of the rocket blast away from the axis. They were provided with $\frac{1}{16}$-in.-thick sides, and each consisted of an eighth of a 3-in.-diameter circle. The centers of curvature were located just inside the center of support, so that a small but definite force was required to move the vane into the blast (Fig. 8).

Each vane arm had an upper extension, provided with a roller, which moved a hinged air vane outward at the same time that the blast vane moved into the jet. The bellows operator for each vane consisted of four 1⅛-in.-O.D. metal bellows soldered end to end, each with 24 convolutions. The length of stroke was 1¾ in. The inside space of the bellows unit when retracted was occupied by a steel tube closed at the inner end, thus reducing to a minimum the amount of nitrogen required for operating the bellows.

Parachute. The 6-ft parachute was contained in a tin box which extended over a part of the cylinder and lower cone of the chamber. It was ejected by a spring, as before, the door being freed by a black-powder release fired by the gyro when the rocket became horizontal, the release using four flashlight cells independent of the magnet-valve batteries. The steel cable for the parachute was fastened around the nozzle of the chamber.

Casing and other details. The casing or housing of the rocket consisted of 0.010-in. 17 ST sheets of cylindrical form, having the same diameter as the tanks, 9 in. Four stationary air vanes were used at the rear end, equally spaced between the movable air vanes. The cap at the forward end was a spun-aluminum ogive. The oxygen-tank sides were heat-insulated by two half cylinders of felt, one on each side, removed just before the rocket was released. The rocket was held vertically in the tower by four rollers that were ejected as soon as it left the tower, the holes for the rods bearing the rollers being filled by plugs, kept flush with the casing surface by springs, as soon as these rods had been ejected.

The nitrogen pressure for the storage tank was supplied by a 200-cu-ft cylinder of nitrogen, with the pressure reduced to 235 psi, instead of by liquid nitrogen in a gas-generating tank. The releases consisted of 0.008-in.-diameter music wire in short lengths, twisted into loops and held by screws placed close together. Fusing the wires by an outside battery of dry cells liberated small levers or arms, which in turn, released the control lever or weights. These electrical releases replaced the blasting-cap exploders previously used.

The rocket weighed 74¼ lb and was 14 ft ½ in. long from the tip of the ogival head to the bottom of the moving air vanes.

Test. When this rocket was tested no flight was obtained, for the reason that the 235 psi caused too much pressure on the valve seat and thus prevented the low-pressure pin of the nitrogen storage-tank valve from being pulled. Moreover, the release lever operated prematurely.

Test of January 31, 1935 (A-2):
Attempted Flight Test

The rocket was repaired, the springs on the nitrogen storage tank were replaced by stronger springs, and the fused wire releases were protected by being enclosed in shallow bakelite boxes. Also, since twisting was found to weaken the 0.008-in. music wire of these releases, it was not twisted into loops but was given a turn around a stud at each end of the wire, the free ends being clamped under screw heads.

Shop tests showed that when the pilot gyro was driven continuously by 35 psi air pressure, there was a slow precession when the square-tube supporting frame was clamped in a vise. This action, found to be due to vibration, was eliminated by using pieces of rubber tubing in the mountings, the gyro then running for 4 min without noticeable deviation.

Shop tests further showed that the bellows-vane operators ceased to move freely after a number of trials. This sticking was found to be caused by filings in the pressure system, which were accordingly removed. Fine wire cloth was used in place of thin silk for the strainers of the magnet valves. At the tower the storage tank was rinsed with nitrogen before being filled, preparatory to a test.

The rocket weighed 74 lb 10 oz and was 14 ft 5 in. long.

No flight was obtained in an attempted test, evidence indicating that only low pressure was obtained through the nitrogen storage-tank valve.

Test of February 16, 1935 (A-3):
Flight Test, Simple Pressure Rocket

The rocket was repaired, and in order to minimize possible damage in this particular test, the automatic guiding devices were omitted. Further, individual valves were used for the storage tank instead of a single composite valve, in order to make the valve operation more positive. Thus a small brass cock, the flow through which was reduced by a plate containing a small hole, replaced the partly open storage-tank valve, and a large brass valve in the same line served in place of the fully open valve previously used. These valves were operated by means of wire loops which passed over the valve arms, or handles, and which thus were removable. These loops were guided in slotted tubes, the valve arms traveling in these slots.

Parachute. The parachute box was located in the space between the gasoline and oxygen tanks, the former being at the forward end of the rocket. The parachute was freed by the use of a fused-wire arm device, instead of by a black-powder explosive pin release as before.

The parachute-releasing device consisted of a ¾-in.-diameter aluminum tube, 11 in. long, containing a weight having a flexibly held disk at the rear end, which, as the rocket decreased in speed, made contact across two insulated pins in circuit with the fused wire just mentioned. This weight would be expected to remain at the bottom of the aluminum tube during the powered part of the rise but would thereafter move forward and make contact owing to the deceleration of the rocket by air resistance.

The casing was streamlined as before and was provided with four fixed air vanes at the rear end. No movable air vanes were employed.

The weight of the rocket was 58 lb and the length 13 ft 6⅜ in.

Test. A short flight was obtained with this rocket, the chamber burning through and showing a white flame during the flight, thus indicating an excess of oxygen. This extra oxygen was probably due to an excess of oxygen-tank pressure over gasoline-tank pressure during the flight, which in turn may have resulted from increased evaporation caused by agitation within the oxygen tank.

Test of March 8, 1935 (A-4):
Flight Test, Pendulum Control

A device was made to prevent the oxygen-tank pressure from exceeding the gasoline-tank pressure appreciably. This device, which may be called an equalizer or differential safety valve, consisted of two opposed 1½-in.-O.D., two-ply Sylphon bellows, fixed at the far ends and connected to a movable closed sleeve on the near ends. One bellows was connected to the oxygen tank and the other to the gasoline tank. A yoke from the movable sleeve bore a pin on the axis of one of the bellows, and beyond its end, this pin operating a small brass valve having a 3/32-in.-diameter opening. In a shop test it was found possible to set this equalizer so that 5 lb excess of oxygen-tank pressure beyond 230 lb opened the valve a distance of 1/64 in.

Pendulum. In order to facilitate making repairs, the gyroscope steering device used in earlier tests was replaced by a short pendulum, the arm of which made electrical contacts in four directions at right angles. Shop tests showed that the pendulum tended to chatter on these contacts when inclined, and hence to make poor electrical connection, but this defect was remedied by cutting the arm into two parts close to the bob and using at this point a flexible joint consisting of a short rubber tube. After this change was made, the bob alone vibrated instead of the pendulum as a whole.

Other equipment. The magnet valves were protected from dust and dirt by being placed compactly in a box made of 1/32-in. sheet iron. The blast vanes were made of 1¾-in.-wide, 4-in.-long, 16-gauge stainless steel, curved cylindrically to 3½-in. diameter of the nozzle. They were located 3½ in. below the edge of the nozzle and 1 in. outward from it. Only fixed air vanes were used.

Each bellows operator consisted of a 2-in.-O.D. single-ply Sylphon bellows, which moved a connecting rod 3 1/16 in. vertically or forwardly. The 35-psi control pressure produced a transverse force of 5 lb at the lower end of the vane and of 6 lb at the center.

The 6-ft parachute was replaced by one 10 ft in diameter in a larger box. The parachute-releasing tube and weight of the preceding test were used again, the weight being held inoperative by a safety wire while the rocket was being transported.

The rocket weighed 75 lb and was 14 ft 7 in. long.

Test. A flight was obtained in which the rocket turned quickly into the wind, thereafter remaining nearly horizontal and rising slightly until near the end of the flight. There was an apparent tendency toward flight correction, which prevented the rocket from moving beyond the horizontal after leaving the tower. The flame was only 8 or 12 in. long, white and pointed, and left a faint black smoke trail. Possibly the excess of gasoline did not burn. The parachute was released soon after the flame ceased, but the rocket was moving so rapidly at this time that the steel connecting cable snapped.

The rocket landed an estimated distance of 9000 ft from the tower. An accurate horizontal measurement could not be obtained, since the pencil moved off the paper of the recording telescope.

Test of March 28, 1935 (A-5): Flight Test, Gyro Control

In this test the gyroscope was again employed for steering, being used with more effective blast vanes. The correcting force, as before, was set to operate for a 10-deg displacement from the vertical.

Changes. A more rigid protecting box was made for the magnet valves by using $1/8$-in.-thick 17 ST aluminum alloy, welded to form a box, the cover of which was held by screws. The fiber end disks of the magnets were replaced by less breakable thin brass ends, insulated by shellacked paper from the enameled wire of the coil.

The concave steering vanes were tapered in order to make possible a greater displacement into the blast. They were $4\frac{1}{4}$ in. long, $2\frac{1}{8}$ in. wide at the top, and $1\frac{5}{16}$ in. wide at the bottom.

The parachute was attached to the rocket by two $1/8$-in. steel cables and was released by the falling-weight device previously used.

The rocket weighed $78\frac{1}{2}$ lb and was 14 ft $9\frac{3}{4}$ in. long.

Test. In the flight that was obtained, successive corrections each side of the vertical took place for several hundred feet, after which the rocket rose at a steep angle. There were occasional flashes at the rear of the blast, accompanied by loud explosions, which may have been caused by the blast vanes' directing the air and flame into the mass of excess gasoline and air, behind the visible rocket blast.

As before, there was no appreciable rotation during the ascent. Toward the top of the trajectory, however, the rocket began to rotate at the rate of about two turns per second. The parachute was not released, even though, after the flight, the wire of the release was found to have been fused.

It appears likely that one or more of the steering vanes became bent or otherwise damaged, accounting for the rotation during the latter part of the trajectory, this rotation causing the failure of the parachute release. Possibly centrifugal force produced by the rotation prevented the weight of the parachute-releasing device from falling.

Test of April 19, 1935 (A-6):
Attempted Flight Test

A further test was made with improved flight-correcting means, consisting of a stronger steering-vane construction and a more protected pilot gyroscope.

Changes. The flat steel vane arms were replaced by arms of $\frac{1}{2}$-in. steel tubing, joined directly to the bellows operators by connecting rods, without intermediate levers for magnifying the motion. The four horizontal arms extending out from the nozzle and supporting both the blast and the fixed air vanes were of double thickness as far out as the vane bearings, which consisted of stronger screws than before. For the 35-psi bellows pressure used, the transverse force was 6 lb on the lower end of the vane, and 7 lb at the center instead of the previous 6 lb.

The gyro was enclosed in a $\frac{1}{8}$-in.-thick 17 ST box consisting of two halves. The sides formed a hexagon, the top and bottom being flat. The outer supporting frame for the gimbals, previously square, was tapered at the bottom by being made in hexagonal form, in order to fit into the box. This box was located just above the liquid-oxygen tank and below the box containing the magnet valves. A test showed that the gimbals moved freely even after the outside of the box had been cooled by liquid oxygen sufficiently to form frost. This result indicated that the cold gas escaping from the tank during filling would not be likely to freeze the gimbal bearings. Four sheet-rubber pads were used as the mountings of the gyro box. Construction of the inner gimbal was simplified by using the gimbal supplied by the manfacturer for the turn-and-bank indicator, a plane surface being milled to accommodate the bakelite support for the copper contact brushes.

Parachute and cap. The 10-ft parachute was placed in the ogival cap, which was arranged, as before, to be released by contact rings on the gyro gimbals when the rocket approached a horizontal position. The parachute was packed by first extending both it and the shroud lines, folding it in the middle, and rolling it into a bundle. The ring on the shroud lines was held by a cable, which passed through four nickel straps brazed to the top of the gasoline tank, on which the cap was mounted. The central point of the parachute was attached by a wire to the cap.

The cap rested on nickel strips placed around the top of the gasoline tank. It was held to the rocket by a loop of wire fastened to opposite sides of the top of the gasoline tank and passing through an eye in the lower end of a short $\frac{1}{16}$-in.-diameter rod. A plug on the upper end of this rod was held until release took place by means of an arm in a $6\frac{3}{4}$-in.-long, $\frac{1}{2}$-in.-O.D. axial steel tube, inside the upper end of the ogival cap and fastened to the apex. Fusing the wire of a release freed the arm and allowed the cap to leave the remainder of the rocket, at the same time unrolling the parachute. The removal of the cap was facilitated by providing a sidewise push by means of a long steel tube fastened to the lower end of the $6\frac{3}{4}$-in. tube and extending obliquely downward. A telescoping sleeve, on the outside, was provided at the lower end with a spur, which fitted in a shallow depression in the top of the gasoline tank at the edge, a compression spring pushing this telescoping tube or sleeve away from the fixed oblique tube as soon as the release operated. The two electric wires to the parachute fused-wire release were made removable by jacks on the top of the gasoline tank.

The rocket weighed 84 lb and was 15 ft $11\frac{1}{2}$ in. long.

Test. In an attempted flight test the rocket was not freed on pressing the release key, but continued to function within the tower for the usual propulsion period. The gyroscope became tilted until the parachute was released, although the cap did not leave the rocket. The cap apparently remained for the reason that the parachute bore against the $\frac{1}{16}$-in.-diameter rod, normally released by the operation of the gyro, which was not free to pass out of the $\frac{1}{2}$-in. steel tube.

Although all the releases at the tower were found to have operated, a shop test disclosed a loose pin in the fused-wire release that operated the lever which freed the rocket. This loose pin probably prevented current from fusing the wire of this release immediately.

Test of May 20, 1935 (A-7):
Attempted Flight Test

In this test the removal of the cap containing the parachute was made dependent upon motion through the air instead of upon a sidewise force within the cap itself.

This removal was accomplished by using a $4\frac{9}{16}$-in.-long, 1-in.-wide, and $\frac{1}{16}$-in.-thick steel strip on a 6-in. arm pivoted close inside the apex of the cap. This strip was curved on a 6-in. radius, and when released at the same time that the cap was released, moved out a distance of $2\frac{7}{8}$ in. from a slot cut in the cap, under the action of a coil tension spring; the air, acting on this exposed portion of the curved strip, tended to tilt the cap.

In order to prevent the cap from sliding off the supports and jamming on the forward end of the gasoline tank, eight horizontal shelf-like lugs were used around the top edge of the gasoline tank, each having a $\frac{1}{32}$-in. raised outer corner to prevent the cap from slipping off.

Gyro protection. To prevent the gyroscope box from becoming cooled before the flight by the oxygen escaping from the top of the oxygen tank during filling, a sheet-tin shield was slid between clips just under the gyroscope box, and two horizontal cuts were provided on opposite sides of the part of the casing around the gyroscope, the metal above the cuts being pulled outward during flight, to prevent inflow of air.

The weight and length of the rocket were practically the same as for the preceding test.

In order to observe at close range what was happening before the launching of the rocket, a 4-ft-deep concrete-lined shelter was made in the ground, 50 ft from the tower. A heavy wooden door, covered with sheet iron, could be raised by hinges on the tower side as a protection, two horizontal slots being made in this door to facilitate observation.

Test. In the test the flame appeared yellowish and the rocket did not rise, the lift apparently being less than 85 lb, the weight of the rocket. An examination indicated that the equalizer had leaked an amount of oxygen gas sufficient to reduce the oxygen-tank pressure and had thus reduced the rate of flow of oxygen.

Test of May 31, 1935 (A-8):
Flight Test, Gyro Control

The brass valve member of the equalizer was replaced by one of steel which could be reground easily and which could also be examined and cleaned before use. Also, the equalizer was set to open at 10 psi excess oxygen-tank pressure, instead of at 5 psi.

The weight and length of the rocket were the same as for the preceding test.

A means for showing when the rocket was lifting more than the loaded weight was used. This consisted of two insulated electrical contacts on the lever that released the rocket, these contacts being bridged by one of the square tubes on the guiding rollers when the rocket rose $\frac{3}{16}$ in. This method gave a visible indication of the lift to the observers at the 1000-ft shelter by causing a fused-wire release to free a pivoted 3-ft angle-iron arm, bearing at the free end a 6-in. square of galvanized iron.

Test. In the test the rocket rose substantially vertically at first, moving four or five times from side to side. It then became inclined, and headed into the wind, rotating slowly after it became inclined. Propulsion did not cease until after it had passed the peak of the trajectory. It landed 5500 ft from the tower, the parachute not having been released.

An examination of the rocket after the test showed that the 0.008-in. parachute-release wire had not been fused. It appeared, however, to have been broken when the rocket landed.

Test of June 25, 1935 (A-9):
Flight Test, Cushioned Gyro

In a shop test with the gyro in place, the vibration of the gyro and gimbals communicated to the containing box caused the axis to tilt gradually, especially when the rocket was inclined. Considerable vibration was noticed when the hand was placed on the containing box. Hence, in addition to two $\frac{1}{16}$-in. pieces of tire inner-tube rubber on the gyro frame and on the gyro box, two mountings were used, at the top and bottom of the frame carrying the gimbals. Each consisted of a pile of five pieces of black sponge rubber $2\frac{1}{4}$ in. long, 1 in. wide, and $\frac{1}{8}$ in. thick. With these additional mountings, very little vibration could be detected with the hand on the box, even though there was noticeable vibration of the frame inside. With the gyro mounted in this way and installed in the rocket, there was no inclination of the axis, whether the rocket was tilted or allowed to remain vertical.

In order to avoid having the blast vanes pushed to one side when not exactly centered in the blast, the lower edges were cut concave, the concavity amounting to $\frac{1}{4}$ in. at the middle. Small movable air vanes were used, in addition to the blast vanes, in this test. These were mounted on the outside of the arms of the blast vanes and were 3 in. long, $2\frac{1}{2}$ in. wide, and 0.016 in. thick, being concave toward the axis of the rocket to the extent of a $3\frac{1}{4}$-in. radius.

Parachute release. The parachute was contained in a tin box, and was ejected by a flat spring when a door was released, as in previous tests. The fused-wire release was actuated by a timer consisting of a small alarm clock from which the escapement arm and alarm parts had been removed. The contact maker consisted of a piece of sheet copper on a brass arm, soldered to the hour-hand shaft. This copper piece had a small but definite freedom of motion, so that contact with two brass points in a bakelite strip was assured. The time interval, nearly the maximum possible, varied from 13.8 to 15 sec.

The rocket weighed $83\frac{1}{2}$ lb and was 15 ft $3\frac{1}{2}$ in. long.

Test. The day of the test was windy. The long yellowish flame observed in the flight was probably due to the wind in the concrete gas deflector igniting the excess gasoline, which usually did not continue to burn after the rocket left the tower. Apparently a gust of wind inclined the rocket just as it became free, the motion pictures showing an inclination of 45 deg when the rocket had risen one length above the tower.

As the rocket headed downward, the chamber burned, probably owing to a large excess of oxygen-gas pressure as the oxygen moved forward in the tank, thus increasing the rate of evaporation.

Test of July 12, 1935 (A-10):
Flight Test

Inasmuch as it appeared possible, after an examination of the rocket, that the yellowish flame in the preceding test had been the result of low oxygen-tank pressure, produced by dirt in the equalizer valve, several strainers were used, in addition to that used between the 250-to-35-lb reducing valve and the magnet valve box, one being used for each magnet valve and one for the equalizer valve. Each consisted of two threaded steel parts, between which was a straining disk of 350-mesh phosphor-bronze twilled wire cloth.

Shop tests showed that when the air jet that rotated the gyro remained for a time either above or below the middle of the gyro disk, the latter gradually became inclined. This action would not, however, be detrimental unless the rocket deviated over considerable periods of time.

The rigidity of the fixed air vanes was increased by increasing the thickness of the aluminum to $\frac{1}{16}$ in., and by using wires as braces, each extending from the bottom of the conical tailpiece of the rocket to the middle of the rear edge of the vane.

The rocket weighed $85\frac{1}{2}$ lb and was of the same length as for the preceding test.

Test. When tested, the rocket rose practically vertically during the entire 14 sec of propulsion period. The oscillations from side to side were of less extent than for previous tests during the first part of the flight but were of larger extent toward the end of the period of propulsion. According to Mr. A. W. Kisk, who observed the flight from the 50-ft shelter, the rocket did not move more than 40 ft from a vertical line through the center of the tower for the first 1000 ft.

The parachute was released just after propulsion ceased, but the two $\frac{1}{8}$-in. steel cables broke, and the parachute floated away by itself. The rocket then described a curved trajectory, becoming horizontal at a distance of 3000 ft from the tower.

The flame from the rocket after it left the tower was white and about a foot long. An additional yellowish flame below this ceased as the rocket left the tower.

Test of September 23, 1935 (A-11): Attempted Flight Test

The frame containing the gyro gimbals, consisting in this case of $\frac{3}{4}$-in.-O.D. square 17 ST tubing split lengthwise to form U-shaped sections, was reduced in size to a rectangle $4\frac{1}{4}$ in. wide and $4\frac{7}{8}$ in. high inside, this frame being $\frac{5}{8}$ in. less in height than that previously used.

A cylindrical containing box of $\frac{1}{8}$-in.-thick 17 ST aluminum was used, consisting of two vertical halves, held together by flanges, each half having a flat top and bottom.

Casehardened pivots were used for the gimbal mountings instead of ball bearings, for the reason that the former were found to run with less vibration when the frame was held in a vise and the gyro was driven by air pressure. Also, the gimbal friction was found to be reduced by this mounting. The angle of the ends of the pivots was 40 deg, and of the casehardened seats, 60 deg.

The gyro assembly weighed 18 oz, and the new box, including the sponge-rubber shock absorbers, 42 oz, this being 6 oz less than for the assembly previously used.

Parachute timer and cable. Since the period of propulsion was 14 sec, the clockwork of the timer was retarded to give a 21-sec period by soldering a 5/8-in.-diameter, 1/32-in.-thick disk to the escapement-wheel pivot.

A doubled 1/4-in. steel cable attached to the parachute was substituted for the 1/8-in. doubled steel cable previously used.

The rocket weighed slightly more than for the preceding test, but the length was the same.

Test. On making the test, a flame showing excess gasoline appeared in the concrete gas deflector, occasionally rising up toward the nozzle but not reaching it. This flame lasted during the entire run of 10 to 15 sec.

Apparently the oxygen gas, which during the filling of the oxygen tank passed down through the chamber, had caused premature burning of the string holding the igniter in the chamber before the run. After ignition, the propelling charge burned entirely outside the rocket.

Test of September 25, 1935 (A-12):
Attempted Flight Test

In this test the igniter was retained in the chamber by one end of a steel arm, 12 in. long and hinged at the other end, held in position by a 1/16-in.-diameter rod, being removable by hand when the flame appeared. In addition, the igniter was supported by the string, as before.

The small steel strainers for the magnet valves were replaced by strainers of 17 ST aluminum, having 3/16-in. holes instead of 1/8 in. as before. The strainers weighed 12 grams each, and the brass tube fittings 11 grams; the previous steel strainers plus fittings weighed 41 grams each.

The length and weight of the rocket were practically the same as for the preceding test.

Test. In the test the release key was pressed after 5 sec of lift, but about this time a gasoline flame appeared near the top of the chamber, followed by a large bright flame. The flame during the short lift period was whiter and noisier than usual, indicating an excess of oxygen.

The chamber was found to have burned through under one of the gasoline orifices, the burning evidently occurring under pressure, since the edges of the hole were found to be bulged.

At the shop after the run, a water test of the two gasoline orifices at 20 psi showed the flows to be 4.09 and 4.73 oz/sec, respectively, whereas the flows originally were 5.25 oz/sec for each. The excess of oxygen was thus considerably greater than in the earlier tests of the series, since the gasoline flow in the present case was reduced in the ratio 8.9/10.5, in addition to which the equalizer had been set to advance the excess oxygen-tank pressure from 3 to 10 psi, and then from 10 to 12 psi.

Test of October 2, 1935 (A-11a):
Attempted Flight Test

The rocket with which a flight had been attempted on September 23 (A-11) was tested again with only the following changes: the equalizer was set for 7.5 psi excess oxygen-tank pressure in order to reduce the proportion of oxygen somewhat, and the timer was set at 19.5 sec in order to permit the rocket to remain longer in the tower before being released.

The weight and length were the same as for Test A-11.

In the test it was planned to release the rocket after 5 sec of lift. After the fourth second, however, a narrow gasoline flame shot up from the top of the chamber, as in the preceding test, followed a second or so later by a large noisy flame from farther down in the chamber.

A hole was found about an inch below one of the gasoline orifices, and also a hole at the bottom of the cylindrical part of the chamber.

The gasoline orifices were examined and were found to give flows with water at 20 psi of 5.30 and 4.75 oz/sec. Further, the flat streams from the elongated or slot-like orifices were stronger at the edges than in the middle, fanning out at about 10 deg. An examination of the gasoline orifice pieces showed that the entering edges of the orifices in Test No. 11, 11a, and 12 had not been beveled or chamfered.

It appeared likely that failure to protect the chambers below the gasoline orifices by the tangential gasoline sheet, where this protection is poorest, may have been due both to lack of the expected rate of flow of gasoline and to divergence of the streams.

Test of October 8, 1935 (A-13):
Static Test

This test was a static, or proving-stand, test of the rocket used in Test A-12, with modified gasoline orifices. These orifices each consisted of steel plugs, drilled to ¼-in. diameter, 5/16-in. O.D. and 3/8 in. long, having No. 29 drill holes in the inner end, which was hemispherical both inside and out.

Tests with water at 20 psi brought to light the fact that chamfering, or beveling, the inner edge of the orifice caused a considerable change in the rate of flow, a slight chamfering increasing the rate from 5.25 to 6.25 oz/sec, and a still further chamfering increasing the rate to 7.75 oz/sec. Adjustment was therefore made by continued chamfering until the required rate of 5.25 oz/sec was obtained.

All the parts used in connection with flights were removed in order to avoid damage. These included the cap, tailpiece, directing vanes, bellows operators, gyro, and accessories.

Test. The flame and roar were very steady during the run, the lift period of which lasted 21.5 sec. This period checked well with the flight tests, 5 sec being allowed to elapse after the rocket lifted its own weight before being released, the period of propulsion thereafter being about 14 sec.

On examination, the chamber was found to have become considerably bulged, apparently by being overheated below and in front of one of the gasoline orifices. It thus seemed likely that the burning in the preceding tests was due to too much spreading out of the gasoline streams where they struck the chamber wall tangentially, as well as too low a gasoline flow from the slotted orifices.

In the present test the overheating appeared due to a wide spreading of the gasoline streams on striking the chamber wall, which occurred notwithstanding the narrow cylindrical form of the streams.

Test of October 29, 1935 (A-14):
Flight Test

The object of this test was to obtain a flight with the rocket used in Test A-13, using the same gasoline orifices but decreasing the lengths of the slots in which they were placed tangentially, from 1⁹⁄₁₆ in. to 1³⁄₃₂ in. The stream from each gasoline orifice traveled 1¾ in. before striking the cylindrical wall of the chamber. In tests with water at 20 psi in both gasoline orifices, the cylindrical wall of the chamber was found to be evenly and completely covered.

The weight and length were the same as for Test A-11.

Test. In this test the rocket was released after lifting for 5 sec. It rose fairly rapidly in the tower and thereafter increased in speed at a moderate rate, becoming inclined as much as 20 deg before correcting itself, first in the plane at right angles to the observers and then in the plane of the observers.

After reaching a height of about ¾ mile practically vertically, it dived sharply to the left and descended under power, striking the ground 12 sec after it rose.

The combustion chamber was found to be intact, there being no evidence of any hot spot or burning.

The stabilizing devices evidently functioned during a considerable part of the flight. The sudden turning and almost straight subsequent path may have been caused by sticking of one of the magnet valves owing to dirt, filings, or rust. It did not seem likely, however, that a steering vane could have remained in the blast continuously without causing the rocket to travel in a curved path.

5

Tests for the Development of a
More Powerful Motor

K Series, November 22, 1935 — February 12, 1936

This series of static tests was carried out for the purpose of developing 10-in.-diameter chambers, in order to obtain a larger thrust than had been possible with the 5¾-in.-diameter chambers. The tests were performed at the launching tower, rather than in the 20-ft tower near the shop, since the former location was more isolated.

The rocket setup for the tests consisted of the chamber, liquid-oxygen tank just above the chamber, and gasoline tank, all in line between two vertical pipes serving as supports. The oxygen line was precooled by liquid oxygen in a jacket around part of the oxygen tubing. Pressure was supplied by a 5-ft cylindrical tank of ¹⁄₁₆-in. sheet nickel, 12 in. in diameter, filled with nitrogen gas before the run, a nitrogen cylinder remaining connected until shut off at a convenient time after the run.

Two steel brackets, on the outside of the support pipes, each engaged a 4⅝-in.-O.D. Sylphon bellows, filled with automobile brake fluid, which served to measure the lift. Connecting pipe lines led to pressure gauges for the lift, chamber, and nitrogen-tank pressures, on an instrument board bolted to the closed horizontal door of the concrete dugout, 50 ft from the tower. Also on the board were a stop watch and two thermocouples that indicated the temperature of the cylindrical part of the chamber and of the nozzle. A 35-mm motion-picture camera was arranged to take photographs of the instruments at the rate of approximately three per second, this camera being so placed that the flame from the nozzle was visible at the right of the instrument board.

The rocket was operated from the 1000-ft shelter, with the electric cable and control keys previously used for flight tests; two 8-in. pressure gauges on the tower, showing the lift and chamber pressures, were observed through telescopes. The performance of the rocket was studied from a partly open shelter 125 ft from the tower.

Test of November 22, 1935 (K-1)*:
10-Inch Chamber

In the first test of the series, the combustion chamber consisted of a 10-in. diameter cylindrical part of $\frac{1}{16}$-in.-thick nickel, 15 in. long, with a 60-deg cone below this, terminating in a nozzle. The latter, of 0.038-in. nickel, was 24 in. long, with a throat of $2\frac{7}{16}$ in. diameter and an open end of $5\frac{1}{2}$ in. diameter. The total weight of the chamber and nozzle was 18 lb.

Fuel injection. The upper end of the chamber consisted of a 45-deg sheet-nickel cone. Between this cone and the cylindrical part was a flat ring, extending $1\frac{1}{4}$ in. inward and having an inverted 45-deg cone. Both the ring and the cone had iron screening on the outside or lower surface, covered with Insalute-Alundum cement, as protection from the heat of the chamber. The liquid-oxygen orifice, at the vertex of the inverted cone, consisted of a $\frac{25}{64}$-in.-diameter circular hole; from this a rod projected, in the direction of the nozzle, bearing a $\frac{3}{4}$-in.-diameter stainless-steel deflector that turned the oxygen backward, i.e., toward the head of the chamber, in the form of a hollow conical sheet.

The gasoline entered through two diametrically opposite tangential orifices, $\frac{13}{16}$ in. below the top of the cylindrical part of the chamber, each consisting of a tube having a rounded inner end in which was a No. 5 axial drill hole. The flow of water at 20 psi through the oxygen orifice was 25 oz/sec, and was 13 oz/sec for each of the gasoline orifices.

The chamber and nozzle were protected from the flame by having the nozzle enter $\frac{1}{2}$ in. in the top of a steel thimble or sleeve, located in the middle of a 3-ft square, $\frac{1}{8}$-in.-thick steel plate, bolted to the lowest set of horizontal angle irons of the tower.

Before the test the lift indicator or gauge was checked by lifting the rocket in the tower with a block and tackle. Before this was done, the lift-pressure line, including the bellows and the two gauges, was filled completely with brake fluid, so that the lift system was tested for leakage at the same time.

Test. In this first test the camera operated for 15 sec, the period of strong combustion being 12 sec. During the latter period the chamber pressure was 94 psi, tank pressure 120 psi, lifting force 450 lb, chamber temperature near the upper end about 120° C, and temperature of nozzle over 375° C.

The chamber became bulged somewhat below each gasoline orifice, evidently from heating. The nozzle was also bulged, just below the narrowest part. The refractory cement on the inverted cone was found to be intact except at two places, where it had become separated from the perforated steel. The oxygen deflector was undamaged.

---

* Dr. Goddard in his records referred to this group of tests as the K series and numbered them consecutively. This numbering system has been preserved in parentheses.

The jet velocity was estimated as 3420 ft/sec; the rates of flow for the oxygen and gasoline were 2.5 and 1.66 lb/sec, respectively, a ratio of 1.52. The flame was whitish and appeared to spread considerably below the steel thimble around the nozzle.

Test of December 3, 1935 (K-2):
Repeat Test, Higher Pressure

The preceding test was repeated, using a higher tank pressure in order, if possible, to obtain a higher jet velocity.

Changes. The chamber was altered by using four gasoline entrance orifices in place of two, in order to reduce localized heating below the orifices. These four orifices were centered 1¾₆ in. below the upper end of the cylindrical part of the chamber, as before. In order to make this change possible without making a new chamber, it was necessary to cut 1¾₆ in. from the cylindrical part. The ⅜-in.-wide slot cut in the wall for each orifice was 1½ in. long, and the orifice end was set back ¾₆ in. from the vertical cut of each opening. The orifice openings were of No. 24 drill size, with the inner edges chamfered, or beveled, and each gave a flow of water of 5.5 oz/sec at 20 psi.

The cemented cone was patched and the oxygen orifice cleaned.

In order to facilitate a more rapid rise of pressure in the tanks, a smaller liquid-oxygen tank was used, in order to decrease the volume above the liquid oxygen. This tank consisted of a 9-in.-long, 9-in.-diameter cylinder with hemispherical ends, as compared with the 9-in.-long, 12-in.-diameter cylinder with conical ends, previously used.

Test. In the test the rocket lifted strongly for 6 sec, the average during this interval being 770 lb and the maximum 797 lb. The tank pressure was 210 psi and the chamber pressure 60 to 70 psi. The chamber temperature was 120° C and the nozzle temperature 370° C.

The chamber showed no sign of heating and was not bulged. Apparently the pressure rose rapidly at the start; the cemented cone was collapsed into the upper 45-deg cone of the chamber because there had not been sufficient time for the pressure to become equalized through the holes in the cone. This condition accounted for the low measured chamber pressure, the line to the pressure gauge probably being plugged by fragments of cement during the run.

The jet velocity was 3380 ft/sec; the rates of flow of oxygen and gasoline were 4.25 and 3.0 lb/sec, respectively. The flame was appreciably noisier than in the preceding test.

Test of December 10, 1935 (K-3):
Repeat Test, Smaller Nozzle

This test was a repetition of the preceding test, with the throat of the nozzle reduced from 2¾₆ in. diameter to 1¹⁵⁄₁₆ in. This change was made because the previous throat area appeared to be too large, an increase in tank pressure from 120 to 210 psi resulting in a somewhat reduced jet velocity.

A new cylindrical part and inverted cemented cone were made for the chamber, the cylinder being 14 in. long and the cemented cone having two rows of $\frac{5}{8}$-in.-diameter holes to help equalize the pressure. A strainer was used in the line to the chamber pressure gauge. The nozzle was 24 in. long and 5 in. at the wide diameter.

Test. The camera did not operate throughout the run, so that it was necessary to estimate the time. This estimate was 12 sec, the average thrust being 516 lb, the chamber pressure 175 psi, and the tank pressure 200 psi. The chamber temperature was 170° C and the nozzle temperature 550° C. The latter reading was secured by using a shunt to reduce the nozzle temperature deflection to one-tenth the previous readings.

After the test the nozzle appeared to have been heated, since it had bulged about 1 in. below the throat all around, although chiefly in one area. The jet velocity was estimated as 3300 ft/sec; the rate of flow of oxygen and gasoline was 2.83 and 2.08 lb/sec, a ratio of 1.37. The flame was intensely white and narrower than in the preceding test.

Test of December 17, 1935 (K-4):
Repeat Test, Higher Injection Velocity

The object of this test was to increase the jet velocity, if possible, by increasing the speed of entrance of the liquids into the chamber, using about the same tank pressure as before.

Changes. For this purpose the flow of water at 20 psi was reduced from 25 to 17 oz/sec through the oxygen orifice, and from 26 to 18 oz/sec through the gasoline orifices.

The inverted cement-protected cone, previously used inside the upper or forward end of the cylindrical part of the chamber, was replaced by a flat disk of 0.050-in.-thick sheet nickel, having sixteen $\frac{1}{2}$-in. holes for equalizing pressure, and a central hole to accommodate the jacketed, cement-protected, axial oxygen-supply tube, bearing the usual deflector for producing an upward-directed spray cone of oxygen. The throat diameter was $2\frac{7}{16}$ in. I.D.

Level recorder. A level recorder was used in both the oxygen and gasoline tanks, in order to measure the rates of flow. Each consisted of a cork float, sliding on two vertical insulated steel rods bearing sets of nickel knife-edges. A nickel contact strip extended across the top of the cork float. A voltmeter reading indicated when the float began to pass away from the upper knife-edges, and another reading indicated when it had reached the lower knife-edges. The distance of travel of the respective floats was $2\frac{7}{8}$ in. and $2\frac{1}{2}$ in., both floats being well under the liquid surface at the beginning of the test.

Test. The Sept camera did not operate during this run, and the duration was therefore estimated by the stop watch. The run was estimated as 14 sec, the thrust being 496 lb, chamber pressure 105 psi, and tank pressure 200 psi. It will be noted that the excess of tank pressure over chamber pressure was 95 psi as compared with 25 psi in the preceding test.

The nozzle became heated to a dull red all over during the latter half of the run, which was terminated when the welded seam of the lower cone of the chamber broke, probably owing to heating.

The jet velocity was estimated as 4470 ft/sec; the rates of flow for oxygen and gasoline were 2.13 and 1.44 lb/sec, a ratio of 1.49. There was a white and relatively small flame close to the nozzle and an additional flame lower down, in the concrete gas deflector.

Test of January 9, 1936 (K-5):
Changes in Injection

In this test the chamber was altered by making the width of the hollow oxygen-spray cone about twice what it had been in the previous tests of the present series, in order to improve the combustion, and using also an increased gasoline flow in order to reduce the heating.

The oxygen injector consisted of two narrow annular orifices, one $3/8$ in. above the other, giving together 17.4 oz/sec of water at 20 psi. The diameters averaged $2 \frac{1}{32}$ in. The two spray cones merged into a single spray cone impinging on the cylindrical part of the chamber in a zone from $5/8$ in. below the top of the cylindrical part down about $1 \frac{1}{2}$ in., being thus $1 \frac{1}{2}$-in. wide at a distance of 5 in. from the chamber axis. The four gasoline orifices were widened to give 5.5 oz/sec each, instead of 4.5 oz/sec.

The perforated 0.050-in. nickel plate at the top of the cylindrical part of the chamber was used again, and the throat diameter was $2 \frac{7}{16}$ in., also as before. The chamber weighed 19.5 lb.

Test. A run was obtained in which the rocket operated satisfactorily, although after the test the perforated nickel disk at the top of the cylindrical part of the chamber was found to have been dished upward and also burned at the central opening. Further, the cement-protected oxygen tube in the chamber was blistered up to within 3 in. of the apex of the upper cone. The nozzle indicated heating, being blued somewhat.

The run was of 5.6 sec duration; the thrust was 541 lb, chamber pressure 140 psi, and tank pressure 200 psi. The jet velocity was 2520 ft/sec, with rates of flow for oxygen and gasoline 4.02 lb/sec, and 2.85 lb/sec, respectively, a ratio of 1.48.

It appeared likely that the wide oxygen spray forced the flame upward and inward from the ring-shaped region on the cylindrical wall where impact took place, thus not only reducing the efficiency of combustion but also causing the nozzle to become heated nearly as much as in the preceding tests. The contact method of measuring rates of flow did not prove reliable.

Test of January 14, 1936 (K-6):
Increased Gasoline Flow

Because of the low velocity obtained in the preceding test, Test K-4 was repeated with the gasoline flow increased about 20 per cent.

The gasoline orifices were the same as in the preceding test, each giving 5.5 oz/sec rate of flow at 20 psi water pressure, or 22 oz/sec for the four. The oxygen orifice, the same used in Test K-4, gave 17 oz/sec in the water test. The 0.050-in. sheet-nickel perforated plate used at the upper end of the cylindrical part of the chamber in Test K-4 was replaced by a 0.050 in. sheet-nickel ring, projecting inward $1\frac{1}{4}$ in. from the upper end of the cylindrical wall.

Heating of the nozzle was reduced by the use of a water jacket that surrounded the nozzle and lower cone of the chamber and contained 21 lb of water. A 2-in.-diameter steel tube outside the jacket connected the upper and lower ends, in order to facilitate convection.

Test. A satisfactory run was obtained, the chamber remaining practically unchanged. The duration was 10 sec; the thrust was 440 lb, chamber pressure 130 psi, and tank pressure 215 psi. The jet velocity was 3060 ft/sec, with rates of flow of oxygen and gasoline 2.6 and 2.0 lb/sec, respectively, a ratio of 1.19. The chamber temperature rose to 150° C, and the water in the nozzle jacket rose 55° C, partly because of a gasoline flame on the 3-ft-square plate supporting the thimble for the nozzle, this flame being caused by a leaking gasoline valve. The float-and-contact method of measuring rates of flow continued to be unreliable.

From the fact that the excess of tank over chamber pressure in Test K-6 was 85 psi, this being only 10 psi under the excess for Test K-4, it appeared likely that the low jet velocity of Test K-6 was due to the larger proportion of gasoline to liquid oxygen.

Test of January 21, 1936 (K-7):
Decreased Oxygen Flow

An attempt was made to learn the effect of decreasing the proportion of oxygen by repeating the preceding test with a reduced oxygen flow. At the same time, sliding contacts on cork floats, in place of the upper and lower contact pieces, were used for measuring the falls of tank level.

The gasoline orifices were the same as before, each giving 5.5 oz/sec flow of water at 20 psi. The oxygen flow was decreased by increasing the diameter of the rod supporting the deflector from 0.189 to 0.230 in., the opening remaining $\frac{5}{16}$ in. in diameter. The deflector diameter was reduced from $\frac{3}{4}$ to $\frac{5}{8}$ in., the spray remaining only $\frac{3}{4}$ in. wide where it struck the 10-in. cylindrical wall. A water jacket was again used.

Each level indicator consisted of two copper wires, in grooves in two vertical fiber rods, the grooves facing each other, and the wires being bridged by a spring-copper strip on a cork float. The wires were 2 in. long for the oxygen tank and 3 in. long for the gasoline tank.

Test. A 10-sec run was obtained, in which the chamber pressure was 120 psi, the tank pressure 215 psi, and the thrust 428 lb. The rates of flow for the oxygen and gasoline, estimated as usual from the falls in tank level, were 2.4 lb/sec and 2.8 lb/sec, a ratio of 0.855, giving 2630 ft/sec for the jet velocity. On the other hand, the rate of oxygen flow from the float indicator readings was 1.75 lb/sec. The gasoline float indicator reading remained constant, possibly because of a short circuit. If the rate of gasoline flow is, however, assumed to be 2.5 lb/sec instead of 2.8 lb/sec, the ratio being 0.96, the jet velocity is 2800 ft/sec. The chamber temperature rose to 155° C, and the water in the jacket rose 44° C.

The chamber showed evidence of having been heated at the upper end. The $1\frac{1}{4}$-in.-wide ring had been roughened by heat at the inner edge, a considerable portion of the refractory cement on the outside of the oxygen tube had been melted up to within $2\frac{1}{2}$ in. of the vertex of the upper cone of the chamber, and about $\frac{1}{16}$ in. had been melted from the bottom of the stainless-steel deflector.

Test of January 28, 1936 (K-8):
Focused Sprays

The object of this test was to determine to what extent low jet velocity was due to the sprays being directed more or less toward the throat, or nozzle orifice.

The liquid-oxygen delivery tube inside the chamber was shortened so that the edge of the deflector was only $2\frac{3}{4}$ in. below the vertex of the upper 45-deg cone. The conical liquid-oxygen sheet passed downward at an angle of 30 deg with the horizontal, and impinged on a 1-in.-wide conical frustum or strip practically perpendicular to the oxygen spray sheet. The narrow end of the frustum was toward the nozzle and rested on a flat ring of 0.050-in. nickel, which projected $\frac{1}{4}$ in. into the top of the 14-in.-long cylindrical part of the chamber. No refractory cement was used except around the part of the oxygen-delivery tube within the chamber.

The oxygen orifice gave a flow of water of 17 oz/sec at 20 psi. The spray was about $\frac{5}{8}$ in. wide at the point where it hit the 1-in.-wide conical ring, which it did with considerable force.

As usual, four equally spaced gasoline orifices were used at the top of the 14-in.-long cylindrical part of the chamber. These consisted of rounded-end tubes with circular chamfered orifices, each giving 4 oz/sec of water at 20 psi. Four additional orifices were used in the 1-in.-wide conical ring or strip mentioned above, these having No. 48 holes in tangential tubes of similar shape, and each giving 1.5 oz/sec of water at 20 psi.

The method may be called the focusing method, since the combined spray of oxygen and gasoline on the 1-in. ring tended after impact to meet within a small region below the oxygen deflector. The nozzle and water jacket of Test K-7 were used again.

Test. When this chamber was tested, a gasoline flame followed by a whitish flame was seen from a hole in the 45-deg upper cone, extending to about 5 in. above where this cone joined the conical strip. The inside of the chamber was undamaged.

Even though the time of the run was short, a comparison with Test K-6, in which the rates of flow of water for the oxygen and gasoline at 20 psi were the same, namely, 17 oz/sec and 22 oz/sec, indicated that the jet velocity was 3560 ft/sec, or 16 per cent greater in the present case, with 35 per cent greater energy efficiency.

Indications of better combustion, or possibly less cooling, were obtained by comparing the chamber pressures for the two tests, these being 124 psi for the former and 137 psi for the latter. The final temperature of the chamber wall was also greater, 175° C compared with 140° C, as was also the heat given to the water jacket.

It is concluded that the focusing method as embodied in the present chamber was somewhat superior to the performance of a chamber with the usual inverted cone and deflector.

Test of February 4, 1936 (K-9):
Large Propellant Flow

The object of this test was to repeat Test K-2, in which the rates of flow of both oxygen and gasoline were relatively large, with the ratio of oxygen to gasoline flow, as indicated by the water tests, in the same proportion as in the A series of flights, namely 6.3 to 10.5, by weight.

The chamber consisted of a 14-in. cylinder with four gasoline orifices giving together a water flow of 32 oz/sec at 20 psi, this being slightly more than three times the corresponding flow for the A series of chamber tests, which was 10.5 oz/sec. The flow for the liquid oxygen orifice was 20 oz/sec at 20 psi, this being close to 18.9 oz/sec, or three times the water flow for the A-type chambers (6.3 oz/sec each). The 1¼-in.-wide flat nickel ring was used at the top of the cylindrical part of the chamber, as before.

Test. A 5.5-sec run was obtained in which the chamber pressure was 130 psi, the tank pressure 180 psi, and the thrust 554 lb. The oxygen and gasoline rates of flow were estimated as 3.64 lb/sec each. The jet velocity was calculated as 2520 ft/sec.

The temperature of the chamber wall was low, 75° C, and the rise of temperature of the water jacket was also low. Increase in the proportion of gasoline to oxygen thus appeared to decrease both the jet velocity and the chamber- and nozzle-wall temperature. The oxygen-level indicator gave 2.6 lb/sec as the rate of flow, compared with 3.64 lb/sec obtained from measuring initial and final levels. The gasoline-level indicator did not operate, possibly owing to the insulating nature of gasoline.

Test of February 12, 1936 (K-10):
Impact Spray

An attempt was made to test a chamber in which sheets of spray impinged from substantially opposite directions, in what might be called an impact-spray method.

The oxygen entered through the usual long tube in the chamber, bearing a deflector at the lower end to give an upward-directed cone of spray, this tube being jacketed with liquid oxygen and having a small return tube to provide circulation, both tubes being covered with refractory cement. The deflector was of stainless steel, 5/8 in. in diameter. The flow was 17 oz/sec for water at 20 psi.

The four gasoline orifices were those used at the top of the cylindrical part of the chamber in Test K-8. The flow rates were checked with water at 20 psi and were found to remain 4 oz/sec each.

In addition to these, four flat-spray orifices were used, directed radially inward from the outer surface of the chamber wall and flush with it; all being located at equal intervals, 27/8 in. below the top of the cylindrical part. Each flat-spray orifice consisted of a 1/2-in.-diameter steel tube pinched together and welded along a transverse line. The two corners were pinched tightly together in a vise, and an elliptical hole was filed in the middle of the welded edge, the long axis coinciding with the line of the edge. Each of these holes produced a flat spray, in a plane at right angles to the line of the edge, from 60 to 80 deg wide, the flow of water at 20 psi pressure being 13/4 oz/sec. When both sets of gasoline orifices were used with water at 20 psi, it was found that the flat sprays were somewhat wider than when tested separately but were otherwise unchanged. The total flow for the eight gasoline orifices was 23 oz/sec with water at 20 psi.

The flat spray struck the conical spray around a circle of about 25/8 in. radius. The angle of impact was 45 deg.

Test. When this chamber was tested, the cylindrical part became heated and broke through after 3 or 4 sec, the opening being in the form of a 6-in.-long slot extending up from the junction with the lower cone, below one of the flat-spray orifices. There was also a break in the nozzle about 5 in. long and ¼ in. wide.

During the short run obtained, the chamber pressure was 140 psi for a tank pressure of 210 psi, the average thrust being 623.5 lb. Again the gasoline-level indicator did not operate. The jet velocity was estimated from the water-flow rates as 4340 ft/sec.

The rise of temperature of the chamber during the few seconds of run was to 169° C, or not much more than usual. The increase in temperature of the water in the water jacket, 15° C, was somewhat less than before. Notwithstanding the moderate jacket temperature, it is possible that the nozzle burned through first and that the tangential flow in the cylindrical part was thereby disturbed, resulting in local heating.

Conclusions from K-Series Tests

Comparisons. It is instructive to compare Tests K-6, K-8, and K-10, for which the rates of flow in the water tests at 20 psi were the same, namely, 17 oz/sec for the oxygen and 22 oz/sec for the gasoline.

Measurement after 2 sec	Test K-6	Test K-8	Test K-10
Lift	442 lb	514 lb	623.5 lb
Chamber pressure	124 psi	137 psi	142 psi
Tank pressure	196 psi	192.5 psi	213 psi
Pressure difference	72 psi	55.5 psi	71 psi
Chamber temperature rise	130° C	170° C	150° C
Nozzle-jacket temperature rise	55.0° C	20° C	15° C
Jet velocity	3060 ft/sec	3560 ft/sec	4340 ft/sec

Inasmuch as the pressure difference, or feed pressure, was about the same for Tests K-6 and K-10, and less for K-8, the rates of flow for the former two were probably the same and were greater than for the latter. The jet velocities for K-6 and K-10 might therefore be expected to be nearly the same, that for K-10 possibly being the higher. In the light of the above conclusion, the greater rise of both chamber and nozzle temperature for K-8 indicates that the impact-spray method may be superior to the focus method, because it combines greater combustion efficiency with the avoidance of severe heating of the chamber.

Injection pressure. The jet velocity in these tests increased with increase in the difference between tank and chamber pressure, as is seen by comparing Tests K-1 and K-4, for which the feed or injection pressures were 30 and 95 psi, respectively, the jet velocity being 3420 and 4470 ft/sec, for about the same proportion of liquids.

Mixture ratio. The less the dilution with gasoline, the greater the jet velocities. Thus for the greater ratio of oxygen to gasoline in Test K-4 to that for Test K-7, 1.49 to 0.855, there was a correspondingly lower jet velocity, from 4470 to 2630 ft/sec.

It is of interest to note that the ratio of oxygen to gasoline flow in the actual tests exceeded the ratio as indicated by the water tests at 20 psi in the proportion from 1.2 to 1.6, averaging about 1.4.

Jet velocity. Although most of the jet velocities were low, it is possible that an accurate flow method would have indicated higher velocities, since the few indications of flow rates obtained by the oxygen-level indicator were lower than rates estimated from the initial and final tank levels. The jet velocities for the various tests were, however, probably in the proper proportion.

Throat diameter. From Test K-3, showing the lack of increase of thrust when the throat diameter was reduced for the same chamber volume, it was concluded that the ratio of volume of chamber to throat area in Tests K-1 and K-2, namely 328, was not so large as to allow much of the gaseous mixture to pass out of the chamber without burning.

Double oxygen sprays. The specific impulse, or impulse per pound of fluids used, was slightly greater for K-1 than for K-5, the respective ratios being 1.08 and 0.895. The wider spray, therefore, gives less efficient combustion, possibly because of disturbance of the tangential gasoline flow, as already explained.

Focusing method. On comparing Test K-6 with K-8, it is seen that the focusing method gives about 16 per cent greater specific impulse. This estimate is made under the assumption that the rates of flow in these two tests are nearly the same.

Impact-Spray method. A comparison of Test K-6 with K-10, assuming equal flows in the two cases, indicates an increase in specific impulse of about 30 per cent for the latter test. The increase in specific impulse for K-10 was probably less than this, however, since the flows probably were greater, owing to the larger pressure difference.

Recommendations. As a result of the K series of tests, it was concluded that higher chamber pressures should be used, and also, in the light of the results obtained in Test K-4, that the feed or injection pressures should be increased, these latter pressures preferably being produced by pumps.

Jacket cooling of the chamber and nozzle also seemed desirable, together with an increase in the oxygen-gasoline ratio from the value 1.49 in Test K-4 to as near 3.5 as possible.

A combination of the oxygen-deflector and tangential gasoline-injection method of Test K-4 with the flat sprays of Test K-10 appeared desirable, with a large number of these flat sprays being directed into the oxygen-spray cone from the nozzle side at an angle of nearly 180 deg.

Liquid hydrogen appeared advantageous as a fuel, since even a dilution of 2 to 1 in the hydrogen, over that required for complete combustion, would increase the total mass by only one-ninth.

6

Flight Tests with 10-Inch-Diameter Motors, in Nitrogen-Pressured Rockets

L Series, May 11, 1936 — November 7, 1936

On May 11, 1936, in New Mexico, Dr. Goddard began the first of a series of rocket flight tests that were to continue for more than two years. Designated by him as the L series of tests, they are described in this and the two subsequent sections. "It was one of the objects of this series," Goddard wrote in his notes, "to produce a flight rocket pressurized by liquid nitrogen. A number of flight tests were made, but they were chiefly with rockets having nitrogen gas pressure storage tanks."

The first six of these experiments, described in this section, had as their object the development of a nitrogen-pressured flight rocket using 10-in. motors embodying principles learned in the K series of tests described in Section 5. In the seventh test, four 5¼-in. motors were used instead of a single 10-in. motor.—Editors.

Test of May 11, 1936 (L-1):
Static Test, Large Rocket

The object of this test was to obtain a satisfactory static test with a rocket of comparatively large size, which could afterward be adapted for flights.

Chamber. The combustion chamber was similar to the 10-in.-diameter chamber used in Test 6 of the K series. The water flows at 20 psi for the single oxygen and four gasoline orifices were, respectively, 17 oz/sec and 22 oz/sec.

The chamber was of 0.037-in. sheet nickel throughout except for the 1¼-in.-wide ring at the top of the cylindrical part, to prevent the tangential sheet of gasoline from rising into the chamber head. The only interior parts in the head end of the chamber were the nickel ring at the top of the cylindrical part and the refractory-covered oxygen line extending in from the apex of the upper cone sufficiently far for the deflector to produce an inverted conical sheet of liquid oxygen, impinging at the upper end of the cylinder. The jacketed tube for the oxygen, within the chamber, was covered with refractory cement, as before. The weight was 16½ lb.

Tanks. The gasoline tank, at the forward end of the rocket, consisted of a 9-in.-long, 17¾-in. cylinder of 0.050-in. nickel, with 120-deg, 0.037-in. frustums and 240-deg, 0.018-in. cones at the ends. Four baffles spaced 5⅜ in. apart, consisting of 0.017-in. 17 ST aluminum sheet, were used, fastened to wires brazed to the side wall of the tank, which weighed 28¾ lb complete. The weight of gasoline planned was three times that used in Test K-6, namely, 90 lb.

The oxygen tank, located 6 in. above the top of the combustion chamber, consisted of a 2½-in.-long, 17¾-in.-diameter cylindrical part of 0.050-in. nickel, with 0.037-in., 120-deg frustums and 0.018-in., 240-deg nickel cones at the ends. Baffles similar to those in the gasoline tank were used. The tank was covered to within 4½-in. of the 120-deg upper cone with ⅜-in.-thick felt, with aluminum foil on the outside. The weight of the tank was 16 lb 11 oz, and the amount of liquid oxygen planned was 78 lb.

The supports between chamber and oxygen tank, and between oxygen and gasoline tanks, each consisted of three 2-in.-diameter, ¾₄-in.-wall steel tubes. The ends in contact with the oxygen tank were, like the tank itself, wrapped with felt and thin aluminum sheet.

The nitrogen tank was located axially, directly below the gasoline tank, and between the oxygen-to-gasoline tank support tubes. It consisted of a 6-in.-long, 7¾-in.-diameter cylinder of 0.037-in. nickel, with 120-deg conical ends. This tank had a single 6-in.-diameter baffle, located in the lower cone. Outside the cylindrical part, separated from the tank by ¼-in. cork spacers and covered with felt and thin sheet brass, was a liquid-oxygen jacket with a cylindrical part 8½ in. high. This oxygen jacket served both to liquefy the nitrogen and to maintain the nitrogen at a low pressure up to the time of the start. When the rocket was released, a spring-operated circular disk valve was released, which dumped the oxygen from the jacket, thereby allowing the nitrogen tank pressure to rise. This valve was a flat disk, 1¾₆-in. in diameter and covered a ⅝-in. hole. On the disk was a washer of kangaroo leather.

Nitrogen liquefier. The liquefier for the nitrogen gas, which was obtained from a commercial gas cylinder through a reducing valve, consisted of six turns of ¾₆-in.-O.D., ¼₄-in.-wall copper tubing of 7 in. average diameter, located on the upper cone of the nitrogen tank. The turns were staggered, so that all the surface could be bathed in the liquid oxygen. The coil terminated at the upper end in an air cock.

Nitrogen regulator. The nitrogen-gas pressure for the oxygen and gasoline tanks was produced by the evaporation of liquid nitrogen in a copper-tube jacket around the chamber and nozzle. A back pressure in the nitrogen tank, sufficient for maintaining the required flow rate, was produced by a regulating valve in the bottom of the nitrogen tank, which allowed enough liquid nitrogen to enter a vaporizer to maintain a high, definite nitrogen-tank pressure.

The 7/8-in.-diameter tapered-seat brass valve disk that served to maintain the nitrogen-tank pressure was located on the side of the cone of the nitrogen tank, and the control means for this valve, being rather long, was located at the side of the rocket. The 1¼-in. steel connecting tube between the valve and the regulator extended at an angle of 45 deg with the rocket axis. It contained a rod that, when pushed by the pressure control, opened the control valve in the tank. This regulator, which was placed vertically, as already stated, pushed the rod through an intermediate bell crank.

The pressure regulator, of simpler construction than the relatively short bellows with springs at the sides that was previously used, consisted of a 12-in. length of 5/8-in.-O.D. seamless corrugated-brass tube. This tube was soldered at the lower end, and the rod that acted on the bell crank was fastened to a cap at the upper end. This cap was held upward by a lever before the run, in order to allow the nitrogen-regulator valve to close. Since the flexible tube used in the present case replaced both the bellows and spring of the earlier regulators, friction was practically absent.

Nitrogen vaporizer. The vaporizer for the liquid nitrogen consisted of strips of 0.013-in. copper, 7⅜ in. long, each bent to a U shape, to form flanges, which were wired to the gasoline-delivery line. A jacket of 1¼-in.-O.D. steel tubing was placed outside these copper strips. The 1¼-in. steel tube for the liquid nitrogen passed to one side of the upper end of this vaporizer jacket. A ½-in.-O.D. copper tube leading to the top of the nitrogen tank from the top of the jacket at the opposite side served to equalize the gas pressure, thus permitting the nitrogen to flow to the vaporizer both by gravity and by the acceleration of the rocket acting on the liquid nitrogen in the tank during flight.

The liquid nitrogen was delivered to the copper-tube jacket around the chamber through a ½-in.-O.D. steel tube which, after leaving the bottom of the tank, looped 1¾ in. above the upper cone of the tank in order to prevent liquid nitrogen from passing to the jacket before the run. This line, provided with an aluminum on-and-off valve, entered the bottom of the copper-tube jacket.

Nitrogen jacket. This jacket was made in two halves, for ease in assembling on the chamber, each having half-round ½-in.-O.D. steel tubes at the ends, to which the copper tubes were soldered. There were eighteen 3/16-in.-O.D. × 1/64-in.-wall copper tubes in each of the two half jackets, extending lengthwise along the nozzle and the lower cone of the chamber. Since these tubes were at a considerable distance apart, except around the throat, heat conduction from the nickel walls was facilitated by wrapping 0.013-in. sheet copper around the nozzle and lower cone. The complete chamber and jacket, with attaching straps around the jacket, weighed 22¼ lb.

Piping. A ½-in.-O.D. steel tube led from the top of each half jacket to the ⅞-in.-O.D. nitrogen-gas pressure tube. This tube was provided with the hose connection for supplying initial pressure and passed to the oxygen and gasoline tanks through aluminum check valves. No reducing valve for supplying control pressure was needed, since the run was to be a static test.

The gasoline line consisted of a ⅞-in.-O.D., ½₂-in.-wall steel tube that passed from the bottom of the gasoline tank, through an aluminum on-and-off valve, to a ¾-in.-O.D. square tube in the form of a ring just above the cylindrical part of the chamber, from which passed the four short tubes to the gasoline orifices of the chamber.

The ⅞-in. liquid-oxygen line was relatively short. Inside the tank it ran from a point near the bottom almost to the top, where it formed a loop, thus avoiding flow or siphoning to the chamber before the oxygen-tank pressure was applied. It passed thence through a 1⅛-in.-diameter jacket tube, 6 in. long, between the oxygen tank and the chamber, and ended in the orifice within the chamber, similar to that used in Test K-6. A 1½-in.-diameter, two-ply metal bellows was inserted in the middle of the jacket tube, to allow for expansion and contraction.

Valves. A safety valve was used on the nitrogen tank. It consisted of a 12-in. length of ⅝-in. flexible tubing, on the free end of which was a ³⁄₃₂-in.-diameter rod passing through a ⅛-in.-diameter valve opening that normally closed by a ball in a small recess or chamber on the end of the steel tube enclosing the flexible tube. The valve was set to blow off at 240 psi.

Parachute release. A similar flexible tube was used in a combination parachute timer and oxygen-tank pressure recorder. For the timing feature, the escapement and balance wheel of a small alarm clock were modified to give one revolution of the minute hand in 100 sec. An electric circuit was closed for the parachute release by the movement of a contact disk on an extension of the minute-hand axis. This axis also bore a paper-covered disk on which a pencil trace of the pressure was made by an arm, which was moved radially by means of a section of spiral thread from a No. 130A Yankee screw driver. In addition, an electric contact was made when the pressure fell to 100 lb, in order to shut off the oxygen tank and thus retain sufficient pressure for operating the gyro and contacts during the coasting period. The weight of the parachute releasing devices was 23 oz.

Controls. As usual, there were two detachable rollers on each side of the rocket to guide it out of the tower. They were ¾ in. wide and 6 in. O.D.

Because of the large number of controls required for starting, the dash-pots were used to operate triggers on new control devices, which could pull a 1/16-in. iron rod forcibly for a distance of 18 in., through a control hole or slot as in a valve or a lever arm.

The 1/16-in. rod to be pulled was fastened to a steel sleeve in the forward end of a 4 ft 5 in. length of 1/2-in. electrical conduit tube. To the rear end of this sleeve were fastened two screendoor springs, hooked together to form a single long spring and attached to a steel block at the rear of the conduit tube. This steel block could be engaged from outside the conduit, through a slot, and locked in place after the spring had been extended rearwardly, thus setting the control ready for operation.

The control was released by a 12-in. lever with a short arm that held the steel sleeve. The long end of this lever was held by the 1/32-in. iron control wire from the dashpot, passing through slots in two flat steel pieces between which the lever moved. Buckling of the springs due to the strong compression on releasing was overcome by a steel tube outside the springs, equal in length to the unstretched springs.

These control tubes were bolted to horizontal angle irons, in the tower, on a rectangular frame of angles whose long vertical sides were provided with holes for easy adjustment of the angles bearing the control tubes.

The Sept camera, taking pictures of the instruments at second intervals, showed the position of the galvanometer used as a lift indicator, the nitrogen-gas pressure, the nozzle temperature, and two indicators consisting of dry-cell voltmeters to show when the liquid-nitrogen regulator valve was open and closed. In addition, a metal sheet was dropped as soon as the rocket had lifted 1/8 in., a can was dropped when the oxygen-tank pressure fell to 100 psi, and a red flare was fired when the parachute timer made contact. The filling of the liquid-nitrogen tank required about 9 min and caused a drop in a nitrogen cylinder from 1100 to 150 psi.

Test. During the 19 sec or so of strong lift, the nitrogen pressure rose from 125 psi to 185 psi, and thus was considerably under the pressure required to cause the 1/16-in. motion in the regulator that opened it at 215 lb and closed it at 225 lb. The regulator valve for the liquid nitrogen was open during the entire run. The oxygen pressure did not fall to 100 psi until after the gasoline flame had appeared at the end of the run, indicating a low rate of flow, even when the oxygen was largely gaseous. The parachute timer operated 6 sec later. The rocket lifted, while operating itself, for 12.9 sec. The nozzle temperature rose to 270° C, indicating that nitrogen was evaporated in the vaporizer at an insufficient rate.

It should be mentioned that a support or cradle, to support the rocket in the tower and produce an initial velocity, was constructed but not used at this time. It consisted of two 27 1/2-in.-I.D. circular rings of 3/4-in.-O.D. square steel tubing, held 50 1/2 in. apart by two vertical square tubes. Two rollers on each side permitted rapid motion in the tower. Each ring was provided with two ⅜-in. tubing arms, extending inwardly. The upper pair were for supporting the top of the gasoline tank, so that the rocket would be suspended thereby and consequently not subjected to compressive forces. The lower pair bore against the chamber. These arms were locked horizontally until the rocket nearly reached the top of the tower, when they were all unlocked by means of cams in the tower, the rocket then passing out of the cradle which was retained by catches after being decelerated by shock absorbers. This cradle was intended for use with a gravity-operated catapult.

Although such a cradle should be light, the weight would be relatively unimportant, since the energy acquired is only that necessary to reach the top of the tower, with a comparatively low velocity.

Test of June 18, 1936 (L-2):
Static Test, Large Rocket with Gyro Control

The object of this test was to repeat the preceding test with the rocket practically unchanged except for the addition of the gyro, magnet-controlled valves, steering vanes, parachute, and streamlined casing.

General alterations. The circular-disk dumping valve, for draining the oxygen bath from around the liquid-nitrogen tank just before the start, was replaced by a 0.001-in. brass disk, the dumping being accomplished by cutting the disk with a wedge-shaped knife member placed on a spring-operated lever and released by a control on the tower.

The pressure regulator that operated the valve in the bottom of the liquid nitrogen tank was set to open ⅛ in., instead of ¹⁄₁₆ in. as before.

The same timer, which gave a record of the oxygen-tank pressure, was used, but the contact that released the parachute was no longer made integral with this timer because of possible uncertainty due to jar. The separate clockwork for the parachute release was freed when the oxygen-tank pressure fell to 100 psi, and operated to make contact 12 sec later.

Control pressure. The 35 psi for operating the gyro and the control vanes was obtained from the oxygen tank by the use of a valve at the bottom of the outlet tube, in the oxygen tank. This valve was allowed to close, and thus to retain gas pressure in the tank, when the oxygen pressure fell to 100 psi. The valve consisted of a flat disk covered with kangaroo leather, motion taking place by means of a rod extending through a ⁹⁄₁₆-in.-O.D. metal packing bellows in the bottom of the tank.

Gyroscope. The rotor of the gyro was from a Pioneer Instrument Company turn-and-bank indicator. It rotated in the original bearings and was held in two cast-aluminum gimbals. The gyro was rotated by a gas stream from the 35-psi control pressure, through a No. 69 hole.

The pivot supports for the gimbals were the same as for the A series of tests, except that the hardened-steel pivot screws were threaded into an aluminum-alloy bushing and held by a lock nut. The adjustment for freedom of turning of the gimbal was thus made independent of the adjustment of the commutator disks, or contact rings, on the aluminum-alloy sleeve. These disks could be turned, and then locked in place, by a nut on this sleeve, which clamped them between itself and a flange.

A Dowmetal box, in two halves consisting of thin dished castings, held the outer aluminum-tubing frame supporting the gimbals. Several layers of sponge rubber were used at the top and bottom of the box. Torsional vibrations were checked by pads of the same material touching the sides.

The half box in which the supporting frame was mounted was held to the rocket by Lord rubber mountings, No. 10 being used at the top and bottom and No. 12 at the sides.

The weight of the gyro, gimbals, frame, box, and mountings, plus 1 ft of rubber tubing for the gyro drive, was 3 lb 6 oz.

Control vanes. The fixed air vanes were of $\frac{1}{16}$-in.-thick 17 ST aluminum alloy, on the lower cone of the 0.020-in.-thick conical aluminum casing, extending out to the 18-in.-diameter width of the rocket at the end of the cone.

The $4\frac{1}{2}$-in. blast vanes were of $\frac{1}{16}$-in. Enduro steel, curved to fit the blast. They tapered rearward from $3\frac{1}{4}$-in. to 2 in., the forward ends being 3 in. below the open end of the nozzle.

The 7-in. movable air vanes were of $\frac{1}{32}$-in. steel 4 in. wide, and were curved on a 9-in. radius and spaced 18 in. apart. A steel link connected the middle of each blast vane with each adjacent air vane, so that each pair of air and blast vanes moved together.

Control valves. The magnet control valves were modified so as to avoid the possibility of chattering of the armatures with consequent partial opening of the valves. An auxiliary magnet was used, which attracted the armature when the main operating magnet was not in use, the magnet valves thus remaining either fully opened or fully closed. The magnetic resistance was reduced by an iron yoke that extended from the far pole back close to the armature.

Current to the auxiliary magnet was controlled by a thick, small magnet, which, together with 3.7 ohms of manganese wire, was placed in parallel with the main valve magnet. This small magnet was provided with an armature consisting of a steel spring, 0.009 in. thick and $\frac{9}{32}$ in. wide, bearing a small copper contact for energizing the auxiliary magnet.

The arrangement for each valve was rather bulky, but two magnet-valve units could nevertheless be contained within each of the Dowmetal boxes that had previously been used to house the four single magnet valves.

Sixteen cells were used for the main magnets, and eight cells for the four auxiliary magnets, two cells in parallel being used for each of the latter. In addition, three cells were used for operating the fused-wire releases, making 27 cells in all, the entire battery system weighing 5.27 lb.

Parachute release. The 10-ft-diameter parachute was held by a 2-ft length of ¾₆-in.-diameter airplane cable fastened to the top of the gasoline tank, the cable and shroud lines being wound around the rolled-up parachute. The 18-in.-diameter ogival aluminum cap was arranged to be released by the timer and to be removed by a small spring-opened parachute, released from a narrow tin box entering along the side of the cap. This box, 13¼ in. long, tapered from 2¼ in. at the top to 2 in. at the bottom. The pilot parachute was folded and placed in this box with the top at the rear end, so that when the upper end of the cover was released the parachute springs forced the door open, the lower end being supported by lugs.

A fused-wire release, on a lever system at the top of the cap, released a spring that in turn pulled a wire and freed the upper end of the box door, and at the same time released a ¹⁄₁₆-in. iron rod on the axis of the cap, by which the cap was held down firmly to the top of the gasoline tank. A 0.020-in. aluminum disk was used under this lever system to prevent entanglement with the parachute lines.

Weights and dimensions. The total weight of the rocket empty was 194 lb, and the length over all, 13 ft 1 in., the movable-vane system extending 7¼ in. to the rear of the nozzle. The diameter of the rocket was 18 in. Weights of particular features and assemblies were as follows:

Chamber and copper-tube jacket	22.25 lb
Gasoline tank	29.00
Oxygen tank	16.50
Liquid-nitrogen tank	8.50
Three 2-in. tube supports between tanks	3.25
Valves (regulator, oxygen- and gasoline-tank safety) and pressure recorder	6.00
Gyro and box, complete	3.37
Two magnet-valve boxes, complete	5.13
Battery, consisting of 27 dry cells	5.27
Cap, complete, less large parachute	8.00
Large parachute	1.50
Two half-cylinder casings	7.00
Door, for hoses and control wires	3.00
Steel ring, four steel arms, and blast vanes	2.92
Steel ring, four steel arms, blast and movable air vanes	4.62
Tailpiece with all vanes, fixed and movable	11.25
Tubing, braces, and supports	83.00

The weights of the oxygen, gasoline, and nitrogen were 78, 84, and 4 lb, respectively, making the total loaded weight 360 lb. The lift for Test K-6, with a similar chamber, was 440 lb, making the net lift for the present test, assuming the same combustion efficiency, 80 lb.

Test. In the test the release key was pressed after about 2 sec of lift, but the rocket did not rise, and the chamber soon burned through. An examination showed that the burning took place under pressure, near the lower end of the cylindrical part. It somewhat resembled the burning that takes place when there is an excess of oxygen.

Test of July 2, 1936 (L-3):
Repeat Static Test

The object of this test was to repeat the preceding test as a static run, with the lift increased by using the greater rates of flow of oxygen and gasoline that were employed in Tests K-1, K-2, and K-3.

Chamber. The flows with water at 20 psi were 24 oz/sec for the oxygen orifice and 26 oz/sec total for the four gasoline orifices, as compared with 25 oz/sec for the oxygen orifice and 26 for the two gasoline orifices in Test K-1. It was found necessary, however, in making the water tests of the oxygen orifice, to replace the ⅝-in. rubber tube by a 1-in. pipe, in order to reduce line resistance for the large flows.

Tanks. No changes were made in the tanks, except for the valve in the bottom of the liquid-nitrogen tank, which was found to leak even after being reground. The leakage proved to be caused by warping of the threaded valve-holder sleeve when it was brazed to the tank. It was reduced by using a packing ring, consisting of asbestos covered by thin sheet copper, between the valve and valve sleeve. The valve motion was decreased from ⅛ to ³⁄₃₂ in. being wholly open at 200 psi and wholly closed at 220 psi.

The lift was measured by means of one of the bellows used in the K series of tests.

Test. When lift commenced, the key which operated the release lever was pressed, but three or four seconds later the chamber burned through along the seam of the cylindrical part, beginning about 4 in. below the upper cone. The nitrogen-gas pressure was about 120 psi until the release lever operated, after which it remained at 150 psi.

The oxygen-tank pressure rose slowly at first but finally exceeded the nitrogen pressure, the lift increasing to 435 lb at the time the chamber burned through. The nozzle temperature rose to 95° C, the rise being rather rapid just before the burning took place, and the chamber temperature rose to 185° C, this being about 35° greater than that for Test K-1.

It was believed that the rather slow rise of oxygen-tank pressure was due to the large gaseous space over the liquid oxygen, and that the burning through was caused by ice, either on the oxygen deflector or in the oxygen tank.

Test of July 16, 1936 (L-4):
Repeat Static Test, Propellant-Tank Changes

The alterations for this static test were intended to produce a more rapid rise of pressure and also to avoid burning of the chamber.

General alterations. The volume of both the oxygen and the gasoline tanks was reduced, in order to decrease the free, or gas, space over the liquids, which were of the same amount as in the preceding tests.

This change involved a considerable alteration in the oxygen-tank piping. Previously, the oxygen delivery line began with a valve in the bottom of the tank, this valve being closed when the oxygen-tank pressure dropped at the end of the run, extended upward to the top of the tank, looped down, and passed out of the tank through a cooling jacket, the latter being concentric and extending down as far as the oxygen orifice in the chamber. A half length of 1½-in.-O.D., two-ply Sylphon bellows was used in this jacket tube, to allow for expansion and contraction.

In the present case the outer jacket terminated 3 in. above the top of the chamber, above which there were a feed line, extending to the bottom of the tank, and a vent line, to the top of the tank. The oxygen tube, between this jacket and the tank, was provided with a section of bellows of the same size. Since the top of the oxygen tank had been lowered, the loop in the original oxygen delivery line now extended above the top of the tank, and hence a similar section of bellows was used in each branch inside the tank.

The valve in the feed line at the bottom of the oxygen tank was closed by a rod that extended to the top of the oxygen tank. It was thus possible to open the valve and precool the jacket at any desired time before the run.

The nitrogen safety valve, which consisted essentially of a 12-in. length of ⅝-in.-diameter flexible tube opening a small ball valve, was found to vibrate so violently after it had opened that the pressure fell from 225 to 150 psi before the valve could close. These vibrations were eliminated by using an 18-in. length of ⅟₁₆-in.-bore copper tube between the nitrogen tank and the flexible tube. A chamois strainer was used in the funnel of the oxygen filler, in order to remove any ice.

Test. After ignition, a gasoline flame appeared, followed immediately by a bright strong flame accompanied by a steady roar. The flame continued steady after the release lever was operated but appeared to become progressively whiter. The time of the strong lift, which averaged 550 lb, was 28 sec, the lift at the end of the run being 599 lb.

The nitrogen-tank pressure rose slowly to 150 psi and then rose more rapidly, becoming 200 about 8 sec after the release lever was operated. The oxygen pressure followed the nitrogen pressure closely, being about 10 to 15 psi below the nitrogen pressure throughout the run. The nitrogen valve remained open, since the pressure did not reach 230 psi, and apparently there was a rather rapid flow of liquid nitrogen through the copper-tube half jackets, since there was frost not only on the ½-in. line leading to the bottom but also on the two ½-in. lines between the tops of the jacket and a strainer. No frost was observed above the strainer, and no frost appeared on the copper-tube jacket, which evidently remained warm.

The temperature 5 in. below the top of the cylindrical part of the chamber rose slowly to 130° C, and 5 in. below the throat, on the nozzle, to 470° C.

The rocket weighed 135 lb empty, the oxygen and gasoline charges being 78 and 84 lb, respectively. From these data, the jet velocity over the 28 sec of run, neglecting the liquids used before and after, was estimated as 2800 ft/sec. As in all the tests in which flow rates were not measured accurately, the calculated average velocity was probably considerably below the true average velocity because of the loss of oxygen and gasoline before and after the run.

An examination at the shop, after the run, showed no damage except to the oxygen orifice, which was burned away on one side. Evidently this happened at the end of the run, when gaseous oxygen entered the chamber; otherwise a hot streak would have been noticed on the cylindrical part of the chamber, owing to a nonuniform oxygen spray.

Test of July 31, 1936 (L-5):
Flight Test, Large Rocket

The object of this test was to obtain a flight with the rocket used in the preceding test, with the addition of the pilot gyro, magnet valves, directing vanes, casing, and cap with parachute.

Chamber and tanks. The chamber was the same as that previously used, after being repaired, as were also the oxygen, gasoline and nitrogen tanks, and the valves and piping. The high and low pressures used were 225 and 35 psi, as before.

Gyro and controls. The gyroscope, guiding vanes, and cap with parachute were all the same as in the test of June 18, 1936 (L-2), second in the present series.

Magnet valves. The magnet-controlled valves, however, were simpler than in the earlier test, being more like those used in the A series, with a single magnet for each valve. Disturbance due to vibration was reduced by narrowing the part of each armature that extended beyond the magnet pole, thereby reducing considerably the moment of inertia of the armature, and by using a coil tension spring, adjustable by a screw and lock nut, instead of a wide compression spring. Five parallel rows of four dry cells each were used for operating the magnet valves.

Casings. The casing was similar to that used previously, except for places cut in the rear cone just above each of the four bellows operators for the steering vanes. Bending out the metal at each of these cuts served to direct air inward to the bellows, thus preventing overheating.

Test. In carrying out the test, the release-lever key was pressed after a strong flame had been observed for about two seconds. The rocket rose slowly after two or three seconds more. It appeared to travel straight for a time, but then leaned away from the observers, a flame appearing from the side of the chamber. It rose about 200 ft and fell about 300 ft from the tower. One of the observers saw the flame issue from the side of the rocket opposite to that toward which it leaned just after it rose above the tower.

Conclusion. It was concluded that the slow opening of the gasoline valve, together with the long distance from the valve to the chamber, delayed the gasoline and allowed an excess of oxygen to generate excessive heat at the start. Pulsations, such as had been observed several times before in the present series of tests, were ascribed to the presence of air pockets in the gasoline line below the valve.

Test of October 3, 1936 (L-6):
Flight Test, Large Rocket

A further attempt was made to obtain a flight, after making the following changes: the cylindrical part of the chamber was made of 0.050-in. sheet nickel instead of 0.037-in.; air pockets were avoided in the gasoline line below the valve, this line being shorter; and liquid-oxygen and gasoline tanks of about half the previous capacity were used in an effort to obtain a greater rate of ascent.

Tanks. The cylindrical part of the liquid-oxygen tank was 11 in. in diameter and $11\frac{7}{8}$ in. long. It had $1\frac{3}{8}$-in.-long, 60-deg conical frustums, capped by 120-deg cones, at the ends. The baffles were circular disks of 0.020-in. 17 ST sheet, fastened to $\frac{3}{16}$-in.-O.D. 17 ST circular tubes, these being held by four vertical $\frac{1}{4}$-in.-O.D. 17 ST tubes on steel studs brazed into the ends of the tank.

The cylindrical part of the gasoline tank was 12 in. in diameter and $18\frac{3}{8}$ in. long, having ends and baffles similar to those for the oxygen tank.

The liquid-nitrogen tank consisted, as before, of a $7\frac{3}{4}$-in.-diameter cylinder, 6 in. long, having 120-deg conical ends, the nitrogen-tank pressure being again produced by evaporating a portion of the nitrogen on the outside of the gasoline-delivery line.

The oxygen line was used without a cutoff valve, beginning $\frac{1}{2}$ in. from the bottom of the tank, looping over inside the tank, where it was 4 in. above the level of the oxygen when filled, and passing out through the bottom. As before, a bellows was used to avoid stresses due to expansion and contraction in the oxygen tube.

Extensive air pockets in the gasoline line were avoided by having the gasoline valve located just below the oxygen tank and by replacing the ring-shaped manifold, from which the tangential tubes had entered the chamber, by a 2-in.-diameter, $1\frac{3}{8}$-in.-long cylindrical box of steel tubing. This was placed below the gasoline valve and served both as a strainer and manifold. From it four ⅜-in.-O.D. steel tubes passed to the tangential entrance orifices in the wall of the chamber.

Controls. The guiding vanes, magnet-controlled valves, gyroscope, and parachute release were all as used in the preceding test.

Weights and dimensions. The rocket was 13 ft 4½ in. over all, and as before, 18 in. in diameter. The weights were as follows:

Chamber	16.87 lb
Copper sheet on lower cone of chamber and nozzle	1.87
2 copper-tube jackets	3.25
Gasoline tank	19.75
Oxygen tank	15.00
Liquid-nitrogen tank	8.50
Three 2-in.-diameter aluminum tube supports	8.25
Aluminum cap	4.25
Parachute	4.00
4 half-cylinder casings of 0.020 in. 17 ST	9.75
Tailpiece, including 4 fixed air vanes	10.00
Piping, braces, regulators, tubing, and parachute batteries (2 sets)	28.00
Gyro, magnet valves and boxes, 5 sets of 4 cells each, ¼-in.-diameter aluminum connecting tubing, wiring, movable vanes, and operating bellows	22.00
Total	151.49 lb

The liquid loads were 40 lb, 46 lb, and 4 lb, for the oxygen, gasoline, and nitrogen, respectively.

Test. When the test was carried out, the releasing-lever key was pressed 3 sec after a strong lift had developed. The rocket rose rather rapidly and traveled straight, even though a fairly strong breeze was blowing at the time. It rose about 200 ft from the tower in 5 sec, when a strong flame appeared at one side of the rocket, which then turned rapidly about a horizontal axis and landed 20 ft from the tower. An examination showed that a hole had burned through the lower part of the cylindrical section of the chamber wall.

The burning through did not appear to have been due to the larger proportion of oxygen, since an even greater proportion was used in the static test, K-4, without damage to a chamber wall of the same size. It appeared likely, therefore, that since the tangential gasoline streams are quickly reduced to a rather low speed in contact with the chamber wall, the centrifugal force, depending on $\frac{v^2}{r}$, is reduced considerably in chambers of large radius. This effect would explain the occasional burning out, especially during an ascent when the tangential sheets tend to move toward the rear. It also would account for the absence of a sudden change in pressure or temperature when the chamber burned through in the static test of July 2, 1936, L-3.

Recommendations. Since the velocity of the gasoline streams is reduced very considerably after passing over a short tangential distance, the burning can perhaps best be avoided by using a number of gasoline orifices at intervals around the chamber, and also at intervals along the lengthwise or axial direction, so that there will be a greater tangential velocity at all points of the surface. Even large chambers can be protected in this way, since the centrifugal force depends upon the square of the velocity and only upon the first power of the radius.

For overcoming the difficulty due to low tangential fuel velocity, four 5¾-in.-diameter chambers might be used, placed close together, with the axes parallel, and with the gasoline introduced oppositely in one pair of chambers in order to avoid rotation of the rocket.

Moreover, the steering of such a four-chamber rocket could be made to take place without moving vanes by using a higher pressure in one or more of the chambers, controlled by magnet-operated bellows valves, or by varying pulsometer or centrifugal pump pressures.

Test of November 7, 1936 (L-7):
Flight Test, Four Motors

The object of this test was to obtain a flight with a rocket having a large thrust, at the same time avoiding the possible tendency for large chambers to burn out because of reduced centrifugal cooling. For this purpose four 5¾-in.-diameter chambers were used, with axes parallel to that of the rocket, each being similar to those used in the A series of tests. The tanks of Test L-6 were used again.

Chambers. Each chamber was of 0.037-in. sheet nickel, with two gasoline orifices each giving 5.25 oz/sec of water at 20 psi, and with an oxygen orifice and ½-in. deflector giving a water flow of 6.4 oz/sec. The ¾-in. liquid-oxygen tube was jacketed by a 1-in. tube covered with iron wire screening and Insalute-Alundum cement. A ring of 0.050-in. sheet nickel was used at the top of the cylindrical part of the combustion chamber, extending inward radially for a distance of 1 in. instead of ¾ in. as in the A series of tests.

The oxygen-orifice tube in each chamber was connected to a small manifold, just below the axially located expansion and contraction bellows, by four inclined tubes of equal length. The gasoline orifices were supplied from a small manifold through eight tubes, also of equal length.

Each chamber, including the short gasoline and oxygen tubes at the top, weighed 6¼ lb. Each half tube jacket consisted of ten ³⁄₁₆-in.-O.D. copper tubes, the 80 copper tubes weighing 4 lb. The eight half jackets weighed a total of 7¼ lb. The complete chamber and jacket assembly, with the associated piping, weighed 44½ lb.

Tanks and piping. The tanks, piping, valves, gyro, magnet valves, and parachute release were the same as in the preceding test. The copper strips in the new vaporizer, for maintaining pressure within the liquidnitrogen tank, were increased in length from 7¼ to 11¼ in.

Supports. The chambers were placed 10 in. between adjacent **axes,** and each was supported by two ¾-in.-diameter steel tubes extending from the upper cone of the chamber forward to an 18-in.-diameter steel tubing ring. The main rocket frame above this ring consisted of three 1½-in.-O.D., 16-gauge steel tubes, each 81¼ in. long. The lower 0.020-in. cone of the rocket casing was of 60 deg and was provided with four 4½-in.-diameter cylindrical extensions for covering the nozzles. The open ends of the nozzles extended about ½ in. into four steel thimbles, on an iron plate in the tower, and ignition was by four separate igniters joined together at the free, or bottom, ends.

Guiding vanes. The moving blast vanes were concave inward, as before, each being 7 in. long, and tapering rearwardly from 5¾ in. to 4⅝ in. Inasmuch as opposite pairs were 16 in. apart, it was believed that guiding would take place by action on the slip stream, after propulsion had ceased.

Weights and dimensions. The rocket was 13 ft 6½ in. long, and weighed 202 lb. Various weights were as follows:

4 chambers	24.75 lb
8 copper-tubing half jackets	7.25
Oxygen tank	15.00
Gasoline tank	19.75
Liquid-nitrogen tank	8.50
Three 1½-in.-O.D. steel support tubes	20.25
Brass and aluminum tube fittings	5.50
Gasoline valve, with ends ready for soldering	1.25
Brackets for tanks	1.50
Square ⅞-in. tubes, in support frame	2.00
Cylindrical casings	7.50
Gyro box and magnet-valve box	1.50

Test. In carrying out the test, the lift indicator light could not be seen with certainty, but the release-lever key was nevertheless pressed after about two seconds of intense flame and roar. The rocket then rose slowly and, after leaving the tower, continued straight to a height of about 200 ft, even though a horizontal whitish flame had already appeared level with the chambers. It then turned over and fell near the tower.

Conclusions. An examination showed that one of the chambers had burned through in the upper cylindrical part, possibly owing to inequality in the flow of oxygen to the chambers at the start, causing excess heating in some of the chambers. If this were the difficulty, it might be avoided by having a more gradual initial liquid-oxygen flow. The straight path, even with a burned place in one of the chambers, indicates that a four-chamber rocket should be as stable, and hence as easily guided, as a single-chamber rocket.

7

L-Series Flight Tests Continued, with 5¾-Inch-Diameter Motors

L Series (Continued), November 24, 1936 — August 26, 1937

Because of the desirability of obtaining stabilized flight tests as early as possible, a return was made to the use of single 5¾-in.-diameter chambers.

Test of November 24, 1936 (L-8):
Fuel Tests

The first tests were made to determine the heating effect of regular gasoline, aviation gasoline, and naphtha on the chamber wall.

Chamber and piping. Three of the chambers used in the preceding four-chamber rocket test were made interchangeable on a single tank-and-piping unit. The piping to the chamber was similar to that previously used. The oxygen flowed from the open end of a tube in a small cup or well in the bottom of the oxygen tank, passed in a loop extending near the top of the inside of the tank and thence passed down from the bottom of the well inside a jacket tube to the bellows for reducing contraction stress, which was located just above the oxygen jacket tube in the chamber.

This latter oxygen jacket space was piped at one side to the bottom of the oxygen tank and at the other side to the top, the former jacket space being filled directly from the tank by gravity. The pressure used in the outside nitrogen-pressure tank was 220 psi.

The gasoline passed down from the bottom of the gasoline tank to the main valve, below which was the combined strainer and manifold, having two ⅜-in. steel tubes leading to the gasoline entrance orifices.

The three fuels tested were as follows:

Regular gasoline	0.753 density
Aviation gasoline	0.692
Naphtha	0.756

Tests. In the test with the regular gasoline, the period of intense lift was about 25 sec, and the flame was small and pointed, being accompanied, however, by a large gasoline flame (due to the excess gasoline) at the rear of the tower. The jet velocity was estimated as 3280 ft/sec, from the lift, 181 lb, the total mass of liquids used, 44 lb, and the time, 25 sec.

In the test with aviation gasoline, the upper cone burned through along the seam after 20 sec of firing and was found to be bulged. It appeared likely that the oxygen was completely used and that the spray produced by the oxygen gas and the gasoline at the end of the run produced an intense heat throughout the head end of the chamber.

In the test with naphtha, the chamber burned out along the cylindrical part after 14 sec of firing, possibly owing to the naphtha tank being empty. In confirmation, the cement gas deflector was without soot, indicating an excess of oxygen.

Test of November 28, 1936 (L-9):
Fuel Test, Increased Oxygen

It was the object of this test to repeat the test of the preceding group in which regular gasoline was used, with the oxygen rate of flow increased so as to produce a greater lift.

Chamber. The chamber was the same as that used previously, except that the oxygen flow was increased by using a deflector stem of 0.153 in. diameter in the No. 2 chamfered oxygen orifice, instead of a 0.167-in.-diameter stem. The flow of water at 20 psi was thereby increased from 6.4 oz/sec to 8 oz/sec. The gasoline flow for each of the two orifices remained the same, giving 5.7 oz/sec of water each at 25 psi pressure.

Test. The flame was rather large and whitish, and the upper part of the cylindrical portion of the chamber burned out after 6 sec of firing. Evidently the oxygen rate of flow was too large, but it is also possible that the tangential speed of the gasoline was not sufficient to provide adequate cooling, the nitrogen pressure during the run being 150 psi as compared with 225 psi in the test of November 24, with regular gasoline.

Test of December 18, 1936 (L-10):
Flight Test, Nitrogen-Gas Pressure Rocket

The object of this test was to obtain a flight with a rocket similar to that tested with regular gasoline on November 24, with the addition of a pressure-storage tank, casing, and parachute, but without gyroscope and guiding vanes.

Chamber. The chamber was similar to the earlier chamber, the water flows for the oxygen and for each gasoline orifice being 6.4 and 5.25 oz/sec, respectively. An inverted perforated nickel cone of 0.050-in. sheet nickel, of about 90-deg angle, was used with the object of avoiding interference with the oxygen spray due to combustion and flow in the upper cone. This new cone extended at the upper, wide end 1/16 in. from the inner edge of the 0.050-in. flat ring to within 1/16 in. of the bottom of the jacket tube, around the oxygen tube in the chamber (Fig. 9).

Tanks. The gasoline tank was of 0.031-in. sheet nickel, the 9-in.-diameter cylinder being 6 in. long, with the ends consisting of bands on which were 120-deg cones. The oxygen tank was of similar construction, with the cylindrical part 14 in. long. The cylinder of the pressure-storage tank, for 225 psi nitrogen-gas pressure, was of 0.037-in.-sheet nickel, 48 in. long, strengthened by a 4-in.-wide, 0.050-in. nickel band around the middle. The cones on this tank were similar to those used for the liquid tanks. All longitudinal seams were welded.

The liquid-oxygen and gasoline tanks weighed 5½ and 7¼ lb, respectively, including the baffles. The pressure-storage tank weighed 22 lb, including two steel tubes that passed through lengthwise. The three tanks were arranged as close together as possible, the gasoline tank being forward and the pressure-storage tank in the middle.

Piping and valves. The gasoline passed through a ½-in.-diameter steel tube from the small cup, or well, at the bottom of the gasoline tank, through the pressure-storage tank, around the oxygen tank, and terminated in a strainer, below which was the aluminum-casting gasoline valve, just above the chamber. The liquid-oxygen line passed up inside the oxygen tank from a well at the bottom, formed a loop at the top of the tank, and passed out of the well inside a gravity-filled jacket, which terminated in an expansion bellows at the oxygen jacket inside the chamber. The bottoms and tops of the two jackets were joined by copper tubing, to provide circulation.

The steel tube passing lengthwise through the pressure-storage tank was bent in the middle, to allow for expansion and contraction; and the final brazing consisted in fastening the tube to a short outer sleeve in the top of the tank, thus avoiding strains due to contraction in the tank.

Two pressure lines were used, one extending from a small hose fitting up alongside the oxygen tank to the bottom of the pressure-storage tank, for charging the latter with nitrogen gas. The other pressure line, passing from a large hose fitting up alongside the oxygen tank had two branch tubes, each containing an aluminum check valve; one branch passed to the top of the oxygen tank, and the other branch, to the top of the gasoline tank. An equalizer, located just above the chamber, was used to vent oxygen gas whenever the oxygen-tank pressure exceeded the gasoline-tank pressure by 5 psi. The vent valve on the tank, to permit escape of evaporated oxygen before the test, was provided with a ball-and-socket stem, to make seating positive on closing.

Supports. The supports between the pairs of tanks consisted of four

⅝-in.-O.D. steel tubes, all being just inside a 9-in. radius to facilitate attaching the casing sections. The support between the chamber and the oxygen tank consisted of three ⅞-in.-O.D. steel tubes extending axially, with short 45-deg elbows facing inward at the ends. The chamber was brought into line with the tanks by cutting the three support tubes in two at the middle, and brazing the ends to 3-in.-long internal sleeves.

Guides. Four roller guides, on aluminum forks, were used, ejected by springs as the rocket left the tower. The ¾-in. square rods holding the forks, and sliding in tubes in the rocket, were placed off center in order to avoid the piping that extended along the axis of the rocket.

Parachute release. The pressure contact maker was similar to previous ones, except that the 2½-in. recording paper disk was not needed, since the use of a gas-pressure tank precluded variations of pressure such as might have occurred with a liquid-nitrogen tank. The contact for the parachute was closed by the clockwork, which was freed when the fall of oxygen-tank pressure permitted contraction of a 12-in. length of ⅝-in. flexible tube to take place. Provision was made against rotation from the twisting of this tube, caused by the spiral form of the corrugations.

The parachute, packed in the usual containing bag, was freed when the bag was pulled off by the removal of the ogival cap at the forward end of the rocket. The fused-wide release, operated by the clockwork contact, freed two long lever arms, the short ends of which held loops on ¹⁄₁₆-in.-diameter rods, held by strong springs to diametrically opposite sides of the top of the gasoline tank.

A knob on one of the ¹⁄₁₆-in. rods held the long end of a third lever, located near the open end of the cap in a short slotted tube, the short end of this lever holding a pin that extended below the cap and rested on the edge of the gasoline tank. The cap was also held by three fixed brackets, fairly close together, on the side of the cap opposite to the rod.

The operation was as follows: when the fused-wire release in the cap operated, the two ¹⁄₁₆-in. rods holding the cap to the gasoline tank were freed, thus loosening the cap. In addition, the freeing of the short rod allowed the cap to fall toward the side where this pin was located, so that no matter in what direction the rocket was moving, the wind would push the tilted cap to the side and thus pull the bag from the parachute. The slot in the short tube allowed the ¹⁄₁₆-in. rod, which had held the lower lever, to pass through and thus become free.

Casings. All the sheet-aluminum casings consisted of two half cylinders. Since the lowest cylindrical casing part, between the oxygen tank and the 27-in.-long lower cone was long, it consisted of an upper and a lower half.

The four fixed air vanes each tapered rearward 26½ in. along the lower cone to a 7-in. width at the open end of the nozzle, thus making a total width of 18 in. across the bottom of the rocket.

Weights and dimensions. The length over all was 14 ft 7 in., the diameter 9 in., and the total weight 78 lb. Some of the weights were as follows:

Chamber	6.25 lb
Oxygen tank	5.50
Gasoline tank	7.25
Pressure-storage tank	22.00
Cylindrical casings	4.00
Lower cone and vanes	5.25
Pressure contact maker	1.18
Nitrogen valve	1.25
2 aluminum check valves	0.62
Parachute timer	0.68
Equalizer, with aluminum strainer	1.25
2 hose valves and clamps	0.93
2 batteries	1.93
Tubing supports between chamber and oxygen tank	3.44

The estimated weight of the liquids was 19 lb of oxygen and 28 lb of gasoline.

The outside nickel pressure tank was not used at the tower, the hoses being connected directly to the rocket from the 2000–225-psi reducing valve. As usual, two felt pieces were kept clamped around the oxygen tank until just before the rocket was released.

Test. In the test the rocket rose as soon as the release key was pressed but turned sharply to the right almost as soon as it emerged from the tower, proceeding thereafter at an angle of about 15 deg above the horizontal. The angle gradually decreased until the rocket struck the ground about 2000 ft from the tower. The sound of the flight was heard at the ranch house, about 8 miles away.

Conclusion. In view of the nearly vertical rise for the first few hundred feet in the flight of December, 1930, in which fixed grooved guides were used, it is possible that the strong ejecting springs of the rollers may have been compressed to a different extent on opposite sides of the rocket, tending to force it to one side as it emerged from the tower.

Test of February 1, 1937 (L-11):
Flight Test, Stabilized Rocket

The object of this test was to obtain a flight with a rocket stabilized both during and after propulsion, but otherwise as nearly as possible like that used in the preceding test.

Chamber. Two changes were made in the chamber. The 1-in.-diameter liquid-oxygen jacket tube around the 3/4-in. oxygen-delivery tube in the top of the chamber was reduced in length where it projected above the chamber, and an entrance-and-exit tube fitting was used on opposite sides, at the top. These fittings had a 1-in. difference in level in order to secure at least some circulation.

Further, the inverted cone was refractory-coated, in order to withstand heating. This was a perforated steel cone, having four holes for equalizing the pressure on opposite sides, covered with wire screening bound by iron wires, and coated with equal parts of Insalute and Alundum cement, as had been done previously with the 1-in. jacket tube.

The inverted cone extended beyond the flat nickel ring at the top of the cylindrical part of the chamber and was cemented, except for this extension, both inside and out, as was the perforated steel ring on the cone. The extension was added in order to avoid bending of this ring. The 0.037-in., $\frac{1}{4}$-in.-wide nickel ring just under this cemented ring was widened to $\frac{3}{8}$-in. Moreover, the $\frac{1}{64}$-in.-wide slots in the gasoline orifices were made in $\frac{7}{16}$-in. steel tubing, having a thick ($\frac{1}{16}$-in.) wall to avoid widening under pressure; the slots being $\frac{1}{4}$ in. deep.

The lower end of the stainless-steel oxygen deflector was grooved, and covered with the same Insalute-Alundum cement. The inverted cone of oxygen spray, extending rearward from the edge of the deflector, had an internal angle of about 90 deg and struck the tangential streams of gasoline where they entered at the top of the cylindrical part of the chamber to form the tangential cooling sheet.

Tanks, piping, and valves. The arrangement and size of the tanks were the same as in the preceding test. The valve necessary for trapping tank pressure for the controls when it dropped to 100 psi consisted of a $\frac{3}{4}$-in.-round valve disk closing a $\frac{7}{16}$-in. hole when the valve rod was freed by the removal of a side rod, which extended $\frac{1}{16}$ in. into a groove near the free end of the valve rod. This side rod was itself freed by a fused-wire release.

The pressure lines consisted of a small hose connection on a tube leading to the bottom of the pressure-storage tank, for supplying initial pressure to this tank as before, and a large hose line joining a tube that passed between the tops of the oxygen and gasoline tanks, through the pressure tank, and furnished with two check valves, also as before.

An aluminum valve on the top of the pressure tank opened at the start of the flight, supplying pressure to the two liquid tanks through the connecting tube just mentioned, first passing through the pressure-cutoff valve described above.

The equalizer, set at 5 psi excess oxygen to gasoline-tank pressure, was located on the top of the liquid-oxygen tank and was piped by $\frac{1}{4}$-in.-O.D. aluminum tubes to the oxygen and gasoline tanks, except for a $\frac{3}{8}$-in. steel tube, extending through the pressure tank. The 200–35-psi reducing valve for the controls was located on the bottom of the pressure tank and was piped to the magnet-control boxes and to the tube containing the small hole by which the gyro was spun during the flight.

The gasoline passed down from the bottom of the well in the tank, through the pressure tank to the strainer and aluminum valve just above the oxygen tank, and finally along the side of the oxygen tank and one side of the magnet-controlled valves and the gyroscope. Thus there were four steel tubes passing through the pressure tank, one being the tube through which the electrical wires passed.

The liquid oxygen passed upward from the well in the bottom of the tank, looped around inside the top of the tank, and thence passed out of the bottom, at one side so as to allow axial space below for the gyro and magnet-control boxes. Below the tank the oxygen line was jacketed by a 1-in.-diameter tube, as before, with a bellows in the middle to reduce contraction stresses.

Supports. The tubing supports were essentially the same as for the preceding test, except that no internal sleeve was used in the middle of the three 3/4-in.-O.D. steel tubes extending between the liquid-oxygen tank and the chamber. The detachable rollers were held in 3/4-in.-square tubes extending transversely between the gasoline and pressure tanks and between the oxygen tank and the chamber, the piping being so disposed as to permit both of these tubes to pass through the rocket axis.

The rollers were on 5/8-in.-square tube shanks, which were pushed outward by slidable plugs in the 3/4-in.-square tubes. Forked levers straddled these steel tubes and ejected the rollers by the aid of long tension springs, which avoided the large forces which had hitherto accompanied the use of relatively short, strong compression springs. Friction was reduced by using a pair of rollers on each shank.

Electric circuits. Two wiring systems were used, one above the oxygen tank, for the pressure-cutoff valve and the parachute release, and the other below the oxygen tank, for the gyro controls. For the former, two parallel batteries, of four flashlight cells each, fired a 0.004-in.-diameter fused-wire release when the nitrogen pressure fell to 100 psi, by means of a 5/8-in.-diameter, 12-in.-long corrugated-tube contact maker, as before. The freed part of the fused-wire release fired another release, which simultaneously allowed the pressure-cutoff valve to close and the clockwork to start; the clockwork, in turn, after 6 to 8 sec, firing the 0.008-in.-diameter fused wire in the cap, freeing both the cap and the parachute.

Five parallel groups of four flashlight cells each were used for the magnet-controlled valves and gyro, grounded on the gyro box.

Flight control. The parachute apparatus, gyro, and magnet-controlled valves were the same as in Test L-7. The movable air and blast vanes were similar to those used in Test L-6, the air vanes again being located at the ends of the 18-in. crossarms at the rear end of the rocket, and connected by links to the blast vanes. The latter were 3½ in. long, were concave inwardly, and tapered in width rearwardly from 2⅜ in. to 1½ in. Each set was operated by a 1½-in.-O.D. single-ply Sylphon bellows, as used in the A series of tests. The four fixed air vanes extended outward to a total width of 18 in. and tapered forward to the 9-in.-diameter rocket casing (Fig. 10).

Weights and dimensions. The length over all was 16 ft 7⅝ in., the diameter 9 in., and the weight empty 102 lb. The center of gravity was 9 in. below the cylindrical part of the pressure-storage tank. The principal weights were distributed as follows:

	6.25 lb
Chamber	
3 tanks, supporting tubes between tanks, check valves, gas-pressure and gasoline valves, regulators and reducing valves, and roller guides	48.00
Chamber, chamber support tubes, and oxygen line	10.50
Casings	5.37
Tailpiece	5.25
Complete air- and blast-vane unit	3.00

Test. When released, the rocket apparently rose more rapidly than ever before and continued to move straight after leaving the tower. At about 150 ft from the tower it began to correct itself, thereafter moving slowly from side to side. This motion was visible from the 1000-ft shelter as well as from the recording-telescope station, located on a line at right angles from the tower. The rocket continued to move upward, at about 10 deg from the vertical, even after propulsion ceased, but finally turned over horizontally and descended at a steep angle. There was a trail of smoke during most of the ascent.

The propulsion period, as timed by the stop watch, was 20.6 sec. The height, from the recording-telescope trace and the readings of the theodolite located close to the 1000-ft shelter, was 1870 ft. On examining the rocket, it was found that the fused-wire release to shut off tank pressure at 100 lb had operated but that the fused-wire parachute release in the cap had not. The chamber showed no sign of heating. One of the rollers remained on the rocket throughout the flight, and the persistent tilt of the rocket was possibly due to the drag produced by this roller. Electrical failure probably prevented the release of the parachute.

Test of February 27, 1937 (L-12):
Flight Test, Gyro-operated Parachute

The object of this test was to obtain a flight with a rocket as used in the preceding test, but with the parachute release operated by the gyroscope, together with fall of tank pressure; with guides consisting of grooved shoes fastened to the rocket instead of detachable rollers; and with a 50 per cent greater liquid load, together with higher nitrogen-gas pressure.

General alterations. The chamber was used without essential change. New tanks were, however, made. The cylindrical part of the oxygen and gasoline tanks was increased by 50 per cent, to 9 and 21 in., respectively, although the cylindrical part of the pressure tank was the same as before. All three tanks had 0.037-in.-thick spun-nickel hemispherical ends. The ends of the 4-in.-wide reinforcing band on the pressure tank were no longer bent outward to form a projecting place over the seam of the tank, but terminated ½ in. from each other, in order to make possible a relatively flat brazing, and hence wirewinding, in later tests.

The valves, piping, and supports were essentially the same as in the preceding test. The gyroscope, however, was placed directly under the oxygen tank instead of over the chamber.

The cutoff valve, for retaining pressure after propulsion ceased, was arranged to operate more quickly by using 0.004-in. instead of 0.008-in.-diameter music wire for the fused-wire release on this valve, the short arm of the release being reduced in length to decrease the tension on the wire.

Parachute release. The parachute release was likewise altered so as to operate more rapidly, by replacing the 0.008-in.-diameter fused wire by one of 0.004-in. diameter. The tension on this wire was reduced by holding the long ends of the levers that released the cap by the long end of a third lever, at right angles to the other two, the short end of which was held by the 0.004-in.-diameter fused-wire release.

The arrangement for firing the fused wire of the parachute release was considerably modified. As before, the corrugated-tube contact maker operated by tank pressure when the pressure fell to 85 psi, and continued to make contact down to zero pressure. This made certain that the parachute would not be released during the firing period of the chamber. In addition, a section of commutator was used on each of the larger insulating segments for the semicircular brass steering contact strips, so that contact would be made, in series with the pressure switch, when the rocket tilted to nearly 90 deg from the vertical in any direction. This segment was of ¹⁄₃₂-in. sheet brass, ½ in. long and ³⁄₃₂ in. wide, having a slot in one end for a 140-thread screw for adjusting the angle of contact, the other end being beveled in such a way as to reduce resistance to motion against the small copper brush.

The flashlight batteries were replaced by Eveready No. 773 radio C batteries, each giving 7½ volts and weighing 248 grams. One set of two batteries was used for the parachute release, and two sets of two each for the magnet-operated valves. The total weight of batteries used was 3¼ lb.

Vanes. The air and blast vanes were the same as in the preceding test except that ¼ in. was cut from the vertical edges of each movable air vane in order to avoid the possibility of one of these vanes catching on the angle irons in the tower that supported the vertical pipe guides for the rocket.

Guides. The detachable rollers were replaced by fixed guides consisting of pairs of ¾-in. aluminum angles, 1³⁄₁₆ in. apart, screwed to steel strips. These guides were 6 in. long on the sides of both the gasoline and pressure tanks, and 24 in. on each side of the space between the oxygen tank and the chamber. The reducing valve on the nitrogen cylinder was set at 225 psi, instead of 210 psi as in the preceding test.

Weight and dimensions. The length over all was 17 ft 5¼ in., and the weight empty 105 lb. The center of gravity, also empty, was 6½ in. below the top edge of the bottom hemisphere of the pressure-storage tank.

Preliminary test. In a preliminary test the pressure-cutoff switch operated prematurely, apparently owing to a momentary fall in pressure when the large hose was pulled off. The bellows of this switch was accordingly connected by a ¼-in. aluminum tube directly to the bottom of the pressure-storage tank. In addition, the liquid-oxygen line to the chamber appeared to be partly clogged during the test, possibly owing to the freezing, on the precooled liquid-oxygen orifice, of some of the gasoline that first entered. This partial clogging might account for the burning out of places on the cylindrical wall of the chamber in earlier tests, particularly in the group of four 5¾-in.-diameter chambers.

Flight test. In the flight test the rocket rose rather slowly in the tower, the flame being accompanied by a large smoke trail. The rocket tilted toward the wind about 20 deg and then returned nearly to the vertical. This action was repeated, after which the rocket continued to become inclined, finally striking the ground under power after about 20 sec of flight. Judging from Test L-11, enough fuel remained for another 10 sec of propulsion.

The impact took place at a very high speed, producing a mushroom-shaped dust cloud and digging a hole 1 ft wide, 2 ft long, and 8 in. deep, besides powdering the ground for some distance on all sides of the hole. The height, from the telescope and theodolite results, was 1500 ft, the landing place being 3000 ft from the tower.

The lack of continued correcting was probably due to a loss of restoring force at high speed, possibly owing to the resistance of the moving vanes becoming greater than the correcting force.

Suggestions. If tanks of 0.018-in. sheet nickel were used, wire-wound both longitudinally and transversely, together with aluminum tubing supports, the weight of the rocket might be reduced from about 100 lb to approximately 50 lb. This reduction in weight would permit adding to the fuel load by an amount equal to the fuel load used in Test L-11, estimated at 19 lb oxygen and 28 lb gasoline, or 47 lb total. In the present test the total load was estimated as 70.5 lb. The combined loads would total 117.5 lb, or enough to furnish propulsion for a full minute.

A good type of vaporizer for use with pumps might be thin metal jackets around the chamber and nozzle, directing fine sprays against the chamber and nozzle surfaces.

Test of March 26, 1937 (L-13):
Flight Test, Higher Acceleration

The object of this test was to obtain a flight with a rocket similar to that used in the preceding test but with a liquid load reduced to that used in preceding tests in order to obtain a greater flight velocity, and with a vane system having less resistance, together with a larger movable air-vane surface.

General alterations. The chamber was the same as that previously used. The lengths of the cylindrical walls of the oxygen, gasoline, and pressure tanks were 6½, 14½, and 48 in., respectively. Hemispherical ends were used on the tanks, the diameters of the cylinders being reduced so that they entered the hemispheres ¼ in. within the flared, or chamfered, edges of the hemispheres, in order to permit making good brazed joints. The gasoline filler opening was recessed, and was placed in the middle of the top hemisphere, in order to avoid interference with the anchoring of the parachute cable.

The 225–35-psi reducing valve was altered so as to produce a greater flow by substituting for the automobile-tire valve previously used an 11/32-in.-beveled-edge brass valve member, engaging a ¼-in.-diameter valve opening. Moreover, the reduced pressure was kept within narrower limits by using a 2-in.-O.D. governing bellows in place of the previous 1½-in.-O.D. bellows. The control pressure was raised from 35 to 42 psi, in order to produce a greater force on the flight-correcting vanes.

The moving air vanes were increased in length and width to 7 and 4 in., respectively, and were moved out to the full 18 in. distance apart. The angle irons in the tower that supported the ⅝-in. pipe guides for the rocket were moved sufficiently apart to permit these larger air vanes to be used. The blast vanes were provided with an adjustable stop, so that the amount of motion into the blast could be set accurately. In addition, the steel connecting link between the moving air and blast vanes was moved up to 1 in. below the cross support for the fixed air vanes so as to be in the slip stream of this cross and hence to reduce the air resistance. The gyro contacts were adjusted so that the vanes operated for a 5-deg angular displacement of the rocket from the vertical instead of 10 deg as before.

Weight and dimensions. The length of the rocket over all was 16 ft 5 in., and the weight empty 100 lb.

Test. When the release key was pressed, the rocket rose rapidly in the tower. It headed into the wind but was restored quickly to the vertical. This correcting continued during the entire period of propulsion, which was 22.3 sec as measured by the stop watch.

Because of dust in the atmosphere, the observer at the recording telescope was unable to follow the flight after the smoke trail ceased, which as seen by the observers at the 1000-ft shelter was several seconds before the end of the propulsion period. The rocket continued to rise farther, becoming too high to follow with the theodolite. The maximum height was estimated as between 8000 and 9000 ft. The rocket turned over during the coasting period and had descended about halfway to the ground before the parachute was released. The latter was considerably torn because of the high velocity of the rocket at the time it was released. The rocket was therefore not adequately checked, and struck the ground about 2000 ft from the tower with a speed sufficient to produce a hole in the ground about a foot in diameter and 6 in. deep. The cap was found at one side, somewhat dented but otherwise undamaged.

Suggestions. It might be advantageous to increase the release pressure of the parachute from 85 to 110 psi, in order to reduce the speed when the parachute opens, and also to reinforce the shroud lines with $\frac{1}{16}$-in.-diameter airplane cable. Larger movable air vanes might be used, particularly movable air vanes that become part of the streamlined casing when not in use. With the center of gravity sufficiently far forward, fixed air vanes might be omitted, and the resistance thereby considerably reduced. Further, a 3-ft-diameter pilot parachute might be attached to the cap, in order to prevent damage to the latter.

Test of April 22, 1937 (L-14):
Flight Test, Larger Air Vanes

The object of this test was to repeat the preceding flight with larger movable air vanes and with a reinforced parachute.

General alterations. The chamber, tank, and piping were used without change, except for the addition of two expansion joints in the gas-pressure line. These consisted of two 0.037-in. nickel disks, 1 in. in diameter, with $\frac{1}{2}$-in. holes, these disks being welded together at the outer edges and brazed to the $\frac{1}{2}$-in. tubing.

The parachute was reinforced by sewing $\frac{1}{16}$-in. Roebling airplane cable, having a breaking strength of 400 lb, to alternate shroud lines of the 12-shroud-line parachute. In addition, the edge of the parachute was reinforced by two salvaged silk shroud lines. A 3-ft-diameter, 6-oz pilot parachute was used for the cap. Contact for the release was made when the storage-tank pressure fell to 90 psi. No changes were made in the gyro, magnet-controlled valves, or batteries.

Large movable air vanes were used, each consisting of a 0.032-in. sheet of 17 ST aluminum alloy, 9 in. wide and 12 in. high, mounted near the end of the steel cross for supporting the fixed air vanes, this cross being reduced to a width of $12\frac{5}{8}$ in. The vanes were moved outward by rods attached to short arms on the edges of the vanes and passing through narrow aluminum tubes on the outer edges of the fixed air vanes. An additional set of bellows operators was used for the movable air vanes, these being located just above the chamber.

In order to make the rocket more visible while in flight, it was painted with black enamel, except for the rear quadrant, which was painted red as before in order to determine if the rocket rotated. A front sight having fine crossed wires was used on the theodolite, this sight being supported sufficiently above the telescope for the latter to point at 30 deg downward when the sights were horizontal. By this means, flight elevations could be measured up to 90 deg.

Weight and dimensions. The length of the rocket over all was 17 ft 9 in., and the weight empty 113 lb. The center of gravity was 14½ in. below the top of the lower hemisphere of the pressure-storage tank.

Test. The rocket rose rapidly through the tower when released, although not so fast as in the preceding test. It corrected once but thereafter became progressively more inclined, being horizontal at the time propulsion ceased. The parachute was not released and the rocket struck the ground about a mile from the tower. A check could not be made on the angle of rise, since the rocket passed directly over the 1000-ft shelter. The propulsion period was 21½ sec, and the smoke was noticeably less than for the preceding test.

Conclusions. It was concluded that large air vanes are not satisfactory in producing stabilized flight. The fact that the parachute was not released was attributed to the time required for the gas pressure to drop to 100 psi after propulsion had ceased.

The resistance of the vane system might be reduced by replacing the fixed air vanes by four retractable vanes turning on two axes at right angles and intersecting the rocket axis at a common point, the vanes turning each way about these two axes.

Test of May 19, 1937 (L-15):
Flight Test, Retractable Air Vanes, Reduced Weight

The object of this test was to repeat the preceding flight test with retractable air vanes and with a general reduction in weight.

Chamber. The chamber was used without change. The oxygen and gasoline tanks differed in having the lower hemispheres replaced by 60-deg and 120-deg cones, as previously used, a complete set of hemispheres not being available. The outer walls were made streamlined by having the 120-deg cones fit inside the cylindrical walls, rather than outside.

Wire-wound storage tank. The pressure-storage tank was wire-wound, both longitudinally and transversely. The cylindrical wall was 48 in. long, of 0.018-in. sheet nickel, and had a welded seam. The conical ends fitted inside this cylinder. The seams were made strong by first brazing the bottom of the groove between the 120-deg cone and the cylinder, then hammering the edge of the cylinder flush with the cone, and finally brazing this edge.

The wire used was No. 14 (0.033-in.) music wire. The transverse windings were ⅛ in. apart, except for three equally spaced 1-in.-wide bands, where the distance apart was 1⁄16 in. The longitudinal wires were looped over 3⁄32-in. pins on the 60-deg cone frustrums, 23⁄64 in. apart, center to center. The free ends of the wire were held between a steel and an aluminum clamping strip, using eight screws.

While winding, it was necessary to apply 10 psi air pressure to the tank in order to avoid distortion. A hand vise used for winding subjected the wire to a 6-lb pull. It was found that the transverse turns, which were more tightly wound, became snug when the tank was subjected to 50 psi pressure, and that the longitudinal turns became snug when the pressure was increased to 250 psi.

It was estimated that in order to have 150,000 lb/in.^{2} tensile stress in all the turns, for 250 psi pressure, there should be nine transverse turns and four and a half longitudinal turns per inch of length. Actually there were six turns per inch for both windings, and hence the tensile stress for the tranverse turns was about 225,000 lb/in.^{2}

Steel lugs, 1½ in. long, mounted on the 60-deg frustums, served to permit bolting the tank to the tube supports extending to the other tanks. The complete pressure-tank assembly weighed 10¾ lb.

Valves and piping. A single aluminum valve was used to open the nitrogen gas from the pressure tank at the start and to close the flow at the end of propulsion. The valve weighed 24 oz complete, as compared with the previous nitrogen-opening valve of 17 oz and the shutoff valve of 11 oz.

The 250–42-psi reducing valve was made with the reduced pressure entering the inside of the regulating bellows instead of the outside. The outer steel tube could therefore be replaced by a light perforated aluminum tube. The bellows was a 2-in.-O.D., 5-convolution Clifford bellows. The valve weighed 14 oz.

The equalizer was reduced in weight from 19 to 16 oz, by cupping or hollowing all the steel parts that could be made lighter.

The system of tubing was the same as before, except that aluminum tubing was used as extensively as possible. No tubes passed through the pressure tank, in order both to simplify wire-winding and to make possible the use of aluminum tubing.

Supports. The supports between the tanks and chamber consisted of ⅞-in. and ¾-in. 17 ST aluminum tubing. Where these joined the nickel of the tanks or chamber they were bolted to aluminum plugs, fitting the tube at one end and forked at the other end to fit over straight steel lugs, brazed to the tank or chamber.

Magnet valves. The magnet-controlled valve system was reduced in weight by replacing the tension springs on the armatures by compression springs, as used in the earlier tests, so that all four magnet valves could be installed in a single Dowmetal box. The time of exhausting through each valve was reduced by using an additional, third, exhaust hole. The weight of the complete set of valves and containing box was 2 lb 10½ oz.

Moving air vanes. The moving air vanes were 10 in. long, 5½ in. wide at the top and 4 in. wide at the bottom. They were constructed of 0.020-in. 17 ST sheet on a welded frame of ½- × ⅛-in. 17 ST strip, and were curved so as to be flush with the outer surface of the lower cone of the casing when retracted, the top edges lying along the top edge of the lower casing cone. They fitted in shallow recesses, both to prevent air from entering the cone when the air blades were extended outward and to keep the rocket surface streamlined (Fig. 11).

A 6-in.-long arm extended upward from the vane, terminating in a 2-in. arm extending inward, the end of this shorter arm being pushed downward by a bellows in an aluminum cylinder. Springs kept the movable air vanes normally retracted, and these were made long in order not to reduce the correcting force appreciably. When extended, the lower edge of each vane was 4⅛ in. from the rocket casing, and the forward edge, 1 in. The force required to move the lower edge of the vane inward, when 42 psi was applied to the bellows operator, was 2½ lb, and the force to move it inward so as to be flush with the casing was 3½ lb.

Fixed air vanes. The fixed air vanes were prevented from extending to the top of the rear cone because of the presence of the moving air vanes, and terminated 1 in. below the bottoms of the latter. The area of the fixed vanes was nevertheless made sufficiently large by extending them to the rear of the crosspiece at the nozzle. Each air vane consisted of two sheets of 0.010-in. 17 ST aluminum fastened to ¹⁄₁₆-in.-flat 17 ST strips.

Blast vanes. The blast vanes were the same as before except that they were ¼ in. wider across the tops, the aluminum-casting bellows operators again being located around the nozzle.

Parachute. A parachute having 450-lb shroud lines, in place of the 100-lb lines previously used, was employed. It weighed, together with the containing bag, 2 lb 3 oz.

Weights and dimensions. Each air vane and arm weighed 8 oz, and each blast vane 4 oz. The total weight of the fixed and moving vanes, together with the various operating devices, was 10 lb 2 oz. The length of the rocket over all was 17 ft 8 in., and the weight empty was 90½ lb. The center of gravity was 10½ in. below the edge of the bottom cone of the pressure tank.

Test. In the test, which was made about 7 P.M., a few minutes after sunset, with a moderate wind, the rocket rose rapidly through the tower and leaned considerably toward the right, at about 150 ft. It corrected itself, however, the inclinations thereafter being of small amplitude, and the rocket traveling almost vertically during the 29.3-sec period of propulsion and for some time thereafter.

When the propulsion ceased there were two bright flashes, accompanied by loud reports, which, in addition to the noise of the flight, were heard at the ranch house 8 miles away. After the roar ceased, a loud whistling noise was heard, possibly owing to the high speed of ascent in the first part of the coasting period. According to several observers, the rocket nearly came to rest at the high point, which was estimated as about a half mile. The parachute was released as soon as the rocket tilted.

The drift in the direction of the wind was about ¹⁄₁₀ mile during the ascent, and ½ mile during the descent. The descent took place so slowly that the observers could have reached the landing spot, near the cross-country road past the tower, by automobile if a start had been made when the descent began.

The rocket was found just before dark, with the directing vanes, as well as the fore part of the rocket, bent to some extent. The chamber showed no sign of overheating. The cap and pilot parachute were found the next morning about 2 miles from the tower and 12 ft from the road.

Conclusion. It was concluded that the moving air vanes used in the preceding tests had produced greater drag than correcting force.

Suggestion. A steering method involving the angular displacement of the tail section of the rocket might be used, to avoid both fixed and moving vanes. Triangular-shaped cover shields or casings might also be used, to extend behind the nozzle during the coasting period, and thereby serve to make the rocket completely streamlined.

Test of July 28, 1937 (L-16):
Flight Test, Steering by Movable Tail Section

The object of this test was to try the movable-casing method of steering, with the rocket made as streamlined as possible.

Chamber. The chamber was similar to that used in the preceding test.

Tanks and valves. An attempt was first made to use 12-in.-diameter tanks of ⅟₃₂-in. aluminum, wire-wound, for the oxygen and gasoline, but these were discarded owing to the tendency for leaks to appear along the welded seams, which could not be repaired without rewinding. These aluminum tanks had hemispherical ends, and slippage on the hemisphere surfaces was prevented by using two rows of short pins on narrow steel bands, placed halfway up the hemispheres. The longitudinal wires were bent around these pins and passed around the hemisphere, nearly to the opposite side. Notched steel strips extended from the steel band toward the wide end of each hemisphere and served to prevent slippage of the transverse windings.

Four vane sections were installed in the tailpiece, with springs to free them so that they could bring the rear streamlining down practically to a point after propulsion ceased, by forming a conical extension of the tail-piece. This feature was not used, since the rocket, being 9 in. in diameter as before, was too small. The oxygen, gasoline, and pressure tanks were the same, as was also the general piping layout.

An improved equalizer was constructed, by which it was possible to hold the excess of oxygen to gasoline-tank pressure much closer to 5 psi than before. It consisted of a tapered-seat valve in one end of a steel tube containing a 1½-in., two-ply bellows, soldered at the other end. A rod bearing a small disk at the free end extended inward from the valve member, and a fork attached to the end plate on the free end of the bellows engaged this disk when the pressure on the outside of the bellows, from the oxygen tank, exceeded the pressure on the inside, from the gasoline tank. This contraction of the bellows served to pull the valve open and to allow gas to escape to the atmosphere. Steel strips limited the motion of the bellows.

The increased sensitiveness was due to the fact that the fork did not touch the rod and disk when the oxygen pressure became too great. This equalizer weighed 10 oz. A single-ply bellows would have been sufficient if there had been no possibility of an accidental severe difference in pressure on the two sides.

A combination oxygen safety and reducing valve for the steering operators was made, weighing 15 oz and consisting of a 5/8-in. diameter, 12-in. length of corrugated tubing. Extension of the bellows caused a ball valve in the free end to be opened by a fixed pin, thus relieving pressure; and contraction caused a rod fixed at the free end to open a ball valve in the fixed end and thus to admit more pressure. The reducing valve was set at 53 psi and the safety valve at 57 psi, thus serving to supply gas for the steering bellows over this range of pressure. A small ballast tank, having a 4¼-in.-long cylinder, 2¾ in. in diameter, with conical ends, was used in the line to the bellows in order to avoid an appreciable drop in pressure when more than one bellows was used.

The magnet-controlled valves were the same as before. The close fit of the movable rods extended only ¼ in. on each side of the middle groove, in order to reduce sliding resistance. These rods were turned in a lathe before being lapped, in order to keep them as straight as possible.

The parachute was released, as before, when the rocket became inclined 90 deg and the nitrogen-line pressure fell to 100 psi.

Steering. For the purpose of steering, the conical tailpiece, containing the combustion chamber, was moved from side to side about pivot points on a ring 35 in. above the open end of the nozzle. Normally this ring was held firmly by gas pressure in four bellows, so that the chamber axis coincided with the axis of the rocket. During steering, pressure was admitted to two bellows, each associated with either one or two units of a four-bellows system. One of the latter counteracted the force of the first-mentioned bellows, and the other, larger, produced a sidewise displacement of the chamber (Figs. 12, 13, 14).

The ring above the chamber permitting the angular displacement was 8 in. in diameter, of ¼- × ¾-in. 17 ST alloy. Two arms from the chamber were pivoted outside the ring, on opposite sides. At right angles to these were pivoted two arms that extended to a fixed ring 4¹¹/₁₆ in. above the first ring. The bellows operators were secured to a third ring 15½ in. above the second ring and were joined to opposite points on the first ring (at right angles to the fixed arms), and to two opposite arms on the chamber, terminating 7½ in. apart and level with the 8-in. ring when the rocket was in normal alignment.

The top of the rear movable casing fitted just inside the cylindrical casing of the rocket, to reduce air resistance. The bending which took place at the level of the first ring necessitated the use of flexible tubing. The axial oxygen line was made flexible by a 1¼-in.-O.D., two-ply bellows, level with the movable steering ring. The oxygen jacket in the top of the chamber was connected by ¼-in.-O.D. seamless flexible tubes. A braided flexible tube was used for each gasoline orifice in the chamber.

Each of the four bellows operators consisted of a 1½-in. single-ply bellows which pushed downward the sleeve that bore the connecting rod just mentioned, using a stop above the bellows, the stop being located inside another 1½-in. bellows. Pressure was applied constantly to the former bellows, and to the latter only during steering.

The actual steering force was produced by a third bellows, 2-in.-O.D., on the sleeve mentioned, which pushed this sleeve upward when pressure was applied. When the operator functioned on one side of the rocket, with the sleeve moving downward, the operator on the other side idled, the sleeve moving upward.

Shop tests. In shop tests, the bellows motion for operation was made ⅜ in., and the sidewise displacement of the nozzle was 3¼ in. With an air pressure of 40 psi, the transverse force required to move the open end of the nozzle, for no steering force, was 2½ lb; and the force required to start the nozzle back, when it was displaced by the steering force, was 4 lb. This ⅜-in. bellows displacement caused the thrust, on steering, to pass about a foot from the center of gravity of the rocket. This corrective force was considered to be too great, however, and accordingly the bellows displacement was reduced to ⅛ in., thus causing the thrust, estimated at 200 lb, to pass 3 in. from the center of gravity.

The gyro, together with the magnet valves, batteries, and a small barograph, was located between the fixed upper ring of the steering system and the bottom of the cylindrical part of the oxygen tank, 38¼ in. above. Because of the amount of this rearward weight, it was decided to add fixed air vanes. These vanes were small, however, extending 12 in. from the nozzle end up the sides of the conical tailpiece, and being 6 in. wide across the rear ends.

Weights and dimensions. The rocket was 18 ft 5½ in. long over all, 9 in. in diameter, and weighed empty 93 lb 5 oz. The center of gravity was 16 in. below the bottom edge of the cylindrical part of the pressure tank. The oxygen tank, together with the support tubes on each end, weighed 13 lb; the gasoline tank, with the support tubes on the bottom, 11½ lb; and the pressure tank, 15 lb 2 oz. The tailpiece, including the air vanes, weighed 2 lb 10 oz, and the cap, including the two parachutes, 4¼ lb.

Test. In the test, at 6:30 P.M., the rocket rose rapidly with but little motion from side to side except at about half the maximum height reached, when it deviated about 30 deg on one side and immediately afterward to the same angle on the other side, thereafter proceeding vertically. After propulsion ceased, the rocket moved gradually toward the left and soon began to descend. There was a loud whistling noise after the powered period.

The rocket descended head downward at first, and thereafter fell at a reduced rate with the axis horizontal. The cap came off when the rocket was about 200 ft from the ground, and both parachutes opened immediately afterward, the rocket being immediately reduced in speed to the terminal velocity with parachute.

The rocket landed about 1000 ft from the tower with the parachute on top, the cap being 50 ft away. It appeared to ascend with the least sidewise drift of any of the rockets, and also to remain more nearly vertical during the propulsion period, except for the large deviation mentioned. From the recording-telescope results the height was estimated as 2055 ft. The barograph gave a smooth curve during the ascent but showed a jerky motion during the descent, evidently owing to friction of the stylus. The maximum displacement of the barograph indicated an altitude of about 500 ft.

Conclusion. It was concluded from the descent with the axis horizontal that the center of gravity of the empty rocket was close to the center of air resistance. The single deviation was considered as possibly being due to the rocket's entering a layer of air having a different wind velocity.

Suggestions. A gravity catapult might be used to give the rocket a substantial initial velocity while in the tower. As a means of avoiding cracks in the welding of aluminum wire-wound tanks under pressure, a bent or corrugated tank surface might be used, which would expand without stretching the metal when the wires were extended under high tank pressure.

Test of August 26, 1937 (L-17):
Repeat Flight Test, with Catapult

The object of this test was to repeat the preceding flight test after removing the slack motion of the tailpiece when in axial position, and using a gravity catapult in order to give the rocket an initial velocity on passing through the tower.

General alterations. The chamber, tanks, piping, and supports were used without change from the preceding test. The pressure contact maker was connected to the combustion chamber at the head end, in order to avoid too low a fall of pressure in the tanks after propulsion ceased. Heat from the chamber was prevented from melting the solder of the $\frac{5}{8}$- × 12-

in. flexible tube constituting the pressure element of the contact maker by using 56 in. of ⅟₁₆-in.-bore copper tube between it and the chamber, and also by reducing the gas space inside the flexible tube by inserting within it a ⁵⁄₁₆-in. steel tube, closed on the inner end.

The equalizer was made more responsive to low excess oxygen-tank pressure by using a coil compression spring on each side of the steel disk on the free end of the bellows, and by using a small spacing screw, held by a lock nut, in the end of the stop rod that limited the amount of compression of the bellows.

The amount of sidewise play of the end of the tailpiece, which was held by the constant-pressure control bellows, was reduced by using, for bearings of the gimbal ring, the ends of screws from which the threads had been turned, and by using a threaded-rod insert in each of the four arms which reduced the displacement, with lock nuts to keep the lengths constant. The backlash or play previously observed was thereby eliminated.

A more sensitive barograph was made, using a 2¼-in. super-sensitive Sylphon bellows in place of two 1⅛-in. single-ply bellows soldered together. As before, a 2½-in. paper disk on a small clockwork was used for the pencil trace.

Weights and dimensions. The weights and dimensions of the rocket were practically unchanged from the preceding test.

Catapult. For the purpose of giving the rocket an initial velocity by the use of falling weights, a cradle, pulled upward by these weights, was used under the lowest (14-in.) set of aluminum guide angles on the rocket, the two upper sets remaining unsupported.

This cradle consisted of two horizontal 15-in. squares of ¾-in. square steel tubing, each enclosing the rocket, and being spaced 23 in. apart by ½-in.-O.D. vertical square steel tubes. Four sets of two grooved rollers engaged the ⅜-in. pipe guides of the tower, on the opposite sides of each square.

Two ³⁄₁₆-in. flexible airplane cables were hooked to opposite sides of the upper square of the cradle and passed over two deep-grooved pulleys at the top of the tower. Thence each passed over a similar pulley, fixed to a strong frame of horizontal angle irons on the tower 30 ft above the ground, under a pulley on the upper end of a 7-ft pipe for holding weights, to be described, over another fixed pulley on the same angle iron frame, and finally to a link on the pipe pulley. The rocket and cradle accordingly moved upward at three times the speed of the falling weights. Six 100-lb, 1-ft-diameter, sheet-iron-covered concrete weights were made, to be held on each 7-ft pipe support by a pin at the bottom, but only one 40-lb weight was used on each pipe support for a first test of the method. Each 7-ft pipe and pulley weighed 14 lb.

Four bumpers or shock absorbers were used at the top of the tower to reduce the speed of the cradle gradually. Each consisted of a ⅞-in.-

diameter tube telescoping inside a fixed 1-in.-diameter tube, the motion being reduced by a strong compression spring. When the concrete weights struck the ground, the cradle was 3 in. below the bottoms of the shock absorbers, each of which had an upward travel of 9¾ in.

Two thin sheet-iron shields were used, on opposite sides of the upper square of the cradle, to prevent the cable, on becoming loose, from moving inward axially and striking the rocket casing. The cradle alone weighed 9 lb, and with these two shields 10½ lb.

A releasing lever having a U-shaped end straddling the rocket casing was used as before, connected by a steel link with a similar lever below, which bore downward on the cradle. A 1⅛-in. rise of the rocket was permitted before the 14-in. guides made contact with the upper lever, so that the lift indicator could be used as usual.

Test. On making the test the rocket rose through the tower more rapidly than usual, but during the main part of the ascent moved slower than for Test L-15, though faster than for Test L-16. The rocket corrected the flight seven times, although the deviations were successively greater. At about 2000 ft it became inclined to the left. While continuing in this inclined path, the parachute was released, carrying the gasoline tank off from the remainder of the rocket. After the test, the vertical ½-in. square tube supports of the cradle were found to have become somewhat bent (Fig. 15).

Conclusions. The large deviations were probably due to the cradle's tilting the rocket as the latter emerged from the tower, the succeeding large displacements finally warping the supports in the rocket and at the same time freeing the parachute retaining rods. The warping of the cradle was believed due either to inertia on stopping or to the fact that the 40-lb weights moved somewhat into the ground, thus pulling on the cradle after it had engaged the bumpers.

Suggestions. A shorter cradle, of 17 ST tubing, might be used, and each set of weights might strike a reinforced-concrete platform, recessed to accommodate the bottom of the 7-ft pipe. It might further be desirable to have any cable guards installed on the top of the tower rather than on the cradle. For large accelerations in the tower, followed by deceleration owing to air resistance, centrifugal separators might be used in the tanks, liquid being taken from the walls, and gas flow taking place through an axial passage.

8

L-Series Flight Tests Concluded, with Rockets Pressurized by Liquid Nitrogen

L Series (Continued), October 23, 1937 — August 9, 1938

The following tests, with pressure produced by a liquid nitrogen pump and engine, were made for the purpose of developing a rocket pressurized by liquid nitrogen.

Test of October 23, 1937 (L-18):
Static Test, Bellows Pump and Engine

The object of this test was to develop a flight rocket in which the oxygen and gasoline tanks were supplied with nitrogen gas under pressure, pumped as a liquid by a bellows pump operated by a bellows engine, and evaporated by the heat of the chamber. In the absence of a relatively large gas pressure storage tank, it was believed possible that the liquid load could be increased 50 per cent over that for the preceding test, the rocket at the same time being considerably lightened.

Chamber. The chamber was used without alteration from Test L-17 except for making the throat more streamlined. This streamlining was done by flaring the narrow end of the nozzle for $\frac{1}{8}$ in. with a tapered pin, and by spinning the opening in the lower cone outward while the nozzle was held in a lathe, using the oxygen-acetylene flame, thus producing a gradually curved part $\frac{1}{2}$-in. long.

Tanks. The oxygen tank was of 0.037-in. sheet nickel, having a $12\frac{1}{2}$-in.-long cylindrical part and hemispherical ends. The gasoline-tank cylinder was of 0.018-in. sheet nickel, 28 in. long, with the usual double cone ends, wire-wound in the same way as with the previous pressure-storage tanks. The weights of the oxygen and gasoline tanks were, respectively, $9\frac{1}{2}$ and $13\frac{1}{2}$ lb.

The liquid-nitrogen tank, from which the nitrogen was pumped, was of 0.037-in. sheet nickel and had a $6\frac{1}{4}$-in. cylinder with 120-deg conical ends.

The outside jacket, for condensing the liquid nitrogen and for keeping it cool before the run, was an aluminum cylinder, $11\frac{1}{2}$ in. long and $6^{13}/_{16}$ in. in diameter, with a 120-deg cone on the bottom, covered with felt, and provided with a dumping valve in the bottom of the cone for preventing condensation of nitrogen under pressure during the run. This dumping valve was similar to that previously used, in which a thin aluminum disk was cut by a knife-edge on a lever, except that the valve and lever were lightened by being made of aluminum alloy (Fig. 16).

The liquefying coil for the nitrogen was located on the top of the nitrogen tank, the liquid nitrogen passing into the tank from the bottom of the coil. It consisted of six turns of $\frac{3}{16}$-in.-O.D., $\frac{1}{64}$-in.-wall copper tubing, having an average radius of 6 in., with the turns staggered to permit circulation to take place around each turn, when placed in the liquid oxygen jacket.

Pump. The pump consisted essentially of a 3-in.-O.D. single-ply bellows having a fixed disk at the top, and being given a $\frac{1}{2}$-in. stroke at the lower, closed, end. The volume remaining in the pump at the end of the up-stroke was reduced as much as possible by a fixed steel tube that fitted freely inside the bellows and had the lower end closed except for the outlet valve. Both this valve and the intake valve, in the closed bottom of the bellows, were as nearly flush with the respective inside surfaces as possible, in order to utilize all the available pump volume (Fig. 17).

Each of the two valves consisted of a $1\frac{3}{8}$-in.-diameter disk of 0.020-in. 17 ST, backed above and below by disks of $\frac{1}{16}$-in. aluminum, the thicker disks being slightly narrower than the $1\frac{1}{4}$-in.-diameter valve openings. By this means, each thin disk conformed to the valve seat and fitted tightly, and at the same time was prevented from bending as a whole by the upper and lower disks. The edges of the thicker disks were rounded, to prevent bending of the thin disks on too small a radius. The nitrogen left the pump through a hollow cone brazed to the bottom of the steel spacing tube, the outlet tube being at the top of this cone.

The fixed part of the pump was held by the upper end of the spacing tube, which projected beyond the bellows, using four steel tubes brazed to this tube and to the bottom of the liquid-nitrogen tank. The lower, moving end of the bellows was soldered to a ring brazed to lugs on the lower ends of four tubes that slid freely in the four fixed tubes, the latter having slots at the bottom to accommodate the four lugs just mentioned. From the center of a cross at the top of the four movable tubes projected a single $\frac{1}{4}$-in.-O.D. steel tube constituting the pump rod and extending upward to the bellows engine, to be described below. Four pump tension springs were used with an engine compression spring to collapse the bellows.

The engine was kept spaced properly with respect to the pump by a $\frac{3}{4}$-in.-O.D. steel tube, from the bottom of which arms extended to the tops of the four fixed tubes. By this means, the stroke was not altered when the nitrogen tank was stretched by internal pressure.

Engine. The engine for operating the pump was placed above the liquid oxygen jacket, and consisted of two 1½-in.-O.D., two-ply Sylphon bellows, soldered end to end. The lower, free end of the combination was soldered to a steel plate, in which the ¼-in. pump rod was fastened. The upper end was fixed in a cap in a containing steel tube, a disk on the bottom of which joined the fixed ¾-in. tube already mentioned and was provided with holes that admitted nitrogen-tank pressure around the outside of the bellows. Radial grooves were provided in the steel plate on the free end of the bellows, in order to permit rapid entry of the gas to the space outside of the bellows.

The space inside the bellows was closed, except for the volume at the bottom taken up by the stroke, by a freely fitting fixed tube, in order to reduce the waste space. A narrow fixed tube in the center led up to a packing gland, through which a rod passed, which in turn was fixed to the plate on the movable end of the bellows.

This central rod served to throw a switch from an ordinary electric-lamp socket that made a positive sliding contact, this being equivalent to a single-throw, double-pole switch. A pin-and-slot slack motion caused the switch to be thrown each way during the last ¹⁄₁₆ in. of the stroke.

Auxiliary engine valve. The engine switch just described served to control the current in a single magnet valve, similar to those used in operating the directing vanes. A ⅛-in. diameter valve rod was moved by the magnet and hinged armature. This rod had a ¼-in.-wide, ¹⁄₃₂-in.-deep groove at the middle, which communicated alternately to ring-shaped grooves in the valve block, for supplying 40 psi pressure and exhaust, respectively; a hole at the middle of the block leading to the bellows operator for the ¼-in. rod of the main engine valve. Resistance to flow was reduced by using large holes in the valve block, leading to the internal grooves, except for No. 52 holes, ¹⁄₃₂ in. deep, just at the grooves. The small magnet valve was protected by a fine phosphor-bronze strainer and also by being enclosed in a ⅛-in.-wall 17 ST aluminum box.

Main engine valve. The main engine valve was similar to the auxiliary engine valve just described, except that it was larger and was operated by the 40-psi control pressure in two ¾-in.-O.D. Clifford bellows, soldered together, with two springs and a yoke for bringing the valve to the exhaust position, the stroke being ⅜ in.

The valve rod was ¼ in. in diameter and had a ½-in.-long, ¹⁄₁₆-in.-deep groove at the middle. The three grooves in the hole in the valve block were ⅛ in. wide, ³⁄₃₂ in. deep, and ¼ in. apart.

The engine and valve operation was as follows: When the engine and pump completed the up, or power, stroke, the engine switch was thrown off, thus de-energizing the magnet of the magnet valve and allowing the springs to collapse the bellows of the main engine valve. This action caused the main engine valve to connect the 250-psi nitrogen-tank pressure with the inside of the engine bellows, and thereby permitted the tension springs on the pump to hold the engine bellows collapsed, and therefore to hold the pump bellows extended.

When, on the other hand, the engine and pump completed the down, or return, stroke, the engine switch caused the magnet to be energized, the bellows of the main engine valve to become extended, and the 250 psi on the inside of the engine bellows to be exhausted, thus allowing the plate on the free end of the engine bellows to be pushed upward by the tank pressure exerted on the under side of this plate. As soon as the engine nearly reached the upper end of the pressure stroke, the engine switch was opened and the process was repeated.

Engine regulator. An automatic arrangement was necessary, as in the 1930–1932 pump and engine tests, to keep the speed of the engine just sufficient to maintain the nitrogen tank at the required pressure. This regulator consisted of a valve rod, similar to that used for the main engine valve, on the free end of a 12-in.-long flexible tube. The cylindrical valve-block hole had two grooves, to and from which relatively large gas flows could take place through radial holes leading to annular spaces on the outside of the valve block.

This regulator was installed in the exhaust line of the engine, each exhaust taking place freely along the groove on the valve rod at low pressure, but being checked when the pressure rose too high and the 12-in. tube became extended. Notches were made, however, in the rearward edge of the ½-in. groove on the rod, so that the engine would not stop abruptly when the normal working pressure was exceeded.

Tests showed that the leakage was sufficient at high pressure to permit the engine to continue to operate slowly, and hence a switch with a sliding contact was added to the regulator, so that the current was cut off entirely above a particular pressure. An additional switch was needed, to keep the circuit open before the run. Also, a safety valve was used for the nitrogen tank, this valve consisting of a 12-in. flexible tube with a ball valve in the movable end, the ball pushing against a fixed pin above a safe pressure.

Ballast tank. A gas chamber, or ballast tank, was used in the liquid-nitrogen pump delivery line in order to help in maintaining pressure during the idling, or return, stroke of the pump. This tank consisted of a ¼-in.-O.D. aluminum tube, about 2½ ft long, plugged at the upper, or forward, end and wrapped in a close spiral around the ½-in.-O.D. steel gasoline line. Any liquid in this chamber tended to become evaporated by the flow of the relatively warm gasoline to the combustion chamber.

Liquid-nitrogen separator. In the 1930–1932 series of tests in which liquid was separated from liquid-gas mixtures, the liquid entered tangentially at the common base of two hollow cones, liquid and gas passing out to the gasoline tank tangentially on the opposite side, and gas alone passing out through a tube in the upper apex to the oxygen tank.

Since this separator would not be very satisfactory if the proportion of liquid were large, a separator consisting essentially of a hollow cone, of increasing rearward taper, was used, the mixture entering the upper end tangentially. The gas passed out of an axial tube in the top, extending halfway down so as to be in a gaseous space. The liquid, on reaching the bottom and continuing to revolve, was guided by curved vanes that stopped the rotation and allowed it to pass out of a hole in the bottom of the separator.

Shop test of engine. In a test in which the engine was tested without the pump, using compressed air, the engine ran at about 5 strokes per second from 150 to 190 psi. It ran slowly at 215 psi and was stopped by the regulator switch at 220 psi. With falling pressure, the switch became closed at 205 psi, and the engine ran full speed at 190 psi.

Copper-tube jacket. The copper-tube jacket around the chamber and nozzle, for evaporating the liquid nitrogen, covered more of the chamber surface, and covered it more completely, than the earlier copper-tube jackets, because its tubes were wound in a spiral. Twelve $\frac{3}{16}$-in.-O.D. $\times$ $\frac{1}{64}$-in.-wall tubes, connected above and below to two semicircular square tubing manifolds, were used. An open spiral of No. 22 iron wire was used in each copper tube for the purpose of breaking up large drops. In winding, a single tube was first wrapped around the nozzle and chamber by means of a spacer equal in width to the other 11 tubes. Weight was reduced by the use of $\frac{3}{16}$-in.-diameter steel tube unions, at each end of the copper jacket tubes. In addition, a small ball valve was used just above each entrance union for the tubes in the lower manifold, to make certain that no liquid entering the copper-tube jacket would tend to return, owing to pressure produced by rapid evaporation, and thus obstruct the flow.

Weight of nitrogen system. The complete liquid-nitrogen unit, consisting of tank, pump, engine, valves, and other parts, together with the copper-tube jacket, weighed $13\frac{3}{4}$ lb. The liquid-nitrogen tank, engine, and pump weighed $6\frac{1}{4}$ lb, and the copper-tube jacket, except for the steel parts, 3 lb. The weight of the regulator was 12 oz; safety valve, 9 oz; magnet-controlled valve and box, 15 oz; main engine valve, 13 oz; separator, 14 oz; and the three operating batteries, together, 25 oz. The weight of all the above accessories was thus $5\frac{1}{2}$ lb.

This $13\frac{3}{4}$-lb system, which, however, did not include the aluminum connecting tube and strainer, replaced the 0.018-in. nickel wire-wound pressure tank weighing 15 lb 2 oz used in Test L-15, and the 0.037-in. nickel pressure tank weighing 23 lb, used in the tests preceding L-15. It should be noted, however, that the capacity of the pump and engine system could be increased considerably without adding much to the weight, the capacity being doubled for about 2 lb increase in weight of the 4⅛-lb nitrogen tank and jacket, whereas the weights for either pressure-storage tank would be nearly twice as great.

Piping and valves. Except for the nitrogen system, the piping was unchanged. The weight of several valves was reduced, however. Thus, aluminum check valves were used in the nitrogen-pressure line to the gasoline and oxygen tanks, in place of steel valves. Further, an aluminum valve, similar to one of the aluminum check valves, was used to shut off the oxygen and gasoline tanks from the nitrogen supply; and a similar valve shut off the gasoline line at the end of the period of propulsion, in order to retain gas pressure for operating the controls and to produce rigidity in the gasoline tank.

Other features. The supports between tanks, the gyroscope, and the parachute release were the same as before. A bellows directive system for movable-tailpiece steering, made of aluminum insofar as possible, with a reduction of about 23 per cent in weight, was tried but not used. The bellows were soldered to thin copper rings, riveted to the aluminum, and fastened with Aluma-weld solder, this solder having a higher melting point than ordinary solder. Leakage developed, however, at some of the Aluma-weld joints, and hence this equipment was omitted, the blast vanes and retractable air vanes of Test L-15 being again employed. The fixed air vanes were made somewhat larger than in Test L-15, because of the additional weight near the rear of the rocket.

Weights and dimensions. The chamber, tanks, and connecting tubing weighed 22½ lb; the weight with the addition of the liquid oxygen and gasoline lines, bellows directors, and copper-tube jacket was 56 lb; the weight with the addition of the nitrogen tank, pump, engine, valves, and gyro was 71.5 lb; the weight of the complete rocket less the ¼-in. aluminum tube and the casings was 89¼ lb; and the complete weight, 105 lb 9 oz.

The length over all was 17 ft 4¼ in., and the center of gravity was 2⅝ in. below the bottom of the cylindrical part of the oxygen tank.

Alterations. Several changes were made after a preliminary test. The 0.004-in. aluminum disk of the dumping valve on the nitrogen-tank jacket was replaced by one of 0.001-in. brass foil. A new pressure contact maker for the chamber was made, having a moving hook of insulating material, which was not moved to operative position until the pressure had risen to 65 or 70 psi. It thereafter made contact when the pressure fell to 45 or 50 psi. Further, a pin was used in the middle of the hose fitting, supplying initial pressure for the rocket, to hold the hose valve on the rocket open until the hose was removed.

Test. In the test the pressure fell after the outside pressure had been cut off, either because the pump pressure was too low or the boiling capacity of the copper-tube jacket was too small. When the run was stopped, the gasoline flow was checked by the cutoff valve, but the continued flow of oxygen caused the chamber to burn through along the cylindrical part.

Test of November 2, 1937 (L-19):
Repeat Static Test

The main object of this test was to repeat the preceding test as a static test, with both the engine pressure regulator and safety valve set to operate at a higher pressure.

The chamber, tanks, and piping in general were essentially unchanged. No flight accessories were installed.

Alterations. Instead of having the fused-wire release for the gasoline shutoff valve operated by the oxygen shutoff valve, closed by the chamber pressure contact maker, the release was caused to operate by the fall of pressure in the oxygen tank, thus making certain that gasoline would continue to flow as long as a considerable stream of gaseous oxygen passed into the chamber.

The pressure contact maker used on the chamber was modified so as to be employed later at high chamber pressures, by substituting a $9/16$-in.-O.D. Clifford bellows for the 12-in. flexible tube, with the pressure applied to the inside.

The dumping valve was improved by using a wide spoon-shaped cutter with a sharply pointed tip for the 0.001-in. brass disk. This cut out a flap nearly as large as the opening in the supporting flanges, and held this flap out of the way thereafter.

The pressure lines to the instrument board and Sept camera were shortened by placing the camera and board on the third horizontal angles of the tower, 15 ft above the ground.

The range of increase of pressure through which the rate of engine operation was reduced was made less by cutting away some of the bottom of the grooves in the engine regulator valve, thus decreasing the size of the small V grooves.

In a test of the engine, using compressed air, the engine began to slow down at 235 psi and stopped at 245 psi. With falling pressure, the engine acquired full speed at 235 psi.

Test. Two seconds after the flame had become steady, the release lever was operated, removing the outside pressure. The nitrogen pressure was steady and just under 200 psi. An indicating arm on the engine showed that it operated slowly several times just after the start, and rapidly at intervals thereafter.

About 10 sec after the start, a small gasoline flame was observed from the side of the chamber that became gradually larger until at 21.3 sec the seam along the cylindrical side of the chamber opened, and the run was stopped.

Conclusions. The burning through of the chamber was probably due to a fault in the welding, since the hole appeared to be very small at first. The seams of the chamber wall might accordingly be brazed over the welding, in order to avoid pinpoint holes appearing under working pressure. Gas outlet lines in the oxygen tank might project 2 in. or so inward from the top, in order to avoid liquid oxygen passing out of these tubes just after propulsion ceased, when the decelerating force due to air resistance was greatest.

Test of November 12, 1937 (L-20):
Repeat Static Test, Brazed Motor

The main object of this test was to repeat the preceding static test with the welded seams of the chamber covered with brazing.

General alterations. Three other alterations were made. (1) A flat disk valve was used in the well on the bottom of the oxygen tank, to close the tube up through which liquid oxygen might pass by inertia at the end of the run, thus preventing gaseous oxygen from entering the chamber. This valve disk was $7/8$ in. in diameter, and the valve rod was released by a side rod, which extended through a short bellows packing. (2) The steel tube leading to the safety valve on the oxygen tank was extended $1\frac{1}{2}$ in. into the top of the chamber, in order to prevent liquid oxygen from passing into it at the end of the propulsion period, during a flight. (3) The illumination of the instrument board was improved by painting white the bottom board, or base, on which the camera and instrument panel were mounted, and also by painting white the inside of the sheet-iron protecting screen, extending up the sides of the base.

Test. A satisfactory test was made, the strong lift lasting for 39.2 sec, the release lever being freed after the first 2 sec. The main flame from the nozzle was short and pointed, as usual, and was accompanied by a secondary flame, below in the cement gas deflector.

The engine operated slowly for a few times and then fairly rapidly, at about 4 strokes per second, during the remainder of the run. The chamber pressure remained at 120 psi. The nitrogen-gas pressure, supplying the oxygen and gasoline tanks, remained closely at 203 psi. The pump pressure averaged about 25 psi higher, varying somewhat and occasionally oscillating. Possibly the pump pressure was unsteady owing to the small volume of the pressure-chamber tube, which was wrapped around the gasoline-supply tube.

The chamber temperature rose to 115° C, and the nitrogen-gas temperature to 75° C. No frost was visible on the nitrogen-gas system. Vapor seen rising from the copper evaporating coil on the chamber was probably from traces of soldering paste.

The rocket weighed $80\frac{1}{2}$ lb, the oxygen about 40 lb, the gasoline, 42 lb, and the liquid nitrogen about 10 lb. The lift averaged 228 lb, and the thrust 3960 ft/sec.

Test of November 24, 1937 (L-21):
Flight Test, Liquid-Nitrogen Pressure Rocket

The object of this test was to repeat the preceding test as a flight test, using the casing, gyro, blast vanes, and retractable air vanes of Test L-18.

Alterations. Among the few changes were the removal of the nitrogen-gas cutoff valve to the oxygen tank, the oxygen cutoff valve used in the preceding test being retained. The control bellows were modified by using internal operating pressure and by replacing the aluminum castings containing the bellows by steel tubes. The length, weight, and position of the center of gravity were practically the same as for Test L-18.

Test. The release lever was operated about 2 sec after the lift indicator light showed. The rocket rose slowly and became inclined soon after leaving the tower, thereafter becoming still further inclined, and struck the ground about 100 feet from the tower.

Conclusions. It seems probable that the rocket would have traveled straight if it had left the tower at a substantial speed. The small excess of lift over weight prevented this, and as soon as the rocket became inclined, the action of the blast vanes reduced the vertical component of the thrust and allowed the rocket to fall, the speed being too low for the retractable air vanes to take part in the action.

STATIC TESTS AT HIGH PRESSURE

The following tests at high tank pressures were made in order to learn to what extent the jet velocity could be increased by raising the chamber pressure. They were also of importance in providing for correct flow measurements by means of visible level indicators, thus making possible more accurate determinations of jet velocities.

Test of December 18, 1937 (L-22):
Static Test, at 350 Psi Pressure

The object of this test was to increase the applied gas pressure to 350 psi, using a 5¾-in.-diameter chamber of the same form as that for the preceding test and with an accurate method of measuring and recording flow.

Chamber. The chamber was of 0.028-in. sheet nickel and weighed 5¾ lb, as compared with the 0.037-in. chamber weighing 6¾ lb used in the preceding test.

Tanks. The tanks were of strong construction, and each contained a cork float, bearing a marker in a gauge glass, which could be photographed by the Sept camera at the usual 1-sec intervals.

The oxygen tank consisted of a 9-in.-diameter, 0.050-in. nickel cylindrical wall, welded and brazed, with 9-in.-diameter, $\frac{1}{32}$-in. spun-nickel hemispherical ends, 11$\frac{3}{4}$ in. apart. The edges of the latter were flared, in order to raise the strength by increasing the amount of the brazing. A split steel ring was clamped around the cylindrical part of the tank while the hemispheres were being brazed, in order to keep the cylindrical part strictly circular.

Because of the larger flows expected at the higher pressures, $\frac{3}{4}$-in.-O.D. steel tubing was used for both the liquid and the gas lines. The oxygen tube passed up from a well in the bottom of the tank, looped around just under the top, as before, and passed out of the bottom, at one side of the well. Thence it passed to the chamber through a $1\frac{5}{16}$-in.-O.D. steel jacket tube having a single expansion bellows, halfway down.

Nitrogen-gas pressure was supplied to the oxygen tank through a $\frac{3}{4}$-in.-O.D. steel tube, bearing a disk located a short distance from the open end, in order to prevent the incoming gas from blowing violently upon the liquid oxygen. The float system, together with that for the gasoline tank, will be described below. The tank weighed 11 lb.

The gasoline tank consisted of a similar nickel cylinder and similar hemispherical ends, the latter 27$\frac{5}{8}$ in. apart. The cylindrical part was reinforced by two 4-in.-wide bands of 0.050-in. nickel, the free ends being brazed over the tank seam in order to permit using a substantial amount of brazing. Gas pressure entered the tank through a $\frac{3}{4}$-in. inside tube, bent so that the outflow was horizontal, and just under the top of the upper hemisphere. The gasoline left by way of a well at the bottom of the tank. The weight, complete, was 33 lb.

The pressure tank consisted of a 9-in.-diameter cylinder of 0.050-in. sheet nickel, with hemispherical ends 47$\frac{5}{8}$ in. apart. It was reinforced by three 4-in.-wide, 0.050-in. nickel bands, equally spaced along the cylindrical part, and was located outside the tower in order to simplify the float system on the rocket.

Floats. Cork floats were used in the oxygen and the gasoline tanks, these floats being sufficiently large to bear the weight of level indicators and to be independent of ripple motion on the surfaces of the liquids.

The indicators slid freely in Pyrex water-boiler gauge glasses, located close together on the top of the gasoline tank, so that they could be photographed at 1-sec intervals by the Sept camera, which was at one side of the instrument board previously used.

Small tubes extended between the top and bottom of each gauge glass, in order to equalize the pressure rapidly at the beginning and end of a run.

The float in the oxygen tank consisted of seven 1$\frac{3}{8}$-in.-diameter, $\frac{1}{2}$-in.-

thick corks, on a 0.0635-in.-diameter straight iron rod, at the upper end of which was a ¼-in.-diameter, ½-in.-long blackened cork indicator or marker, held between small soldered disks. This marker traveled in a ¾-in.-diameter, 8¾-in.-long water-boiler pressure gauge glass, held in the usual brass fittings with dry asbestos packing, a light ring preventing this packing from being squeezed out along the glass tube.

The float traveled freely in a cage, or guide, in the oxygen tank, consisting of four 3⁄32-in. equally spaced vertical rods. The iron rod extending upward from the middle of the float to the marker, at the top of the gasoline tank, passed through the latter inside a 7⁄16-in.-O.D. steel tube. Leakage of gasoline into this tube, and hence down into the liquid oxygen, was prevented by brazing a sleeve or jacket tube around this guide tube, 2 in. above the top of the gasoline tube, this tube being open to the air at the lower end, 2½ in. below the top. Any leakage from this tank, therefore, passed harmlessly into the air.

A strong outflow of gas was prevented, in case of gauge glass breakage, by having the iron rod to the indicator pass through a hole only two drill sizes larger than the 0.035-in. diameter of the rod. Beyond this small orifice, a side outlet led, by way of a 3⁄16-in. copper tube, to the fitting at the upper end of the gauge glass, for equalization when the tank pressure was rising or falling rapidly, as already mentioned.

The gasoline float was smaller, bearing the shorter 0.035-in.-diameter rod to the small level indicator. It consisted of six 1⅜-in.-diameter, ½-in.-thick corks, sliding in a 1 13⁄32-in.-O.D. perforated steel guide tube, brazed at the top to the upper hemisphere of the gasoline tank.

The brass fittings for each gauge glass were mounted on an angle iron, these angle irons being held as close together as the size of the brass fittings permitted, using short cross angles. The measuring scales consisted of white-enameled sheet-iron strips beside the gauge glasses, with black divisions in inches.

Valves. The oxygen valve consisted of a 1-in.-diameter disk, lapped on the rim of the ¾-in. hole in the supply line that passed upward from the well in the bottom of the tank. This valve was held open ¼ in. until the pressure cutoff on the chamber made contact, when a fused-wire release freed a pin in a side bellows packing, at the top of the tank, releasing an axial rod that pulled up the valve member on a yoke, by the action of a coil compression spring.

The gasoline-valve disk, also of 1 in. diameter, closed the opening in the bottom of the well in the tank, from which the gasoline flowed downward to the chamber. This valve disk was movable up and down by an arm on a rotating rod, extending into the well from the outside through packing. The valve was held tightly shut before the run; was opened slightly by a spring, on the release of a pin, at starting; was thereafter opened fully by pulling a second pin; and was caused to close at the end

Fig. 1.   Dr. Robert H. Goddard at work on a liquid-propellant rocket in his shop at Roswell, New Mexico, November, 1935.

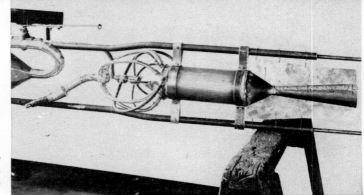

Fig. 2. Combustion chamber used in first test of March 4, 1930.

Fig. 3. Nitrogen bellows pump used in test of January 26, 1932.

Fig. 4. Gyroscope and associated parts installed in . rocket tested April 19, 1932.

Fig. 5. Gyro-controlled rocket, with casing, tested April 19, 1932. Left to right, N. T. Ljungquist, A. W. Kisk, L. C. Mansur, C. W. Mansur, R. H. Goddard, C. Gustavson.

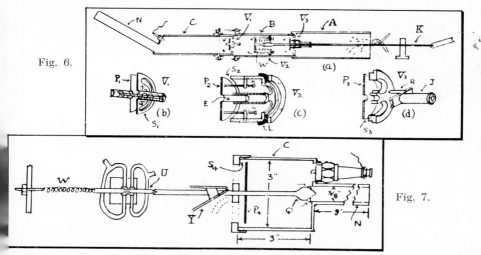

Fig. 6.

Fig. 7.

Fig. 6. Fixed chamber with positive charge displacement. This drawing, from Dr. Goddard's notebook, shows the apparatus used in this experiment. A is the mixing chamber; B, the displacement chamber; and C, the combustion chamber. Detail of the three valves V_1, V_2, and V_3 are shown in the lower sketches.

Fig. 7. Fixed chamber with explosions automatically controlled. A drawing from Dr. Goddard's notebook, sketching the apparatus used. C is the combustion chamber; P_4, a valve plate operating against the ground valve seat S_4. The valve rod is normally held against the valve seat by tension spring W, and bears rod U passing through valve block to control fuel flow. Y is the fuel spray device, consisting of two ⅛-in.-diameter steel tubes, the air escaping from a 1/16-in. hole in one tube, drawing up the fuel (ether) by suction through the other. N is the nozzle, and Q, the plug on the end of the valve rod. Mechanism used to delay return of valve to seat is not shown.

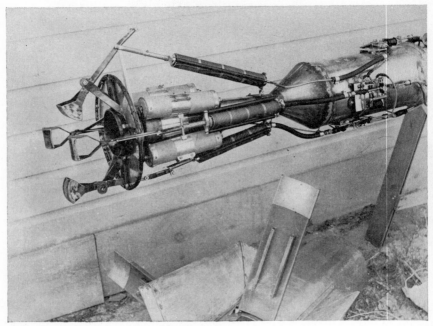

Fig. 8. Combustion chamber with vane assembly, showing extensions with rollers, which moved in grooves on the movable air vanes, at lower right. January 15, 1935.

Fig. 9. Combustion chamber, before upper cone was attached, for rocket tested December 18, 1936.

Fig. 10.   Rear view of tailpiece, showing air vanes
and blast vanes used in rocket tested February 1, 1937.

Fig. 11.   Rear view of tailpiece for rocket tested
May 19, 1937.

Fig. 12.   Detail of the movable tailpiece used for steering of rocket tested July 28, 1937.

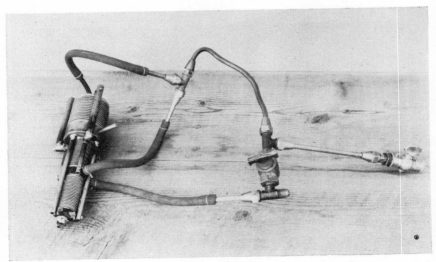

Fig. 13.   Bellows director used in rocket tested July 28, 1937.

Fig. 14. Directing bellows assembly for rocket tested July 28, 1937.

Fig. 15. Rocket in flight, August 26, 1937.

Fig. 16. Assembled nitrogen tank, engine, and pump used in test of October 23, 1937. The tank and copper-tube condensing coil were placed in a liquid oxygen jacket. The bellows engine or motor was inside the aluminum cylinder at right center. The lower tube is shown provided with an aluminum T for testing the pump and engine. It was afterward shortened and connected with the bottom of the copper-tube jacket around the combustion chamber and nozzle.

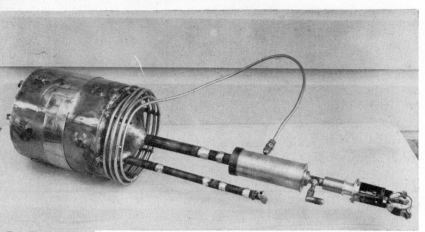

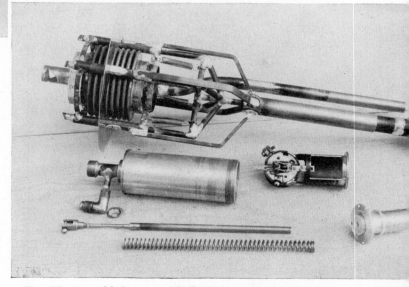

Fig. 17. Assembled nitrogen bellows pump, with engine parts, used in rocket tested October 23, 1937. The intake tube is at left, close to bottom of the nitrogen tank. At center are four movable steel tubes joined to a single rod which was pulled upward by the engine, and was returned by the engine compression spring (shown at bottom) and the four pump tension springs.

Fig. 18. Pump mounting, form A, 1938.

Fig. 19. Pump and turbine assembly, form B, 1938.

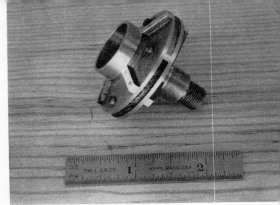

Fig. 20. Impeller for gasoline, January 6, 1939.

Fig. 21. Close-up view of pump system for rocket tested January 24, 1939.

Fig. 22. Turbine regulators used in rocket tested January 24, 1939.

Fig. 23. Gas generator chamber and head, used in rocket tested April 28, 1939.

Fig. 24. Oxygen reducing valve used in rocket tested May 18, 1939.

Fig. 25. Parts of oxygen reducing valve for rocket tested May 18, 1939.

Fig. 26. Nitrogen reducing valve used in rocket tested August 4, 1939.

Fig. 27. Parts of nitrogen reducing valve used in rocket tested August 4, 1939.

Fig. 28. Combustion chamber and main valves used in rocket tested November 18, 1939.

Fig. 29. Liquid nitrogen tanks used in rocket tested November 18, 1939.

Fig. 30. Oxygen tank with compressive supports used in rocket tested November 18, 1939.

Fig. 31. Oxygen tank cylinder and baffles used in rocket tested November 18, 1939.

Fig. 32. Complete rocket, without casings, tested November 18, 1939.

Fig. 33. Complete vane system of rocket tested February 9, 1940.

Fig. 34. Front and rear pieces juxtaposed to provide view of the complete rocket tested February 9, 1940.

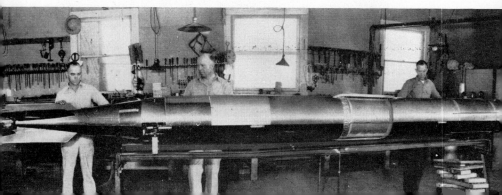

Fig. 35. Winding copper-tube jacket of motor used in rocket tested April 12, 1940.

Fig. 36. Pumps and turbines used in rocket tested April 12, 1940. Oxygen pump is shown at left, gasoline pump at right.

Fig. 37. Gas generator installed in rocket for test of August 1, 1940.

Fig. 38. Rocket in launching tower, ready for test of August 1, 1940.

Fig. 39. Completed oxygen pump used in rocket tested April 1, 1941.

of the run by the fall of pressure in the chamber, which operated a fused-wire release.

The two check valves were similar to those previously used, except that they were simplified by being made of steel, and were of brazed construction, the final brazing being at a sufficient distance from the valve seat to avoid distortion due to heating.

The equalizer was that previously employed, being again set to vent oxygen when the oxygen-tank pressure exceeded the gasoline pressure by 5 psi.

The ball safety valve for the oxygen tank was the same as before except that a 10-in. length of narrower ($\frac{1}{4}$-in.-I.D.), seamless corrugated tubing was used, in order to withstand the higher pressure. A pressure of 350 psi caused an extension of $\frac{11}{32}$ in., the valve being set to open at 375 psi. The extra space inside was taken up by a loose aluminum tube closed at the ends.

The chamber cutoff, or contact maker, was tripped into operative position when the pressure rose to 55 psi, and contact was made at the end of the run when the pressure fell to 35 psi.

Supports. The tanks were held by $\frac{7}{8}$-in.-O.D. steel tubes, four of these tubes extending downward from the oxygen tank to angle pieces, which could be bolted to a horizontal square tubing frame, held above the chamber by four $\frac{3}{4}$-in.-O.D. steel tubes. This method of mounting permitted chambers to be used interchangeably.

The rocket was 13 ft $4\frac{3}{8}$ in. long and weighed 73 lb.

Controls at tower. Pressing the first key, at the 140-ft shelter, fired the igniter. The first dashpot then allowed the gasoline valve to open part way. The second dashpot opened it fully and at the same time permitted a small flow of nitrogen to take place, by the opening of the small by-pass valve in the outside nitrogen line. This second dashpot also pulled the pin that allowed the vent valve on the oxygen tank to close, pulled off the two felt pieces on this tank, and finally opened the large outside nitrogen valve and freed the arm holding the igniter in place. After the run, the nitrogen pressure was shut off and the tanks were vented.

Test. Two or three seconds after the igniter key was pressed, the rocket commenced firing without any noticeable preliminary gasoline flame. The flame was narrow, rather yellowish, steady, and noisy. The time of the strong flame was 30.5 sec.

The average chamber pressure was 170 psi, nitrogen-gas pressure 340 psi, and oxygen-tank pressure 335 psi. The average lift was 258 lb, the weight of oxygen being $35\frac{1}{3}$ lb and that of gasoline $50\frac{3}{4}$ lb. The oxygen and gasoline rates were 1.46 and 2.1 lb/sec. The jet velocity was 3710 ft/sec or, correcting for the head of liquid in the thrust pressure line to the instrument board, 4100 ft/sec.

The temperature of the nozzle, 4 in. down from the throat, was 35° C;

that of the chamber, 5½ in. down from the upper cone, on the cylindrical part, was 135° C.

Test of December 23, 1937 (L-23):
Static Test, Larger Chamber

The object of this test was to repeat the preceding test with a larger chamber, in order to obtain, if possible, both a higher thrust and a higher jet velocity.

Chamber. The combustion chamber consisted of a 7-in.-diameter cylinder, 13 in. long, of 0.037-in. nickel, with the usual 90-deg cone at the top, and a long tapered nozzle on the lower, 60-deg cone. This nozzle was 1¹¹⁄₁₆ in. in diameter at the throat, widening to 3½ in. at a 17-in. length. The lower cone was spun to a gradual curve, for a ¾-in. distance, at the throat.

The usual 90-deg inverted Insalute-Alundum-covered cone was used inside, on the 1-in.-O.D. steel-tube jacket over the ¾-in. oxygen-entrance line. A ⅝-in.-wide copper deflector on a ¼-in. stainless-steel stem produced a thin conical sheet of oxygen, which struck the cylindrical wall ¾ in. below the flat nickel ring, which latter extended ½ in. inward radially. The oxygen-orifice rate of flow, for water at 20 psi, was 9.8 oz/sec.

Three tangential gasoline-orifice tubes were used, spaced at equal distances around the top of the cylindrical part, giving a combined flow of water of 15.75 oz/sec at 20 psi.

The cylindrical wall was cooled by a water jacket consisting of ½-in.-O.D. aluminum tubing, wound in an open spiral over a sheet of 0.013-in. sheet copper, soldered around the chamber, the ends of the aluminum tube ending in a tin cup to permit convective cooling. The chamber, without the jacket, weighed 9½ lb.

Test. The flame did not appear to be quite as small, bright, and noisy as in the preceding test. The intense period lasted 22.3 sec. The nitrogen pressure gradually rose from 250 to 335 psi, the chamber pressure rising rapidly at first and then more gradually, from 140 to 169 psi. The oxygen-tank pressure rose to 330 psi, being 8 to 10 psi below the nitrogen pressure at the start, and only 3 to 4 psi below toward the end of the run.

The weights of oxygen and gasoline used were 35⅛ and 50¾ lb, respectively, and the flow rates were 1.62 and 2.52 lb/sec. The average thrust was 466 lb, and the jet velocity was 3900 ft/sec.

The temperature of the nozzle was 550° C, and of the chamber 15° C.

Conclusions. It would appear that the comparatively intense heating of the nozzle was due either to the narrow taper, causing heat to be communicated to the nozzle wall, or to the lack of cooling by the tangential gasoline flow for large radii. Tangential orifices for gasoline might be used at intervals along the chamber wall just inside the throat, and also along the nozzle, in order to secure adequate cooling.

Test of January 11, 1938 (L-24):
Repeat of L-22, with Higher Pressure

The object of this test was to repeat Test L-22 with the 5¾-in. chamber, raising the applied nitrogen pressure from about 350 to 450 psi.

Tanks. The cylindrical wall of the oxygen tank was reinforced by adding a 4-in. wide, 0.050-in. nickel band in the middle, with two 1¾-in.-wide bands on each side. The valve that was to close at the end of the run was simplified by having the valve seat, into which outflow took place downwardly, in a short section of ¾-in.-O.D. steel tube, four ⅜-in. tubes or arms extending up from this to the ¾-in. steel delivery tube that extended through the top of the tank. These four ⅜-in. tubes formed a cage for a 3-in. long, 1⅜-in.-diameter cork float that bore loosely a 1-in. valve disk on the bottom. When the float was in the raised position, the valve disk was 4⅝ in. above the seat, so that there was only a slight tendency for the float to be drawn down prematurely by the flow.

The gasoline tank was reinforced by adding two more 4-in.-wide, 0.050-in. nickel bands. After a pressure test to 455 psi, it was found advisable to add a ½-in.-wide band at each end of the cylinder.

The pressure tank was also reinforced by four additional bands, of such widths as to make the unprotected spaces between band and hemisphere about ½ in. wide. A protecting cone was brazed on the bottom hemisphere, to prevent scratching and denting during handling.

Valves and piping. The half length of 1½-in.-O.D. two-ply bellows, used in the oxygen jacket line, was tested up to 475 psi with the ends prevented from spreading apart, and was found to be satisfactory.

The flexible tube of the oxygen safety valve became extended ⁹⁄₃₂ in. at 475 psi but returned to 11⁵⁄₃₂ in. each time pressure was applied and removed thereafter.

Gauge protection. Steel reinforcing pieces were made for the gauge glasses but were not found necessary, at least below 455 psi. Each consisted of a ¹⁄₁₆-in. steel tube loosely fitting the glass tube, split lengthwise. To each side a ⅛-in.-thick steel strip was brazed, these strips serving as flanges. Holes ¼ in. in diameter were drilled along the split tubes, ⅜ in. between centers, so that at least one end of the ½-in.-long level indicator would be visible at the camera. Bolt holes in the flanges permitted fastening the pairs of strips around each gauge glass. The space between the tube sections and the glass was designed to be filled with cement.

A test at 425 psi pressure showed that the brass blocks that held the ends of the gauge glasses tended to separate, that is, to move outward along the gauge glasses. This separation was prevented by using two ⅛- × ½-in. steel strips between each pair of brass blocks. When this was done, the gauge-glass assembly withstood the pressure without appreciable alteration, and hence the perforated protecting tubes just described were not considered necessary.

The weight of the rocket was 80¼ lb.

Equipment at tower. The 2000-to-350-psi reducing valve previously used was modified to give greater reduced pressure. This valve had consisted of four 1½-in.-O.D., two-ply bellows with atmospheric pressure inside, sliding freely in a steel tube and thereby moving the long arm of a lever, in another steel tube at right angles, the short arm of which opened the valve from the 2000-psi nitrogen cylinder. A long coil tension spring was hooked to the long end of the lever, which the bellows operated, this spring being in a steel tube opposite to that containing the bellows.

These three containing tubes, forming a tee, were reinforced by ¼-in.-thick split tubes, held to the outsides by flanged clamps, closely spaced.

Inasmuch as the bellows were not suitable for the high reduced pressures to be used, the pressure inside the bellows system was kept constant at 250 psi. This pressure was produced by a needle valve, from the high reduced pressure, using a ballast tank of 0.050-in. sheet nickel, which had a cylindrical part 6 in. in diameter and 7½ in. long, with 60-deg conical ends. The system was sufficiently tight that the leakage was not over 1 psi per hour. The safety valve was a regular 250-psi valve, with a lever added having a ¾-in. short arm and a 4½-in. long arm, the latter being provided with a coil tension spring. The valve was set to blow off at 500 psi, this high pressure being necessary because of the large and continued drop, once the safety valve opened. Suitable high-pressure gauges were used on the reducing valve.

Test. The strong flame appeared suddenly, without any preliminary gasoline flame, and lasted for 30.5 sec. The yellowish flame around the concrete gas deflector was large and remained so during the run.

The nitrogen storage-tank pressure, which was initially 440 psi, fell to 240 psi at the start and gradually increased to 390 psi. The oxygen-tank pressure was 6 to 7 psi below the nitrogen pressure during the early part of the run, and 3 or 4 psi below later. The gasoline-tank pressure, on the other hand, remained about 25 psi below that for the oxygen tank. The chamber pressure became steady at about 175 psi. The chamber temperature was 130° C 5 in. below the upper cone, and the nozzle temperature was 390° C 4 in. below the throat.

The rates of flow of oxygen and gasoline were 1.31 and 1.82 lb/sec, respectively. The average lift was 300 lb and the maximum lift 422 lb, the average jet velocity being 4100 ft/sec.

Conclusions. It is likely that the fall of nitrogen pressure, at the start, was due to the cold oxygen, since the free initial volume in the tops of the oxygen and gasoline tanks was small. The nitrogen first entering the oxygen tank probably cooled and condensed, and the oxygen became warmed up to the temperature at which the saturated vapor pressure is 300 to 400 psi. Such condensation of nitrogen would be expected to take place more and more slowly, as the warmed layer of oxygen became thicker. In flight, agitation and sloshing would tend to delay the rise of tank pressure.

Test of February 2, 1938 (L-25):
Static High-Pressure Test, Increased Oxygen

The object of this test was to use 430 psi tank pressure with a 5¾-in. chamber, with the proportion of oxygen to gasoline increased, and with the oxygen tank initially at 430 psi oxygen pressure.

Chamber. The chamber used in the preceding test was altered by increasing the oxygen orifice so that the flow with water at 20 psi was raised from 6.4 oz/sec to 7⅜ oz/sec. Because it was believed that a considerable time would be required to raise the vapor pressure of the oxygen to 430 psi, the 1-in. jacket tube in the chamber, surrounding the ¾-in. oxygen-delivery line, was not filled with oxygen, in order to avoid frost forming on the oxygen orifice, and was connected at the upper end to the upper cone of the chamber by a short tube so as to equalize the pressure inside and out.

Valves. The oxygen line passed from the oxygen valve, on the bottom of the well on the oxygen tank, to the chamber, having a half 1½-in., two-ply bellows just above the oxygen jacket in the chamber to equalize pressure. The oxygen line was covered from the wall to the bellows by a jacket tube, from the top of which one line led to the bottom of the tank and another to the top.

The oxygen valve was designed to hold high pressure in the tank until released and to remain open thereafter. It therefore opened in the direction of flow, or downward. The valve disk was held somewhat loosely on the top of the valve rod, the seat being metal to metal and a 9/16-in.-O.D. bellows being used as packing on the valve rod. Two levers were used, the second folding back under the first to save space and being insulated by bakelite plates and screw bushings from the pin that freed the lever. This insulation prevented frost from forming, and holding the pin.

It was found that a 4-lb tension was sufficient to hold back 450 psi. Above 300 psi, however, there was a slight though not serious leakage of gas. In starting the flow of oxygen, first a pin was pulled that allowed the valve disk to open 1/32 in., a second pin thereafter allowing the valve to open fully, to ¼ in.

The supply line was closed, at the end of the run, by a valve disk on the bottom of a cork float, which disk engaged a metal seat, the float traveling in a cage consisting of six 3/32-in.-diameter rods, each 10 in. long.

Equalizer. The equalizer, having a 1½-in.-O.D., two-ply bellows, previously used, was tested up to 450 psi but was found to be unsatisfactory, since the convolutions became distorted and hence were no longer parallel.

A new equalizer was therefore designed, in which a group of seven %₁₆-in.-O.D. bellows was used. The open ends were soldered to holes in an iron plate, fixed in an outer 2⅛-in.-O.D. steel tube. Rods extended from the closed ends to a steel sleeve, slidable in the outer tube, from which slack-motion fingers could pull a knob on the small escape valve and thereby vent excess oxygen to the air. At the closed ends of the bellows these rods were screwed to a perforated steel plate sliding in the outer tube, in the gasoline-pressure side, with an adjustable coil compression spring bearing against this perforated plate. This spring was adjusted so that the oxygen excess pressure was under 10 psi for 430 psi gasoline-tank pressure.

The safety valve on the oxygen tank was dispensed with, the equalizer serving the purpose satisfactorily. A further change was the addition of a vent valve, closed by pulling a pin just before the run, in the gas-pressure line between the two tank check valves, in order to prevent any leakage of oxygen through the oxygen-tank check valve from entering the gasoline tank.

A preliminary test showed that the rapid flow of gasoline tended to close the valve in the bottom of the tank. Therefore a double valve having two valve disks and two seats, resembling the valve assembly in the oxygen tank, was used. The outlet-valve member, in the bottom of the well, was held against a Vellumoid seat by a bellows-packing valve rod, held firmly by a lever. Pulling one pin allowed the valve to open %₆₄ in., and pulling a second pin allowed the valve to open fully, the lever then falling away from the free end of the valve rod.

Instead of a float valve, to close the tank after the run, a disk valve was used on the bottom of a long rod, extending into a tube at the top of the gasoline tank and freed, after the run, by pulling a releasing pin in a bellows packing.

Condensation system. It was planned to have 430 psi pressure in the oxygen tank before making the run. However, a shop test with a small tank cooled initially to liquid-oxygen temperature showed that a comparatively long time would be required for the pressure to rise by the conduction of heat from the outside air through the cylindrical wall. The level of oxygen in the tank would, moreover, be considerably lowered by the evaporation.

A shop test was then made to produce a rapid rise of pressure by condensation of gaseous oxygen. For this purpose, a 3-in.-diameter, 5-in.-long cylindrical tank having conical ends, completely covered with felt, was supplied with gaseous oxygen through two ⅛-in.-diameter crossed tubes at the bottom of the tank, each tube having four staggered No. 60 holes. It was found that the pressure could be raised quickly to 430 psi, the volume of the liquid oxygen increasing by about 30 per cent.

The condensation system for the rocket was somewhat similar and consisted of four vertical $\frac{5}{16}$-in.-O.D. steel tubes, plugged at the upper ends and extending 4 in. from the bottom of the oxygen tank, about halfway up the hemisphere. Each tube was drilled with eight holes along a spiral of $1\frac{1}{8}$-in. turns and was connected to a vertical tube outside the tank, enclosed in a jacket tube connected with the oxygen tank. This outside tube was to condense any water vapor in the oxygen before it could reach the holes.

Because of danger due to the presence of hydrocarbon vapor with the oxygen at over 400 psi, the oxygen tank and pipe fittings were all cleaned thoroughly with carbon tetrachloride. In addition, Insalute cement was used on pipe joints, and soap on all fine threaded parts.

Controls at tower. The oxygen-tank pressure was raised before the run by means of a 2100-psi oxygen cylinder with a 2000-psi gauge, located just behind the 50-ft dugout and connected to the condensation system by 75 ft of $\frac{1}{4}$-in.-diameter copper tube. Nitrogen pressure from outside the tower was used on the gasoline side of the equalizer during the condensation, in order to avoid loss of oxygen gas.

In starting the test, the first dashpot weight, which opened the gasoline valve part way, freed the second dashpot weight at the end of the stroke. This second dashpot then performed a number of operations: it opened the gasoline valve completely, closed the emergency vent between check valves, allowed the felt pieces on the oxygen tank to be pulled off, opened the small nitrogen-gas valve outside the tower to lead pressure from the storage tank to the rocket, closed the vent on the gasoline tank; and when halfway down it opened the oxygen valve part way and allowed the igniter supporting arm to drop at the same time. The third dashpot weight then allowed the oxygen valve to open fully.

Test. In a preliminary test the oxygen pressure rose to 430 psi in 6 min, the tank level rising $3\frac{1}{4}$ in., although the pressure fell to 375 psi after the cylinder was disconnected. The time could have been shortened considerably, however, since the valve on the cylinder was closed frequently in order to determine the steady pressure in the tank. On the day the actual test was made, pressure rose to 400 psi in 7 min, falling to 375, the tank level rising $2\frac{3}{8}$ in.

About 3 sec after the igniter key was pressed, the rocket began operating, with a very loud roar that continued thereafter. There was no noticeable preliminary gasoline flame. The yellowish-white flame at the rear of the concrete gas deflector appeared to be whiter and brighter than usual. A rather large gasoline flame appeared at the end of the run, before the tanks could be vented. The period of strong lift lasted for 16 sec.

The chamber pressure averaged 208 psi, the nitrogen pressure 420 psi, and the oxygen pressure 402 psi. The average rates of flow of oxygen and gasoline were 1.73 lb/sec and 1.9 lb/sec. The average lift was 477 lb, and the jet velocity was 4180 ft/sec, although the velocity as measured by the flow rates was 5340 ft/sec.

It should be noted that in the present test, the rise to steady thrust and pressures was about 3 sec, whereas for the preceding test, at 440 psi applied nitrogen-gas pressure, the time was nearly 20 sec, indicating a considerable nitrogen condensation in the present test. Tests L-22 and L-23, at lower nitrogen pressures, also showed a slow rise, occupying about 10 sec. It is possible that the 3-sec rise in the present test was caused not by condensation but by choking or gas bind in the oxygen line until it was thoroughly cooled.

At 5 in. below the top of the cylindrical part, the temperature of the chamber rose slowly, from 130 to 155° C, whereas the temperature of the nozzle, 4 in. below the throat, rose considerably at once, to about 500° C.

Conclusions. A high-pressure nitrogen tank, used without pumps, has the disadvantage of requiring very high pressure in order to store any considerable amount of nitrogen, since the temperature of oxygen at 430 psi, namely −132° C, is 15° C above the critical temperature of nitrogen. Probably the best that can be done is to surround the nitrogen tank with oxygen at −132° C, and to warm the nitrogen in a jacket around the chamber and nozzle.

At high pressures, cooling jackets in which flow takes place may be required around the nozzle, and perhaps around the chamber also.

FURTHER FLIGHT TESTS, USING LOW-PRESSURE TANKS

Notwithstanding the increased thrust produced by a particular chamber at increased pressure, it appeared simplest to develop improved flight performance by low-pressure tank rockets, using, however, a somewhat greater pressure than in the earlier tests and reducing the over-all weight as much as possible.

Test of March 6, 1938 (L-26):
Flight Test

In the first test of the present flight series it was planned to increase the lift by adjusting the equalizer for a greater oxygen supply.

Chamber. The chamber was the 0.028-in. sheet-nickel chamber used in the preceding pressure test, with a ½-in.-diameter copper oxygen deflector, the oxygen orifice giving a flow of water of 6.4 oz/sec at 20 psi.

Tanks. The liquid-oxygen tank consisted of a 0.037-in. nickel cylinder, 6½ in. long, between two 9-in.-diameter hemispheres. The ½-in.-diameter oxygen line began at the bottom of a 2-in. diameter well on the bottom of the tank, passed up and looped around inside the tank, and then passed out of the bottom, inside a jacket tube. A disk was used on a cork float to shut off the oxygen after the run, the seat being at the bottom of the well.

A round disk baffle of 0.018-in. nickel was used halfway up the bottom hemisphere, and three thin aluminum disk baffles on an aluminum-tubing frame were used in the cylindrical part. The total weight, without the felt and supports between tanks, was 7 lb 3 oz.

The gasoline tank consisted of a 14½-in.-long, 0.018-in.-thick cylinder, having double frustums of cones of 0.037-in. nickel at the ends. As with the nitrogen pressure-storage tanks, provision was made for wire-winding. Pins of ³⁄₃₂-in.-diameter welding rod were brazed to the narrow parts of the ends, these pins being ²³⁄₆₄ in. between centers.

The transverse turns on the cylinder were wound ⅛ in. apart using a steel spacer of this width, except that at a 1-in. width in the middle the turns were ¹⁄₁₆ in. apart. A single wire was used for both the transverse and the longitudinal turns. At the end of the cylindrical part, where the wire was bent at a considerable angle in changing from transverse to longitudinal windings, a slotted tube was brazed, into which the wire was slipped.

Seven narrow steel lugs were brazed to the ends of the tank before winding: three on the upper end, for supporting the cap, and four on the bottom end, to be bolted to the tubing supports between the tanks.

The tank was supported during winding by a rod brazed to the middle of the top and passing through a disk bolted to a flange on the bottom of the well. This rod was provided with a handle.

Float. In place of a system of baffles in the gasoline tank, a float was used, which slid freely on a 1⅝-in.-O.D. aluminum tube 16 in. long placed axially in the tank. This aluminum tube was held in place by being clamped to the ½-in.-O.D. steel pressure tube and a ⁵⁄₁₆-in. tube containing the electrical wires for the parachute release, both of which passed up on the inside.

The float consisted of an 8-in. circular disk of 0.010-in. 17 ST sheet with a hole in the center. This disk was covered on both top and bottom with 1⅝-in. diameter, ½-in.-thick corks, cut into hexagons so as to fit close together and fastened to the disk with 0.010-in. tinned-iron wires.

This disk was prevented from tilting to any considerable extent by four ³⁄₁₆-in. alumnium-tube vertical triangles, the tops of which were wired to the under side of the float. At the bottom they were welded to a ring of the same size tubing, connected by radial arms to a smaller ring, which slid freely on the 1⅝-in.-diameter aluminum tube.

Two baffles of 0.010-in. 17 ST aluminum were used in the lower cone, held by iron wires brazed to the inside of the cone. The weight of the tank complete, with a sheet-aluminum cylindrical top on which the cap rested, was 9½ lb.

After a test at 460 psi pressure, the longitudinal seam buckled inward when the pressure was relieved, probably owing to the stretching of the sheet nickel produced by the pressure. The initial tank pressure chosen for the flight was 250 psi.

Pressure tank. The pressure tank consisted of a cylinder of 0.018-in. sheet nickel, 9 in. in diameter and 48 in. long. The transverse and longitudinal turns were spaced the same as those for the gasoline tank, except that there were three 1-in.-wide spaces along the cylindrical part where the windings were spaced ⅟₁₆ in. apart. A rod extending through the tank and provided with a handle was again used for winding. The tank was tested to 460 psi pressure, whereupon the seam of the cylinder bulged inward, as in the case of the gasoline tank. The tank weight, complete with four narrow lugs at each end for connecting the other tanks, was 15 lb.

Valves and piping. The reducing valve, of 14 oz weight, was the same as that used in Test L-15, set at 40 psi reduced pressure. The equalizer, weighing 13 oz, was that used in Test L-16, set for 10 psi excess oxygen-tank pressure.

Aluminum valve casings were used for the pressure-tank valve and the gasoline valve, these parts being bolted to the flanges on the bottom of the two respective tanks. The design of the pressure-tank valve was similar to that of the high-pressure oxygen-tank valve. A metal valve disk on a rod pressed against a seat provided with a Vellumoid ring, this rod extending through a ⁹⁄₁₆-in. packing bellows and being released by a lever. The valve weighed 8 oz.

The outlet valve for the gasoline tank was bolted to the flange on the well in the bottom of the tank. It was likewise provided with an aluminum valve disk that bore against a Vellumoid ring seat, and was released by a lever. The lever was freed sufficiently by the first control pin to permit the valve to open ⅟₆₄ in., a second pin thereafter allowing the valve to open fully, to the extent of ⁹⁄₃₂ in.

A gasoline-shutoff valve, provided to stop the flow at the end of the run, had a similar valve disk and seat, the valve travel being ⅜ in. The valve rod was released by a bellows-packed side rod, close to the bottom of the gasoline tank, also released by a lever. The weight of the valve assembly, including wire cloth around the support for the shutoff valve, to serve as a strainer, was 10 oz.

The two check valves, to which the pressure hoses were attached, were lightened by using aluminum insofar as possible. The previous combined weight was 24 oz, the present weight being 12 oz. The tank check-valve casings consisted of two aluminum parts, screwed together and provided with hexagonal flanges. Aluminum tube fittings, to fit the ½-in. tubing line, were welded to these two parts. The weight for the gasoline line was 3½ oz, and for the oxygen line, 4 oz. The pressure contact maker, piped to the chamber as before by $\frac{1}{8}$-in.-O.D. copper tubing, was set to trip on a rise of pressure to 55 psi, and to make contact on a fall to 37 psi. A combined strainer and Y branch for the two gasoline tubes to the chamber was made as light as possible. Its weight, together with these two tubes, was 7 oz.

The liquid-oxygen line passed out of the tank and down inside the outer jacket tube, directly to the jacket inside the chamber. It was not necessary to allow for contraction, since flexibility was provided by the bend at the top of the line, inside the oxygen tank. An expansion bellows was used halfway down, in the jacket tube, and both this jacket and that inside the chamber were provided with a supply tube from the bottom of the oxygen tank, and a vent or return tube to the top of the tank. A small ballast tank was provided in the 40-psi line, near the bellows operators for the vanes, in order to avoid fluctuation in pressure.

Supports between tanks. The supports between the tanks and chamber were considerably lightened by using $\frac{3}{4}$-in. 17 ST aluminum support tubes, with solid-aluminum connecting pieces at the ends; these pieces were round where they fitted into the tubes and were forked or slotted where they were bolted into the narrow lugs on the gasoline and pressure tanks. The chamber was supported by four steel tubes passing upward to a 9-in.-O.D. ring of $\frac{3}{4}$-in. steel tubing, perforated for lightness.

The oxygen tank was connected to this by three $\frac{7}{8}$-in.-O.D. aluminum tubes, each 33 in. long, to provide room for the gyroscope and magnet valves besides keeping the center of gravity well forward. The aluminum tubes fitted at the ends into steel tubing sleeves. The bolts used in assembling these support pieces were provided with steel sleeves, to avoid crushing the aluminum tubing and lugs. As a precaution against the tanks' becoming separated when the parachute was released, a $\frac{1}{8}$-in.-diameter airplane cable was fastened to the bottom of the gasoline tank and to the top of the oxygen tank, passing around the pressure tank.

Casing and guides. The casings were made of 0.010-in. 17 ST sheet aluminum throughout, except for the rear cone around the chamber and nozzle, which was of 0.016-in. sheet for greater stiffness. The fixed air vanes were also of 0.016-in. sheet. The aluminum-angle guides were $\frac{1}{16}$ in. thick, being made of angles formed by cutting $\frac{3}{4}$-in. square 17 ST tubes lengthwise, along a diagonal.

Directing system. The movable air and blast vanes were those used in Test L-21, with the weight reduced as much as possible by the use of aluminum supports.

Gyro and magnet-control valves. The gyroscope was used without modification. The magnets, however, were of higher resistance, to make it possible to employ the same batteries for both the control valves and the parachute release. The use of higher EMF for this purpose tended to reduce weakening of the batteries during the flight.

Each magnet was wound with 100 ft of No. 30 enameled copper wire and thus had about twice the previous resistance. Four radio C batteries, consisting of two sets of two in parallel, were used, giving 15 volts. It was found that a $\frac{3}{16}$-in. length of 0.004-in.-diameter music wire could be fused across the four magnets. The weight of magnet valves and box complete was 49 oz.

Parachute release. The 10-ft-diameter parachute, provided with 450-lb shroud lines, was released on the completion of three operations: when the chamber pressure fell, when the gasoline fused-wire valve release operated, and when the rocket became tilted 90 deg with respect to the axis of the gyroscope. A barograph with a metal bellows was used, in a box of $\frac{1}{8}$-in.-thick sheet iron in order to make the total weight $4\frac{1}{4}$ lb, which was close to that of the official N.A.A. barograph to be used in later tests.

Weights and dimensions. The length over all was 17 ft 6 in., the diameter 9 in. The weight of the chamber, three tanks, supports, oxygen line, aluminum valve on the gasoline tank, and gyro without the protecting box was 49 lb. The weight complete was $87\frac{1}{2}$ lb, the center of gravity being $16\frac{7}{8}$ in. above the top of the cylindrical part of the oxygen tank. The oxygen load was 21 lb and the gasoline load 26 lb.

Test. Three seconds after the igniter key was pressed, a strong flame appeared with little or no preliminary gasoline flame. The lift-indicator light appeared immediately after, and the rocket was accordingly released. The rocket rose through the tower more rapidly than usual and continued straight, without appreciable smoke. At 400 or 500 ft, however, the flame suddenly stopped, and a small gasoline flame appeared thereafter at intervals.

The rocket coasted upward for a short time, and as soon as it turned over horizontally the parachute was released and opened, the cap descending at one side. The small parachute in the cap did not open, since there was not enough slack between the parachute and the place where the cable was fastened.

Conclusion. The premature shutting off of the oxygen was probably caused by the rapid flow out of the tank, together with the downward current in the middle of the tank, produced by the upward or forward motion of the oxygen, due to warming, along the uncovered side walls.

Apparently there is needed, in the oxygen tank, an oxygen shutoff valve that will close when the chamber pressure drops; this cutoff valve, in turn, operating the gasoline cutoff valve and releasing the parachute as soon thereafter as the rocket becomes turned through 90 deg.

Test of March 17, 1938 (L-27):
Repeat Flight Test

The object of this test was to repeat the preceding test with a shutoff valve in the oxygen tank, and with a gasoline tank of larger capacity.

Chamber. A stronger chamber was made, of 0.037-in. sheet nickel. This weighed 6¾ lb, being 1 lb heavier than the 0.028-in. nickel chamber.

Tanks. A new gasoline tank of larger capacity was constructed, so that the oxygen tank could be filled to the top of the cylindrical part. The new weights of oxygen and gasoline were 21½ and 34 lb, as compared with 16 and 28 lb in Test L-15. The cylinder of the new tank was 20½ in. long, the increase in tank length being 6 in. The weight complete, without wire, was 9¼ lb; the wire weighed 1½ lb.

As an indication of the thinness of the tank wall, which withstood 460 psi when wired, it may be mentioned that in the course of repairs made after the test the conical ends were cut off with an ordinary can opener.

Valves. A shutoff valve was used in the oxygen tank in place of the float, the valve disk previously used on the float now being held on the lower end of a rod, the upper end of which was released by a removable side pin that passed through a bellows packing at the top of the tank, as in Test L-22. A compression spring to assist in closing the valve was also used, held in the cage that served previously to guide the cork float.

Batteries and wiring. The wiring was the same as before except that an additional fused-wire release was used, to free the lever on the oxygen release valve. Two of the three fused-wire releases were therefore of the contact-making type, the fused wire freeing a lever, thus opening a circuit, and immediately thereafter allowing a spring member to close another circuit. The heavy current load that would be caused by several fused-wire releases operating at the same time was thereby avoided. In the present case the chamber contact maker caused the first fused-wire release to fire and thereby to close the oxygen tank. This operation closed a circuit that shut off the gasoline, thereafter causing a third circuit to fuse the parachute release in the cap, as soon as the rocket tilted 90 deg with respect to the gyro axis.

Weight and dimensions. The length over all was 18 ft, and the weight was 88¾ lb.

Controls at tower. The Sept camera was mounted on a board, at an angle of 60 deg with the ground, so that a motion picture could be obtained of the rocket ascending through the tower and just beyond it.

Test. The release key was pressed as soon as the lift-indicator light was seen, this following the appearance of the flame very quickly. The rocket rose rapidly but not quite so fast as in the preceding test. It corrected its motion from side to side until it reached about 800 ft, when it became inclined. The cap and parachute were torn away when the rocket became horizontal, or nearly so. Propulsion ceased at about the same time, when the height as measured by the recording telescope was 2170 ft. The rocket landed about 3000 ft from the tower. There was little or no smoke during the flight.

An examination showed that the cast-iron snap ring that fastened the ⅛-in. airplane cable to the steel ring on the parachute shroud lines had been broken in two. A test of the barograph in a bell jar indicated that the trace observed in the flight represented a height of 720 ft.

The Sept camera showed pictures of the rocket from the middle of the tower to 20 ft above it.

Test of April 20, 1938 (L-28):
Repeat Flight Test, Stronger Parachute Connection

The object of this test was to repeat the preceding test, using a stronger connection between the parachute and the cable, using a delay in freeing the gyro in the tower to avoid disturbance due to vibration when the pressure hoses were pulled off, and also using an accurate barograph.

General alterations. A new chamber was constructed, of 0.031-in. sheet nickel, the water flows at 20 psi pressure being 6.4 oz/sec for the oxygen orifice, and 5.25 oz/sec for each of the gasoline orifices. The weight was 5⅝ lb. The weight of the gasoline tank was 10¾ lb, and of the pressure tank, which had a 0.016-in. nickel cylinder, 14½ lb. The aluminum disks on the ends of the valve magnets, for retaining the wire, were replaced by bakelite disks, which had better resistance to shock.

A ⅛-in. airplane cable was looped twice through the ring on the parachute shrouds, and extended, doubled, to the top of the gasoline tank. Another ⅛-in. cable was looped through this at the top of the gasoline tank and around the bottom of the oxygen tank, in order to avoid separation of the tanks, in flight.

Barograph. An official National Aeronautic Association barograph was used, set by the National Bureau of Standards to record over a range of 10,000 ft. The dimensions of the containing box were 6¾ × 4⁵⁄₁₆ × 4⅛ in., and the weight was 62 oz.

N.A.A. committee. An observing committee, arranged for by Mr. W. R. Enyart of the Washington office of the National Aeronautic Association, was present. The committee had charge of sealing and shipping the barograph, and consisted of a group which could be brought together on short notice. The chairman was Colonel D. C. Pearson, and the other members were Major John E. Smith and Captain Howard H. Alden. They were, respectively, the superintendent and the heads of the physics and mathematics departments of the New Mexico Military Institute.

Barograph mounting. It was originally planned to install the barograph in the detachable ogival cap at the front end of the rocket, the barograph being held between two aluminum plates. In order to provide sufficient room, an aluminum cylindrical extension, 8½ in. long, ¹⁄₁₆ in. thick, and 9 in. in diameter, was fastened to the rear of the cap, the 10-ft rocket parachute and a 6-ft cap parachute being contained within this cylinder. It was found, however, that the stress on the two rods that held the cap to the remainder of the rocket was too severe because of the added weight; accordingly, an empty cap, provided with a 3-ft pilot parachute, was used, as before.

The new location of the barograph was in the space between the gasoline and oxygen tanks, the support tubes being lengthened by 12 in., to 25¼ in., to provide sufficient room. It was suspended at the four corners by rubber bands, in accordance with the N.A.A. requirements, these bands being rings cut from an inner tube and doubled, so as to be about 3 in. long when stretched. Sidewise displacement was prevented by two cross braces, on opposite sides, on which were bound three and four layers, respectively, of ⅛-in.-thick sheet sponge rubber.

Weights and dimensions. The length over all was 18 ft 5¾ in., and the weight was 90⅝ lb. The fuel weights were 21.5 lb for oxygen and 34 lb for gasoline.

Test. The N.A.A. committee sealed and installed the barograph before the test. As usual, the flame appeared about 3 sec after the igniter key was pressed, the lift indicator light showing about 1 sec later, when the rocket was released.

The rocket rose fairly rapidly through the tower, and thereafter headed into the wind, correcting itself, as before, each time the inclination exceeded 5 deg. A smoke trail appeared after the rocket had risen about 500 ft. The inclination continued to increase, however, and the rocket struck the ground at a considerable distance from the tower, without the parachute opening.

The maximum height was estimated as 4215 ft, at 2400 ft horizontal distance from the tower, the landing taking place at a measured distance of 6960 ft from the tower. The time to reach maximum height, the period of propulsion, and the total time of flight were, respectively, 23.3, 25.3, and 44 sec.

The rocket made a hole in the ground 14 in. in diameter and 6 in. deep, telescoping all the parts severely. The barograph showed no record, inasmuch as gasoline had washed the camphor smoke from the drum. The barograph was flattened to a thickness of ½ in.

Conclusions. The alterations made in adapting the rocket for the new barograph may have caused damage to the electrical connections for the parachute release.

Considerably greater heights might be reached with a similar rocket, having tanks of 50 per cent greater capacity and with the pressure tank at 280 to 300 psi nitrogen pressure.

Test of May 26, 1938 (L-29):
Repeat Flight Test

The object of this test was to repeat the preceding test with satisfactory parachute release.

General alterations. It was necessary to remake a considerable part of the rocket, but the changes were kept to a minimum. The chamber and tanks were constructed the same as before, except that the guide for the shutoff valve in the liquid-oxygen tank was reduced in size. The support tubes were of ¾-in.-O.D. 17 ST alloy throughout, except for the steel tubes joining the chamber to the 9-in.-diameter perforated steel ring, 10⅛ in. above the top of the cylindrical part of the chamber. The equalizer was, as before, set for 10 psi excess oxygen-tank pressure.

The fiber washers holding the adjustable commutator rings on the gyroscope gimbals were strengthened by reducing the hole size from ⁵⁄₁₆ to ¼ in., the aluminum sleeves on which the washers were mounted being made smaller to this extent.

The magnet-operated valves were improved by making the various movable parts line up better than before and by making the supports for these parts more rigid. The four assemblies were also reduced in size.

The 1½-in.-O.D. Clifford bellows operating the movable air and blast vanes were stiffer than those previously used, requiring a force of 8 lb for a ⅜-in. compression, as compared with a previous force of 5 lb. To take care of this greater stiffness, the reducing-valve pressure was accordingly raised from 42 to 50 psi. The weight and size of the rocket were practically the same as before.

Gyroscope. The gyro settings were adjusted so that correcting took place for a 3-deg, instead of a 5-deg displacement. Because of this change, and also in order to make certain that precession in the rocket was avoided, the gyro and box, without the cover, were checked in the shop by being clamped in a frame of tubing of the same form as the support in the rocket, a 1-in. pipe extending 33 in. above this frame and another 44 in. below. The upper pipe was suspended by a simple universal joint on a horizontal pipe 100 in. above the floor, the free end of the lower pipe being just above the floor.

A buzzer was used to check the commutator adjustments, with the aid of a 10-in.-diameter circle on the floor, about the point of rest. Any tilting of the gyro was indicated by a sharp pointer, clamped so as to be near the rotor but not to touch it. After adjustment by means of this swinging frame, no further adjustment was found necessary in the rocket displacement tests, which were conducted in the 20-ft tower at the rear of the shop.

Test. The start was the same as usual, a large flame being seen about 3 sec after the igniter key was pressed, the lift-indicator light showing a second later, and the release lever being operated immediately afterward.

The rocket rose with the usual speed through the tower but veered to one side immediately thereafter and struck the ground 500 or 600 ft away without any evidence of correcting. The greatest height was about

140 ft. Examination of the barograph indicated a displacement of about
1/32 in. The same committee was present.

Conclusion. It seems likely that a gust of wind like those which had
been noticed at intervals during the day tilted the rocket while the speed
was low and thus caused a decrease of lift owing to the operation of a
blast vane. This explanation could not be checked by the wind sock,
however, which was wrapped around a support at the time of the run.
The barograph displacement was of the expected order, for the rate of
displacement of 1 in. per 5000 ft.

Suggestions. For great ranges, it may be desirable to use high pressure
combustion with low tank pressure, brought to as high a degree of
streamlining as possible by the use of movable casing steering.

Three stages of propulsion would appear to be desirable. First, a
turbine propeller should be used with blades in a streamlined housing, up
to the limit of good propeller operation, possibly 6 to 8 miles. The rocket
chamber could thus be much smaller than would be needed if direct
rocket action were employed.

When the dense region has been passed, the turbine-propeller parts
should be dropped off, by parachute, the speed then being maintained, by
liquid fuel rocket chamber, just under that which produces great resistance. High pressure centrifugal pumps would be desirable, with either
circulation cooling or porous wall cooling of the chamber, and with water
introduced both above and below the throat.

In the region where the air is very rare, possibly above 20 miles, the
type of chamber should be that which is best adapted for propulsion in
practically a vacuum. Detonating rods might be used in a 90-deg cone,
giving a reflection jet type of propulsion, since the cone at the open end
could be as wide as the rocket casing without introducing a drag due to
a partial vacuum across the rear.

Test of August 9, 1938 (L-30):
Repeat Flight Test, Increased Oxygen

The object of this test was to repeat the preceding test with a greater
proportion of oxygen, in order to increase the lift.

General alterations. The oxygen rate of flow was increased by decreasing
the diameter of the spindle for the oxygen deflector in the chamber, the
water flow at 20 psi being increased from 6.3 to 7 oz/sec.

The pressure tank was one previously made for 300 psi instead of 250
psi, to be used with oxygen and gasoline tanks of 50 per cent greater
capacity. The transverse windings were spaced 0.052 in. apart instead of
1/16 in. as before, and the 70 longitudinal wires were looped over pins
spaced 1/4 in. apart on the tank ends. The weight, before adding the pins,
lugs for attaching the other tanks, and pipe fittings, was 9 3/4 lb; complete

ready for winding, 10½ lb; and after winding, 15 lb, this being 8 oz more than for the tank previously used.

The valves were the same as before except for the check valves, which were made from solid 1⅜-in. 17 ST bar stock instead of from castings, in order to avoid corrosion. As before, brass sleeves were used in aluminum valve parts, for soldering the ⅜₆-in. bellows.

The tubing frame, in which the gyro was suspended for adjustment in the shop, was altered by making the mountings adaptable for the various gyro protecting boxes that were on hand.

Test Attempted June 14 and 15, 1938

The equipment was set up on June 14, with Colonel Pearson of the N.A.A. committee present. The wind became too gusty for making a test, however, and a guard was left at the tower during the night. The next day also proved to be too windy, and a trip was made to the tower to make everything fast for the night. On arriving at 4:30 P.M., however, it was found that a twister, accompanying a severe thunderstorm, had demolished both the tower and sheet-iron shelter, the rocket of course having remained in the tower.

A new tower and sheet-iron shelter were erected, advantage being taken of the construction to make the tower stronger by the use of 2½- × 2½- × ³⁄₁₆-in. corner angles and 1½- × 1½- × ³⁄₁₆-in. horizontal angles up to 20 ft, with 1¼- × 1¼- × ⅛-in. angles for the other 60 feet.

The rocket was repaired, the chief alteration being the use of guide shoes made by milling grooves, ⅜ in. wide and ⅝ in. deep, in ¾-in.-square 17 ST bars.

Test Attempted July 25, 1938

In this test, for which Colonel Pearson and Captain Alden constituted the N.A.A. committee, there was a loud explosion 3 sec after the igniter key was pressed, at the moment when a strong flame usually appeared. It was found that the cylindrical part of the chamber had been blown to pieces.

The explanation appeared to be the high level to which the oxygen tank had been filled. It was noticed that the occasional surges of oxygen through the delivery tube to the chamber, toward the end of the tank filling, occurred more frequently in this than in preceding tests, and it seemed likely that one of these surges occurred at the moment when gasoline was entering the chamber.

Alterations. The tendency toward surging in the oxygen-delivery tube was reduced by having this tube on the outside of the tank instead of being inside the tank as before, and extending upward from the bottom of the well to a distance of 2 in. above the top of the tank, thence passing downward and entering a jacket tube at the point just below the bottom of the tank. This jacket was not joined directly to the tank, as before, but was connected to the bottom of the tank by a small delivery tube, and by another small tube, serving as a vent, to the top of the tank.

As an additional precaution, a level indicator was made, consisting of a small cork float with a rod on the top, guided by a cage consisting of four narrow rods. This was inserted in the opening for the vent valve in the oxygen tank at intervals, toward the end of the filling, and gave an indication of the level of the oxygen.

The lever system, for the parachute release in the cap, was made more rigid in order to avoid the possibility of the lever arms' slipping past each other when the cap was being fastened to the rocket, as had sometimes occurred previously.

Final Test

In the test of August 9, 1938, the N.A.A. committee consisted of Captain Alden and Mrs. (Dr.) Alden. Captain Alden, as before, wound and installed the barograph. This was, as before, a standard N.A.A. official barograph, set for 21,000 ft altitude, with the needle about $\frac{1}{2}$ in. above the bottom of the smoked drum, which had a period of rotation of 1.18 hr. The weight remained 63 oz.

The rocket was set up on August 8, but a test was not carried out because of wind. The test was finally made at 6:30 A.M. on August 9, in a moderate breeze.

Although the lift-indicator light was seen soon after the flame appeared, accompanied by a loud pop, the release-lever key was not pressed until the flame became more intense, a second or two later.

After a few slight swings back and forth about a line inclined 5 deg from the vertical, the rocket proceeded along this line with no further appreciable deviation. It appeared to continue in the same path even after propulsion had ceased, although this was uncertain because by then the rocket was almost invisible. Apparently the parachute opened at the maximum point of the ascent, and thereafter the rocket was observed to swing considerably from side to side until it landed, 0.4 mi to the rear of the tower. The reduced nitrogen pressure was 240 psi.

The highest point could not be obtained from the recording telescope and theodolite readings, since the theodolite was taken down before readings had been made. The height was, however, estimated as 4920 ft, from the curve of the telescope, allowing for the general direction of the maximum point as seen from the 1000-ft shelter. Only a small amount of smoke appeared from the rocket during the ascent until just before propulsion ceased, this reduced amount probably being due to the increased rate of flow of oxygen. After the test about $8\frac{1}{2}$ lb of gasoline was found to have remained in the gasoline tank.

The trace on the barograph showed a nearly vertical line for the rise, of slightly under 1/2 in. and a sloping line for the descent, the width of the graph at the bottom being about 5/32 in. In addition, the trace showed a short line extending downward at the start, and another similar line at the highest point reached. The former was explained by a pop or slight explosion in the chamber when the firing started, and the latter by the sudden checking of the flight when the parachute opened.

The line was irregular or wavy during the latter part of the ascent, and was particularly so during the descent, this aberration possibly being due to slight explosions in the chamber when the oxygen tank became empty during the ascent, and to the swinging of the rocket from side to side on the parachute during the descent.

The barograph was removed and sent to Washington by Captain Alden. The official record was 6565 ft above sea level, or 3294 ft rise above the ground.

9

Experiments toward Development
of Propellant Pumps

P Series, September 1938 — February 28, 1939

Convinced that suitable propellant pumps would be necessary to lighten the rocket further, thus making long ranges possible, Dr. Goddard resumed, at termination of the L series of tests, the pump development he had begun during 1932–1934 at Clark University (see Section 3). The long series of pump tests that followed, which he designated as the P series, commenced in the autumn of 1938 and continued until 1941, ending in flight tests of pump-fueled rockets. These highly significant pump developments are the subject of this and the two following sections.
—Editors.

PRELIMINARY PUMP DEVELOPMENT

From September to December, 1938, tests were carried out on several small centrifugal pumps, one made and tested at Clark University in 1932–1934, and the others constructed just prior to September. They were designated as forms A, B, C, D, and A′, the last a modification of form A (Figs. 18, 19).

Pump design. Each pump consisted of an impeller closed by conical sides with a conical deflector opposite the intake and a small number of spiral, rearward-directed vanes; four radial vanes on the outside of each wall of the impeller, to act as seals; an annular expanding passage from the outlet edge of the impeller to the volute; and a long narrow-tapered outlet nozzle extending tangentially from the volute.

The pump casing consisted, for convenience of manufacture, of three plates, one fitting against the inlet side of the impeller with small clearance, one fitting the shaft side, and one serving as a spacer between these two and forming the outer surface of the volute. The three parts were held together by screws that engaged threaded holes in the casing plate on the shaft side.

In the tests at Clark University the radial vanes on the sides of the impeller had been found to prevent leakage through the shaft opening in the pump housing for several hundred psi pressure, the vanes acting like two centrifugal pumps, one on each side of the main pump. The pressures of each of these two pumps were greater than that produced by the impeller because of absence of radial flow.

Bearings. The bearing housing consisted of a tubular part containing the ball bearings, having a flange at one end, which was fastened by the above-mentioned screws to the intake side of the pump casing; three strengthening webs extended from this flange to the tubular part. In the oxygen pump, the bearings were heat-insulated from the pump proper by a bakelite ring under this flange, and also by a small bakelite ring located between the two halves of a slinger disk, to be described below.

Suction or intake pressure of about 30 psi was used on the pumps. Leakage around the shaft opening in the housing, when the pump was idle, was prevented by a pneumatic seal on the outside of the pump housing, consisting of two metal bellows of different diameters. Each was concentric with the shaft, and the free ends were soldered to a brass sealing ring. Four compression springs kept this ring away from an annular flange on the pump side of a disk on the shaft. This disk was provided on the far side with radial vanes and served as a slinger disk, with the vanes running close to a slinger housing equipped with a tangential outlet tube, or drain. This metal-to-metal seal was ground to a tight fit, and was kept closed while there was pressure on the supply tank by means of air pressure applied to the space between the two bellows.

Turbines. The turbines, of 17 ST aluminum alloy, consisted of disks having blades milled in the edge by means of a small milling cutter, the turbine blank being rotated about a horizontal axis in a jig during the cutting. A shroud ring used on the outside of the blades was fastened by a small screw to each blade and was strengthened by music wire in a groove on each side of the screws.

Air nozzles were used to drive the turbine. These were beveled in the usual manner as for De Laval turbines, and were either piped individually through copper tubes or mounted on a manifold consisting of a hollow torous ring of rectangular section into which the air entered tangentially in the same direction as the nozzles.

Pump dimensions. Certain features were the same for all the pumps. Thus the intake and outlet tubes were of ¾ in. diameter. The impeller parts were held together with small screws and were sweated with solder, the impeller blades being just thick enough to provide adequate strength at the screw holes. The annular passage from the outlet edge of the impeller to the volute extended outward radially at an angle of 60 deg, becoming equal in width to the volute. The volute, owing to the fact that the pump casing consisted of flat plates, was of rectangular cross section, and increased from a very small width to a square outlet cross section. This volute passage terminated tangentially in the 5-deg tapered outlet nozzle, which changed gradually from square to circular section. The impellers were of steel, except for pumps D and A′, which were of brass. The radial sealing vanes on the outside were $\frac{1}{8}$ in. high.

The shafts rotated in double-row self-aligning SKF No. 1202 ball bearings, except that the bearings for pump A were No. 5202A. All the pump casings were of 17 ST aluminum except that for pump C, which was of brass, this pump being one of those made earlier at Clark University. Pump D was provided with a large-diameter impeller and a narrow volute, in order to be most effective for pumping the low-density gasoline later.

Pump A′ was pump A modified by using a brass impeller having the inner passages made as smooth as possible, with both the axial and radial clearances around the impeller reduced by about 50 per cent and with self-aligning bearings.

In the table below, all except the first and last two columns refer to the impeller, the angle subtended by the impeller blade being given with reference to a point on the shaft axis.

Turbine dimensions. The turbines were $3\frac{9}{16}$ in. in diameter and $\frac{7}{16}$ in. wide. The outer shroud ring was $\frac{3}{32}$ in. thick, and the turbine blades were $\frac{1}{4}$ in. deep. They were 28 in number and were cut by a $\frac{3}{16}$-in.-diameter end mill, on a radius of $\frac{3}{8}$ in. to the center of the mill, to form the curved surface of the blade.

The air nozzles were of 6-deg taper and had $\frac{5}{32}$-in.-diameter throats, with the nozzle axes 30 deg to the plane of the turbine. The hollow ring-shaped steel manifolds referred to were of $\frac{1}{16}$-in. sheet steel, rectangular in section, $5\frac{3}{4}$ in. O.D., of $\frac{3}{4}$ in. width inside radially and 1 in. width axially, supplied with compressed air tangentially through a $\frac{3}{4}$-in.-diameter steel tube.

TABLE I

Pump Dimensions

Pump form	Diameter, inches	No. of blades	Inside width, inches		Side clearance, inches		Angle subtended by blade, degrees	Volute width, inches	Outlet nozzle length, inches
			At intake	At outlet	Axial	Radial			
A	$1\frac{1}{2}$	2	$\frac{3}{8}$	$\frac{3}{32}$	0.006	0.011	270	$\frac{3}{16}$	$6\frac{1}{4}$
B	$1\frac{1}{2}$	2	$\frac{3}{8}$	$\frac{3}{32}$	0.006	0.011	270	$\frac{3}{8}$	$3\frac{3}{16}$
C	$2\frac{1}{2}$	3	$\frac{1}{4}$	$\frac{3}{32}$	0.017	0.009	180	$\frac{3}{8}$	$3\frac{3}{8}$
D	$1\frac{3}{4}$	2	$\frac{3}{8}$	$\frac{3}{32}$	0.0075	0.010	300	$\frac{7}{32}$	5
A′	$1\frac{1}{2}$	2	$\frac{3}{8}$	$\frac{3}{32}$	0.003	0.006	270	$\frac{3}{16}$	$6\frac{1}{4}$

Pump setup. The pump casings were mounted on a heavy brass base plate 3/4 in. thick, over a sink. Water was supplied from a galvanized tank above the sink to which air pressure could be applied. The water passed from the tank through a large wire-cloth strainer backed by a perforated plate, thence through a Venturi tube for flow measurements to an inlet gate valve close to the pump. Before each run, a globe valve in the outlet line was set as nearly as possible for the desired pressure.

As a precaution, strong C clamps were used along the edge of the pump casing for tests at high pressures, and a 1/4-in.-thick iron plate was used between the pump and the operators for the same reason.

Compressed air for driving the turbines was supplied from a galvanized-iron tank outside the shop, through a 2-in. pipe. A large gate valve close to the turbine nozzles was used to apply this air pressure.

The intake or suction pressures, outlet or delivery pressures, turbine air or manifold pressures, and turbine tank pressures were all measured by gauges. The rpm was measured by a thermogalvanometer, as will be described. The temperature of the bearing housing was measured by means of a copper-constantan thermocouple and a Weston No. 325 d-c galvanometer, the maximum deflection of 50 divisions corresponding closely to 500° C.

The flow measurement was made as a pressure difference produced by a Venturi tube of 0.018-in. sheet nickel. The large diameters, at the ends, were 1 1/16 in. inside, and the narrow diameter was 5/8 in. The entrance cone was 3 in. long, and the exit cone 8 1/2 in. long. Holes for measuring the pressure were made at the large end of the entrance cone and at the constriction.

Flow measurements. The flow-measuring device finally used consisted of mercury in a glass U tube, with water replacing all air in this tube as well as in the connecting lines.

Some work was done on a device which would have been easier to use but which was less simple in construction. It consisted of a 15-lb pressure gauge of 2 in. dial diameter, mounted in a steel box having a thick plate glass front or window. The gauge and box were filled with water, as were also the connecting lines to the Venturi tube. The recordings were small, however, the indication being but 1/2 psi for a 3 to 4 lb/sec rate of flow.

A more sensitive differential pressure gauge was then made, consisting of four 3-in.-O.D. metal bellows in line, fastened at the top to a closed steel cylinder and at the bottom to a movable plate bearing a vertical rod which served as a height indicator. The space inside the bellows was connected to the narrow part of the Venturi, and the space outside to the wider part. A marker on the top of the rod was visible through a glass tube. The motion produced by this bellows indicator, though of sufficient magnitude, was too sluggish to be usable. Increasing the number of holes around both parts of the Venturi increased the rate markedly, but the lag was still excessive.

Rpm measurements. An elongated iron nut, 1⅜ in. long, ½ in. wide, and ⅛ in. thick, was used on the turbine end of the pump shaft. This rotated %4 in. away from the poles of a U-shaped magnet having straight sides.

A d-c coil was used on the bottom of the U, and an a-c coil on each leg, all of No. 26 enameled copper wire. A single dry cell was connected to the d-c coil through a rheostat, and a Weston No. 425 thermogalvanometer was used with the a-c coils. The rheostat was set so that 12,000 rpm measured by a tachometer gave a deflection of 4.0 divisions. The calibration for higher rpm was obtained by the use of a tuning fork. The speed-deflection relation was practically linear, for although the reading was proportional to the current squared with the current increasing as the speed, the a-c resistance increased simultaneously with the frequency.

Instrument setup. The pressure gauges, U-tube manometer, thermo- and d-c galvanometers, and stop watch were all mounted on the 1-ft-square instrument board, used for previous instrument recordings. Recording was by a Sept motion-picture camera, set to take exposures at 1-sec intervals. The thermogalvanometer was mounted horizontally, with a small mirror to reflect the scale toward the camera.

Two photoflood lamps in aluminum-covered reflectors were used to illuminate the instruments during the run, these being so placed that there was no direct reflection into the camera from any point. Care was also taken to have the camera and instrument board sufficiently braced to reduce vibration.

Method of conducting a test. Tests were carried out in such a manner as to obtain not only a photographic record but also a sufficient number of readings by several observers to make possible the planning of the next test. These observers noted the level of one arm of the U-tube manometer, the pitch of the sound from the pump (which was compared with that of a 256 tuning fork, after the run, to obtain the rpm), the thermogalvanometer reading, and the pump delivery pressure.

The test was started when one operator pulled a cord that opened the pump intake gate valve, and immediately afterward pulled a cord that opened the turbine air valve. The arm of this air valve closed switches at the same time, turning on the photoflood lights and also the direct current to the rpm magnet. The water intake valve was opened before the air valve in order to prevent the pump from racing.

As soon as the mercury in the manometer ceased to oscillate, after starting, a switch that operated the camera motor was closed. This motor was allowed to run until the manometer reading began to fall noticeably, whereupon it was stopped and a signal was given for the two cords to be released, thus allowing the two valves to be closed by coil tension springs. A further frame was taken a minute later, in order to find to what extent the temperature of the turbine air tank had fallen during the run.

Results. A number of tests were carried out for three different initial air-tank pressures, namely 100, 150, and 180 psi. The initial pressures at the turbines during the test were somewhat less, however, owing to the time required for the manometer to become steady and for the pump to acquire full speed.

For pump A′ it was found necessary to cut off the very thin part of the middle section of the casing piece at the place where the volute started, because in one test this part became bent and thereby plugged the entrance to the outlet nozzle.

Two-stage turbines did not give quite as high efficiencies as single-stage turbines, possibly because of imperfect blade form. There was some leakage through the slinger-housing drain tube for the tests with pump forms B, C, and D. In the tests with pumps D and A′, the individually piped turbine nozzles were replaced by the turbine manifold described above.

The bearing housings remained practically at room temperature during the runs but showed a 10 to 20° C rise a half minute to a minute after each test, possibly because the outer parts of the bearing housings were kept cool by the cold exhaust blast from the turbines during the run, and became warm from the somewhat heated bearings afterward.

The air-tank pressure rose about 2 psi one minute after the tests, indicating a negligible amount of adiabatic cooling during the runs. The greatest over-all efficiency, as estimated on the basis of the number of BTU's lost by the turbine air tank, was about 12 per cent.

The last four items in Table II are for large flows and also for pressures approximating 550 psi, which was the pressure planned for use in later pump flight tests, the oxygen and gasoline flows for these tests being estimated as 3 to 5 lb/sec, and 1.5 to 3 lb/sec, respectively.

TABLE II

Data for 180 Psi Initial Air-Tank Pressure, Single Turbines

Pump type	Turbine air pressure	Pump pressure		Flow		Rpm	Pump hp output
		Intake	Delivery	Lb/sec	Gal/min		
A	170	32	750	1.37	9.8	46,000	4.37
B	168	35	568	1.13	8.2	30,000	2.70
C	163	33	375	1.12	8.1	21,000	1.77
D	160	34	730	1.63	11.7	39,000	5.05
A′	160	35	820	1.63	11.7	41,000	5.57
A′ (large flow)	155	32	350	3.20	23.0	39,000	4.70
A′ (flow for 550 psi approx.)	157	34	600	2.53	18.3	39,000	6.42
D (large flow)	157	32	450	3.33	24.0	38,000	6.40
D (flow for 550 psi approx.)	163	32	620	2.43	17.3	35,000	6.35

A pressure-flow curve for pumps D and A', at 155 psi turbine air pressure from initial tank pressures of 180 psi, showed the graph for the former to be practically a straight line from 3.5 lb/sec at 400 psi to 1.5 lb/sec at 730 psi, whereas the graph for form A' was somewhat concave toward the pressure axis, from 3 lb/sec at 440 psi to 1.5 lb/sec at 850 psi.

Recommendations. Considerable pump weight could be saved by using Dowmetal for the casings and bearing housing in place of 17 ST aluminum alloy, the respective densities being 1.8 and 2.8. Further, although adding somewhat to the weight, the shaft diameter should be increased from 1/2 in. to 5/8 in. in order to have the impeller held more rigidly.

STATIC TESTS WITH PUMPS USING VARIOUS METHODS OF TURBINE DRIVE

From January 6 to February 28, 1939, static or proving-stand tests were carried out, in which several methods of pressure feed were used for the turbines. As a result of these tests, it was concluded that a small chamber producing hot oxygen gas should be developed for operating the turbines.

Test of January 6, 1939 (P-1): Pump Test, Oxygen Gas Pressure

In this test the pressure in the turbine manifolds was produced by oxygen gas, supplied as liquid to a copper tube jacket around the chamber and nozzle, through a reducing valve in a by-pass between the pump and chamber. In addition, the speed of each turbine was reduced sufficiently to maintain a pump pressure of 550 psi by flow regulators installed in the turbine manifold, the starting taking place by means of outside pressure applied to the rocket gas-pressure system.

Chamber and jacket. The combustion chamber, similar to previous 5 3/4-in.-diameter chambers, was made of 0.037-in.-thick nickel sheet. The flow of water through the oxygen orifice at 20 psi pressure was 9 13/16 oz/sec. This was larger than for pressure-tank feed, inasmuch as high pump pressures would be expected to increase the velocity of the tangential gasoline sheet and hence the protection afforded by it. The water flow through the two respective gasoline orifices at 20 psi was 7 9/16 oz/sec and 7 17/32 oz/sec. The oxygen deflector, of copper, was 5/8 in. in diameter.

The copper-tube jacket was wound spirally over as much of the chamber and nozzle surface as possible, extending from within 1 3/8 in. of the top of the cylindrical part of the chamber to within 4 5/8 in. of the bottom of the nozzle. Spirals of 0.020-in.-diameter iron wire, pulled out so as to be rather open, were used in the copper tubes to break up drops.

Twelve ⁹⁄₁₆-in. O.D., 0.020-in.-wall copper tubes, each 12 ft 4 in. long, were used for the jacket, making 148 ft in all. The ends were flared and held in small steel unions. Heat conduction was increased by using aluminum strips or wires of somewhat triangular section between the coils, such as had been used in the 1930–1932 tests. These were so shaped as to be in contact both with the chamber and with each of the two adjacent copper tubes. The total weight of chamber, copper-tube jacket, and ½-in.-square tubing manifolds for the ends of the jacket was 17¼ lb.

Tanks. The gasoline tank, at the top of the rocket, was of sheet nickel, the 9-in.-diameter cylindrical part being 27¾ in. long and having hemispherical ends. The sheet-nickel Venturi tube, as used in the preliminary pump tests, extended axially from the bottom.

The oxygen tank was 9 in. in diameter, with the cylindrical part 26 in. long, also having hemispherical ends. The Venturi, extending similarly from the bottom of the tank, was provided with a jacket tube, kept filled with liquid oxygen through holes around the outlet orifice of the tank.

Below the oxygen tank was a 9-in.-diameter spherical nickel tank, which acted as a storage or ballast tank to maintain the gas pressure from the copper-tube jacket as constant as possible, thus preventing any momentary drop in the power supplied to the turbines.

Oxygen pump. The oxygen pump was the 1½-in.-diameter impeller pump designated as form A′ in the preliminary pump tests with water. Heat insulation was secured by using a bakelite ring between the pump casing and the flange on the slinger housing, as well as small bakelite rings or washers under the heads of the screws holding the casing sections together. The bearings were similarly protected by making both the shaft and the flange, which bore the steel seat for the double bellows seal on one side and the slinger vanes on the other, in two parts, with a bakelite ring between these two flange sections. The orifice for the seal was 1⅛ in. O.D. and ¹⁄₁₆ in. wide. This seal held 30 psi air pressure in the pump for 20 psi operating pressure in the double bellows.

Both the pump and the strainer, which was located a short distance from the intake side of the pump, were covered with ⅜-in.-thick felt and aluminum foil.

Gasoline pump. The gasoline pump was the 1¾-in.-diameter impeller pump designated as D in the preliminary water tests. A new brass impeller was made, however, which had 0.006 to 0.008 in. axial clearance on each side and 0.004 in. radial clearance (Fig. 20).

The shaft was in two parts, coupled by the steel flange, which had on one side the 1½-in.-O.D. by ¹⁄₁₆-in.-wide seat on the brass ring of the double bellows seal, and the slinger vanes on the other side. In order to simplify construction by using the same form of pump housing for both pumps, an aluminum ring was used between this housing and the gasoline-pump casing, of the same size as the bakelite ring for the oxygen pump. The casing sections of both pumps were coated with shellac before assembling, this coating being at a sufficient distance from all parts of the volute passage to avoid clogging.

Leakage of gasoline to the outside of the pump from the narrow annular space between the slinger housing and the shaft was prevented by the use of a narrow brass ring, which extended between this housing and the bearing housing and was covered on the outside with wet asbestos in order to make a tight packing. Gasoline could, of course, still pass to the outside air, but only through both ball bearings.

Pump mountings. Each pump was fastened to a 2- × 2- × ¼-in. angle iron, by means of a steel bracket bolted to one of the webs of the bearing housing. The turbine manifold was similarly fastened to this same angle iron. The angle iron for each pump was bolted to a horizontal 10-in.-square frame consisting of ⅞-in.-O.D. square steel tubing, these frames being held 9¾ in. apart by ⅞-in.-diameter round steel tubing at the corners, the ⅞-in.-diameter tube supports for the chamber and pressure sphere extending outside from the corners of the squares. The pumps, with axes parallel, faced in opposite directions in order to reduce the total angular momentum to a low value when the pumps were mounted for flights. The gasoline pump was placed below the oxygen pump.

A side tube between the on-and-off valve and the chamber led down to a large-capacity 200-psi reducing valve, which will be described below, and thence, through a check valve, to the copper-tube jacket, which evaporated the oxygen for driving the pumps. A side tube just above the reducing valve led to two oxygen turbine regulators, for controlling the pump speed, which will also be described below. It was not necessary to jacket the oxygen line, because both the supply tubes and the pumps were filled by gravity down to the on-and-off valves. A simple wrapping of these oxygen lines with inch-wide strips of felt and aluminum foil therefore afforded sufficient thermal insulation.

Lines and valves. The gasoline line led from the gasoline Venturi to the strainer and pump, and thence to the gasoline on-and-off valve just above the chamber, to which connection was made through two branches. A side tube just above the on-and-off valve led, as in the case of the oxygen, to two turbine regulators.

The gasoline on-and-off valves each had a ⅞-in.-diameter orifice, closed by a flat valve member. The seat was metal-to-metal for the oxygen and metal-to-Vellumoid for the gasoline. A 9/16-in.-O.D. bellows was used for each valve as the seal for the valve rod.

The oxygen-gas pressure line extended up from the copper-tube jacket to the 9-in. pressure-storage sphere, a branch leading through a shutoff valve to a Y which in turn led to the two turbine manifolds. The hose, for supplying starting pressure from an outside tank, was connected to a fitting on the 9-in. pressure sphere. The check valve below the 200-psi regulating valve was for the purpose of preventing passage of gas back through this regulating valve before the oxygen pump was up to full pressure. The shutoff valve, which was in the line to the turbine manifolds, was closed to prevent racing at the end of the run. The 9-in. sphere was provided with a high-pressure safety valve, and the oxygen and gasoline tanks with low-pressure safety valves.

The 30-psi tank pressure line entered by way of a short tube extending between the oxygen and the gasoline tanks and leading to the tops of these tanks. A check valve was used between this entrance and each of the respective tanks in order to avoid mixtures of vapors in the tanks.

Oxygen regulating valve. The oxygen regulating or reducing valve referred to above, for reducing 550 psi liquid-oxygen pressure to 200 psi, consisted of a conical brass valve member engaging a ¼-in. hole. The movable member, which served to open the valve, consisted of the outlet tube connected to the outside piping by a flexible braid-covered section. This tube was mounted in the free end of a 2-in.-diameter, two-ply bellows. A disk in each of the outlet tubes engaged a short projection on the conical valve member, the force produced by the bellows being opposed by the action of seven strong coil tension springs outside the bellows, which springs opened the valve on fall of pressure.

Turbine regulators. In addition to maintaining a constant pressure of 200 psi in the manifolds by means of the reducing valve, it was also necessary to reduce the flow through the turbine nozzles sufficiently to reduce the pump pressures to 550 psi. For this purpose, tapered rods were used in the throats of two opposite nozzles of each of the four nozzles on the two turbine manifolds.

Each nozzle rod was guided so as to be axial with respect to the turbine nozzle and extended into a large tube communicating with the turbine manifold. In this large tube were four %6-in.-O.D. bellows on a yoke fastened to the valve rod, the free ends of the bellows being closed by a plate. By this means, the pump pressure exerted force on the free ends of the bellows, and excess of pressure thus tended to close the nozzle openings.

On the end of each large tube opposite the manifold was a 1¼-in.-O.D. bellows contained within a smaller tube, the free end being soldered to a disk on the end of the valve rod. This bellows was supplied internally with 30 psi pressure and acted like a compression spring, exerting a constant force tending to keep the nozzle closed.

In operation, when the pump pressure fell, the force on the four %6-in. bellows from the manifold pressure exceeded the force on the outside of these bellows due to the pump pressure, and the nozzle opening was accordingly widened. The reverse operation took place when the pump pressure rose.

Connection from the pump delivery lines to these regulators, as already stated, was from points between the on-and-off valves and the chamber. The passage of liquid oxygen to the regulators was avoided by wrapping the ³⁄₁₆-in. copper tube to the regulator nine times around the gasoline delivery line, thus forming a heating coil. In addition, felt was used in the oxygen turbine regulator to prevent direct contact of gas from the manifold with the metal parts around the recess containing the pump pressure.

An indicator to check the operation of the turbine regulators was used in shop tests. This consisted of a freely sliding ¹⁄₁₆-in.-diameter rod resting against the movable end plate of the 30-psi bellows, with the regulator in such a position that this rod was vertical. The upper end of the rod could be seen inside a glass tube held in a packing gland.

Controls at tower. Pressure for starting the turbines was obtained from the 12-in. diameter, 5-ft-high nickel pressure tank used in previous tests. This was supplied with 200 psi of nitrogen gas from a commercial cylinder just before and during the run, through a large-capacity reducing valve also previously used. From this 12-in. tank a tube passed through a 30-psi reducing valve, also of large capacity, operated by a 5-in.-diameter bellows and seven strong coil tension springs. This valve supplied pressure to the oxygen and gasoline tanks. A smaller reducing valve, from this 30-psi valve, supplied 25 psi for the bellows seals on the two pumps. The oxygen and gasoline tanks were rinsed with nitrogen just before the run.

The lift was measured by means of a single bellows of 13 sq. in. cross section, as used in the K series of tests. A downward force was applied to the bellows by one end of a channel-iron lever, the other end being pushed upward by the rocket. The bellows, as well as the turbine line to the pressure gauge on the instrument board, was completely filled with brake fluid and was placed under a small initial pressure in order to detect the presence of leaks.

Starting. Pressure was first admitted to the 12-in.-nickel tank from the commercial nitrogen cylinder just before firing of the igniter, which as usual set the first kerosene dashpot in operation.

This dashpot allowed the gasoline on-and-off valve to open ¹⁄₃₂ in. by a coil tension spring on the valve lever arm, which struck a stop pin and thereby prevented full opening.

The first dashpot then released the second dashpot, which pulled a number of pins. These closed the vent valve on the oxygen tank, opened the oxygen on-and-off valve, opened the gasoline valve fully, allowed 30 psi to pass to the oxygen and gasoline tanks and 200 psi to flow to the turbine gas-pressure line through a small valve outside the tower, and relieved the 25-psi pump seal pressure, thus allowing the pumps to rotate freely.

The second dashpot operated the third dashpot, thus opening a large gate valve outside the tower to apply full starting pressure to the turbines. The time of stroke of this dashpot was increased from the usual 2 sec to

2½ sec, in order to provide adequate time for starting the turbines. At the end of the stroke, a valve shut off the 200 psi outside pressure supply.

Stopping. The run was stopped by pressing a key that operated the lever previously used for freeing the rocket in making flights. This lever shut off all the outside pressures and at the same time applied the 25-psi seal pressure. It also shut off the oxygen and gasoline on-and-off valves on the rocket, besides allowing the shut-off valve in the line to the turbine manifolds to close. The oxygen and gasoline tanks were afterward vented by valve cocks, using long cords.

Two tubes extended from the slinger-housing drain tubes of the pumps to the outside of the sheet-iron shield around the tower, in order to avoid fire along the sides of the rocket.

Instruments. Of the copper-tube connecting lines, that to the lift gauge was ⅜-in.-diameter in order to avoid lag, and that from the gasoline delivery pipe was ¼ in. for the same reason. All the other connections were of 3⁄16-in. O.D. and 1⁄64-in. wall except the lines at high pressure, for which the wall was 1⁄32 in.

The pressure gauges measured the lift, oxygen- and gasoline-tank pressures, oxygen- and gasoline-pump pressures, gas-storage-tank pressure, and chamber pressure. The d-c galvanometers measured the rpm of each pump, and the U-tube manometers measured the rates of flow. The copper tubes extended 15 in. above the top of the oxygen tank, to prevent liquid oxygen from passing down to the mercury U tube. Above the level of the tank they passed through a tube containing water in which a circulation could be maintained by convection. Both tubes were covered with thin flanged copper sheet in order to produce good thermal contact with the water, thus preventing the rise of liquid oxygen in either tube.

Test. The flame appeared two or three seconds after the igniter was fired, accompanied by a loud report. It was short, white, and noisy for two or three seconds, and was followed by a flame that evidently was produced by much less pressure.

An examination of the pumps immediately after the test showed that the oxygen-pump shaft turned with a noticeable viscous drag, the bearing lubricant evidently being very cold. The gasoline bearings gave uneven resistance to turning. An examination showed that rust had accumulated on a steel spacer sleeve between these bearings. This rust evidently had been driven into the bearings, probably by a flow of gasoline.

The gas pressure produced by the copper-tube jacket was evidently not sufficient to drive the pumps at the required speed, an appreciable pressure being shown only in the first two frames, taken at 1-sec intervals by the Sept camera. From the data contained in these, the lift was estimated to be 502 and 463 lb, respectively; the chamber pressures, 90 and 85 psi; oxygen-pump pressures, 430 and 350 psi; gasoline-pump pressures, 230 and 200 psi; both oxygen-tank and gasoline-tank pressures, 4 and 6 psi; both oxygen and gasoline rpm's, 15,000 and 12,000 rpm; and gasoline flows, 1.5 and 2.4 lb/sec. The oxygen-flow rate was uncertain, owing to a large initial U-tube displacement. Apparently the boiling of oxygen in the connecting tubes was sufficient to mask the relatively small pressure difference due to flow.

The low turbine drive pressure may have been the result of gas bind in the 200-psi liquid-oxygen reducing valve, in which case a large-capacity gaseous-oxygen valve might be used beyond the copper-tube jacket, this valve being of the pneumatically balanced slotted-sleeve type; and two pressure-balanced $\frac{9}{16}$-in. bellows might be used for the packing or seal, and a 30-psi bellows, located outside, for operating the valve sleeve.

Test of January 24, 1939 (P-2):
Pump Test, Outside Pressure

The object of this test was to use 200 psi outside pressure for driving the turbines, in order to study pump operation of the rocket during a fairly long interval of time. No change was made in the chamber, but since no cooling flow took place through the copper-tube jacket, a water tank or jacket was used around the chamber and turbine jacket in order to prevent over-heating.

Pumps. The only alteration of the pumps was in substituting shellac for water in the asbestos packing placed over the thin brass ring that closed the space between the gasoline-pump slinger and bearing housings. This substitution was made in order to avoid the rust that had previously been found on the steel shaft and the bearing sleeve (Fig 21).

Turbine regulators. The previous turbine regulators were not completely satisfactory, inasmuch as the closing pressure could not be adjusted without changing the pressure in the low-pressure bellows. Further, an appreciable motion of the valve rod required a considerable pressure variation.

In order to overcome these difficulties, new regulators were made in which the opening in the turbine manifold around the valve rod was sealed to the outside air by a $\frac{9}{16}$-in. bellows so placed that pressure was applied to the outside. The valve rod was moved by pressure up to 30 psi applied inside a 2-in.-diameter single-ply bellows. The movable end plate pushed the valve rod, which normally was forced outward by the manifold pressure exerted on the $\frac{9}{16}$-in.-bellows (Fig. 22).

The motion of the valve rod was varied by altering the pressure within the 2-in. bellows and retaining this pressure at any desired value. This result was accomplished by using, for each pair of regulators, one of the small pneumatically balanced magnet valves used previously for vane control in automatic steering. The rod of this small valve was kept normally in the open position by a small coil compression spring, thus allowing flow at 30 psi to pass to the turbine regulators. Rise of pump pressure caused the extension of a 10½-in. length of %₂-in.-O.D. by ⅛-in.-I.D. seamless brass tube. The movable, closed end of this tube shut the valve at the proper pump pressure and opened it to the exhaust position on a further rise of pump pressure.

Level indicators. The oxygen Venturi had been found to be unreliable when used with an outside mercury manometer, and hence both level indicators were replaced by 8-oz cork floats that operated rheostats. In this way the levels in the oxygen and gasoline tanks were each measured over a 22-in. vertical distance. Each cork float was prevented from turning about a vertical axis by two fixed vertical rods, one on each side of a spiral or twisted aluminum strip, ½ in. wide by ⅛ in. thick, located on the axis of the float. This strip was pivoted at the top and bottom and bore a contact arm near the top, in a steel box above the tank. This arm slid on a horizontal 0.020-in.-diameter manganin wire, which made a nearly complete circle and constituted the rheostat. The twisted strip was turned by vertical motion of the float, being between two rollers fixed to the top of the float, each having a clearance of 0.002 in. with respect to the strip.

The d-c galvanometers used had scales for both positive and negative current and therefore were connected across the contact arm and the midpoint of the circular rheostat wire. A 100-ohm series resistance gave satisfactory maximum deflections.

Controls. Except for the fact that pressure was not generated on the rocket, the control arrangements were the same as before. A larger outside gas-supply space was provided by using a 9-in. diameter, 4-ft nickel tank in addition to the 12-in.-diameter tank. An 8-in. diameter, 2-ft-long tank was used for the bellows-seals reducing valve in order to allow for any leakage, this tank being filled initially to any desired pressure by means of a globe valve on the 200-lb pressure line. The seal pressure could therefore be applied after the run, even if all the other tanks had become empty.

A larger-diameter line was used from the 30-psi reducing valve outside the tower to the rocket tanks, in order to produce more rapid rise of tank pressures.

Test. The two pressure tanks were filled at 200 psi pressure in about 6 sec before the igniter was fired as compared with 4 sec for the preceding test. A strong flame appeared two or three seconds after the igniter was fired, although it became yellowish for a moment, indicating an excess of gasoline. It remained white from this time until the end of the run, being accompanied by a yellowish-white flame at the rear of the tower.

After the test it was found that the gasoline pump turned freely but that brass particles from the impeller entrance produced an occasional resistance to turning of the oxygen pump. These had evidently rubbed on the pump casing, eventually breaking off and causing the irregular flame at the beginning of the run. The brass of the impeller entrance was brittle, and hard enough to dull a sharp lathe tool, possibly owing to heating by friction and quenching in liquid oxygen.

The run was of 25 sec duration, during which time the pump pressures gradually decreased owing to inadequate pressure supply, the outside tank pressure falling from 200 psi to 107 psi in 4 sec. The maximum pump pressures were 530 for the oxygen and 250 for the gasoline, the former thereafter continuing about double the latter.

The tank pressures rose to 28 psi within 2 sec, the rapidity probably resulting from the larger supply line. The chamber pressure was uncertain, owing to a poor tube connection to the gauge. The level indicators did not prove reliable, since the readings were erratic. Average flows, however, were estimated, these being 2 lb/sec for oxygen and 2.5 lb/sec for gasoline. These flows, for an average thrust of 624 lb for 23 sec, gave 4450 ft/sec jet velocity.

The rise of temperature of the water jacket around the chamber, namely 39° C, seemed small in view of the large excess of oxygen-pump pressure over gasoline pressure. This small rise appeared to be especially noteworthy when the degree of chamber heating was compared with that for pressure tanks.

Test of February 7, 1939 (P-3): Repeat Test, Oxygen Gas Pressure

The object of this test was to repeat the first test of the present series, in which the turbines had been operated by oxygen evaporated from the turbine jacket on the chamber, using additional turbine nozzles supplied by outside pressure for starting.

Chamber jacket. The resistance to flow of the turbine jacket around the chamber and nozzle was reduced by using larger-diameter tubing and dispensing with the open coils of iron wire used inside for breaking up the drops.

The new jacket was made of $\frac{1}{4}$-in.-O.D., 0.035-in.-wall, soft aluminum tubing in twelve 8-ft lengths extending from $3\frac{1}{4}$ in. below the top of the cylindrical part of the chamber to $5\frac{3}{4}$ in. above the bottom of the nozzle. Brass SAE union parts were used on the tapering ends, with steel union parts turned down for lightness on the $\frac{5}{8}$-in.-O.D. square tubing half-circle manifolds, at the ends of the jacket. Heat conduction was increased over the surfaces of the nozzle and the lower cone of the chamber by using No. 14 aluminum wires between the tubing turns. The jacket was clamped tightly against the wall by sheet-iron bands, bolted together along wide flanges while the jacket tubes were being wound under tension.

A shop test of the jacket using gas from a nitrogen cylinder gave pressures of 19, 45, and 60 psi in the 9-in. nickel sphere for pressures at the bottom of the jacket of 23, 50, and 75 psi, indicating a much lower resistance than for the ³⁄₁₆-in.-O.D. copper tubes previously used. It was protected against flame while in the tower by a conical frustum of 0.018-in. sheet nickel extending upward from the bottom of the nozzle.

Pumps. Owing to the scoring of the oxygen-pump casing caused by brass particles in the preceding test, the clearance at the sides of the impeller was increased from 0.008 to 0.010 in., and at the edge from 0.007 to 0.010 in. Further, the clearance around the impeller inlet opening was widened to ¹⁄₆₄ in., in order to avoid any more rubbing.

Turbines. No turbine regulators were used, the openings left in the manifolds by the removal of the regulators being closed by plugs. Each pump was started by two steel nozzles located on the opposite side of the turbine from the four nozzles used for regular operation. These starting nozzles were piped from a Y branch through two ¹⁄₂-in.-O.D. copper tubes. All Y branches, in both the starting and the regular running piping, were of gradually changing cross section. The use of outside starting nozzles made a check valve unnecessary between the jacket and the 9-in. tank.

Oxygen reducing valve. The resistance to flow in the 200-psi oxygen reducing valve was decreased in two ways: by reducing the mass of metal as well as the space into which the liquid oxygen passed from the valve; and by using the pressure in the 9-in. sphere for valve bellows operation rather than the reduced pressure of the oxygen after it had passed through the valve.

An ¹⁄₈-in. rod, used to open the conical valve member previously employed, was soldered to a ⁹⁄₁₆-in. bellows that served as packing against the outside air. The 2-in. bellows, for moving this rod, was piped to the 9-in. nickel gas-storage sphere, and hence responded immediately to changes in turbine gas pressure.

Recording instruments. The circular wire rheostat for measuring fall of oxygen-tank level was replaced by a 0.020-in. manganin wire that passed up the sides and over the top of a ¹⁄₄-in.-diameter vertical bakelite rod, on the cork float. Fixed copper brushes served as connections to the rheostat wire. This change was made in order to avoid the friction in the oxygen tank that was caused by the twisted strip in the preceding test. The gasoline-level circular wire rheostat was again used, without change.

Controls at the tower. The smaller 9-in.-diameter 4-ft nickel pressure-storage tank was not used for the reason that the outside pressure was needed only for starting. A cord passing over a pulley was, however, fastened to the end of the lever arm of the valve that shut off pressure from the 12-in. nickel tank to the rocket, in order to boost the turbine speed manually, if desirable, during the run. The time of fall for the third dashpot, which allowed the starting pressure to flow, was increased to 3 sec.

Test. Although the rocket continued to operate during the 12-sec run after the starting pressure had been shut off, the turbine pressure gradually fell, thus indicating a lack of adequate pressure from the chamber jacket. There was, however, a pressure rise soon after the start, owing possibly to a large rush of oxygen taking place as soon as the jacket had become sufficiently cooled. The flame was whitish and varied in intensity, probably owing to the variation of turbine pressure.

The lift was considerable, since the nozzle rose above the steel thimble on the base plate in the tower and thereby became bent at the throat when the rocket dropped, after the run. The chamber was otherwise undamaged except for a small hole in the inverted inner cone. The tank pressures rose fairly rapidly to 26 psi. The oxygen-pump pressure remained about 200 psi above the gasoline-pump pressure until both pressures had fallen considerably. The temperature of the oxygen gas from the chamber jacket was 120° C. The bearing temperatures, on the other hand, fell below air temperature, probably owing to the drop in temperature accompanying the expansion of the fairly cold oxygen from the turbine.

The maximum pressures were: turbine pressure 195 psi; oxygen-pump pressure 600 psi; and gasoline-pump pressure 400 psi. The maximum lift was 671.5 lb. From the rates of flow, namely 2.15 lb/sec oxygen and 2.28 lb/sec gasoline, the velocity was estimated as 4820 ft/sec. The mixture ratio was 0.94. According to the photographs, the maximum chamber pressure was 290 psi and occurred a second after the maximum pump pressures, possibly indicating a lack of complete mixing at the time the liquids entered the chamber.

Recommendations. Because of lack of substantially instantaneous mixing, it was believed that many fine sprays of oxygen might be superior to a single sheet, and also that sprays impinging from practically opposite directions might be used advantageously in connection with a tangential curtain of gasoline just sufficient for cooling the chamber wall.

Production of warm oxygen gas sufficient for operating the turbines might be obtained by increasing the rate of oxygen flow through the jacket, provided variation of pump pressure did not seriously alter the mixture ratio.

Test of February 28, 1939 (P-4):
Pump Test, Chamber Gas Pressure

The purpose was to test the operation of the turbines by gas from the top of the chamber, this gas being cooled by means of oxygen sprays before leaving the chamber.

Chamber. Gas for driving the turbines was led from the upper cone of the chamber through a 20-in. length of $\frac{9}{16}$-in.-O.D., $\frac{1}{16}$-in.-wall steel tube, to a $\frac{3}{4}$-in.-O.D. steel tube that passed to the turbines. Liquid oxygen was introduced into the upper cone through three No. 60 holes that directed streams inward radially against the jacketed oxygen-entrance tube. At high pressures these streams were converted to sprays on impact with the jacket. Copper tubes, ³⁄₁₆ in. O.D., led oxygen from the pump delivery line to these holes.

Inasmuch as the aluminum-tube jacket around the chamber and nozzle was not used, protection against undue heating was obtained by the use of a conical tank containing water, placed around the chamber as in the test of January 24, except that the tank in the present case was made high enough to cover the upper cone of the chamber.

The 9-in. pressure-storage sphere was not used, in order to avoid possible accumulation of an explosive mixture. The thermocouple for the turbine gas was placed just before the branch to the two turbines.

Results. After the igniter was fired, a sharp hiss was heard and white vapor was seen to pass from the nozzle, evidently under pressure. A short time later there was a flash, the upper cone of the chamber being blown off.

It seemed probable that the explosion was largely due to the low rate of initial flow of gasoline through the partially opened gasoline valve, this slow starting of the gasoline failing to produce an initial flame throughout the chamber.

Apparently combustion took place in the chamber for a short time, since there was considerable lift shown in one frame, accompanied by 180 psi chamber pressure, 440 psi oxygen-pump pressure, and 220 psi gasoline-tank pressure. The turbine gas temperature dropped below air temperature, indicating the absence of normal combustion in the upper cone of the chamber before the explosion took place.

Recommendations. The bleed method as described of obtaining gas for the turbines from the chamber might be used successfully if the gasoline valve were opened fully at the start, rather than part way. An alternative method would be to use water in place of oxygen for the sprays, this water being contained in a small tank supplied with oxygen gas from a side tube in the pump high-pressure line. The liquid oxygen would be converted to gas by first passing through a coil under the water.

10

Static Pump Tests Continued

P Series (Continued), March 24, 1939 — August 4, 1939

As a result of the foregoing tests it was concluded that a small chamber to produce hot oxygen gas should be developed for operating the turbines.

Accordingly, a gas generator or small chamber, supplied with a large excess of oxygen for the purpose of furnishing warm gas to the turbines, was developed in a series of 11 tests, made from March 24 to April 28, 1939 (Fig. 23).

The first chamber tried was similar in general to the chambers used for thrust, except that the gasoline entered axially in a conical sheet and the oxygen entered tangentially.

The cylindrical part of the small chamber was 1⅝ in. O.D. and 8 in. long, the outlet tube for the gas in a bottom cone being ¾ in. This outlet tube led to a cone on which was a 2⅛-in.-diameter steel disk, ¹⁄₁₆ in. thick, having eight ⁵⁄₃₂-in.-diameter holes, these being practically equivalent to the eight nozzles used in driving the two pump turbines. A powder igniter was installed in the inverted cone.

Both liquids were admitted through valves that could be adjusted during the run by turning small wheels. Chamois strainers of 2-in. diameter, backed by perforated aluminum, were used between the turbines and the on-and-off valves. A pressure gauge and a thermocouple were used to measure the pressure and temperature, respectively, of the gas produced. A nitrogen pressure of 250 psi was applied to the two tanks.

Tests. In the first test the chamber burned through about 1 in. below the upper cone before the pressure produced in the generator exceeded 25 psi. The gasoline flow was accordingly decreased. Further, the mass of metal at the oxygen inlet of the gas generator was reduced by dispensing with the hand-operated oxygen needle valve, and in addition the line from the oxygen tank to the generator was provided with a liquid-oxygen jacket. The chamber burned out in this case also, beginning about 2 in. below the upper cone.

The gasoline rate of flow in the generator was then reduced by using a small spray nozzle without the needle valve, this nozzle being located axially in the vertex of the upper cone of the generator. This upper cone was refractory-lined, and the inverted cone was dispensed with.

The spray orifice consisted of a No. 80 hole, $\frac{1}{64}$ in. long, backed by a $\frac{3}{16}$-in.-long aluminum-plug rotator in a $\frac{3}{16}$-in.-diameter drill hole with double spiral grooves. The spray had the form of a solid cone, of 42-deg angle.

Ignition. Ignition of the spray was by a spark plug, the terminal being close to both the spray orifice and the spray cone. The spark passed to the rim of the No. 80 hole, the spray nozzle being made slightly conical so that this rim was close to the spark-plug terminal.

After each of the earlier tests the porcelain of the spark plug was found to have become cracked. This cracking, which appeared due to liquid oxygen striking the plug while it was heated, was avoided by using a steel ring at the upper end of the cylindrical part, which prevented the liquid oxygen from flowing or splashing into the upper cone of the gas generator.

Arrangements were made whereby the fall of level of the oxygen tank could be recorded by the Sept camera. For this purpose a float was used in the oxygen tank, having a wire extending upward to a head that was visible in a glass tube.

Liquid-flow adjustment. With the above spray-head gas generator, a run was obtained at 125 psi steady pressure for a tank pressure of 250 psi, the rate of flow of oxygen being 0.179 lb/sec, and the temperature rise about 60° C. A roar was heard, but no smoke or vapor appeared from the eight gas-outlet holes.

It therefore became evident that the flow of both liquids, particularly the gasoline, should be increased. Widening the gasoline orifice, however, produced a narrow stream instead of a spray, and it therefore became necessary to use a new spray head, in which the lengths of the passages in the rotator were much less.

Gasoline spray head. The form of gasoline spray head finally used consisted on the outside of a brass plug having a $\frac{1}{2}$-in. hole, at the bottom of which, at the center of the cone left by the drill end, was a No. 25 hole, chamfered on the inner edge by a 60-deg countersink.

A rotator member, provided with a number of entrance openings, was screwed into this brass plug, the part engaging the above conical end being $\frac{3}{16}$ in. in diameter and having a conical dent formed in the end by a $\frac{1}{8}$-in. drill, the cylindrical wall or hole produced by this drill being only $\frac{1}{64}$ in. deep. The edge of the resulting narrow rim was tapered to fit the cone in the $\frac{1}{2}$-in. hole, and two tangential grooves of semicircular section were filed in this edge, opposite each other. A water test at 30 psi gave a flow through the spray orifice of 14 oz in 3 min.

Strainer. It should be mentioned that after the above spray head had been tested, the strainer and spray head were incorporated into a single unit, using a phosphor-bronze wire-cloth disk of 150 mesh, ½ in. in diameter. With this strainer, explosions occurred in the tube on the generator at starting, even when oxygen gas was introduced in the upper cone opposite to the spark plug in order to produce positive ignition of the gasoline as soon as it entered.

It appeared probable that a fine spray of gasoline in air was produced by passage through the small strainer at the start of the run. The previous 2-in.-diameter strainer was again employed, using 150-mesh wire cloth, at the entrance to the spray head, and smooth runs were obtained thereafter.

Final form. In the final form the tangential oxygen orifice was increased from a No. 40 hole to No. 29, and a $1\frac{3}{16}$-in.-O.D., 6-ft-long steel tube from the generator to the eight outlet holes was used, bent to the same U shape as required on the rocket. In a 10-sec run, the gas generator pressure remained steadily at 180 psi for 250-psi tank pressures. The rate of flow for the oxygen was 0.49 lb/sec, and the temperature rise of the gas in the tube from the gas generator was 62° C.

A considerable saving in weight might be effected by introducing water tangentially into the gas generator and condensing the resulting steam, which would be prevented from leaking around the turbines by labyrinth packing; the uncondensed carbon dioxide being allowed to escape.

STATIC TESTS WITH PUMPS USING AN OXYGEN-GAS GENERATOR TURBINE DRIVE

From May 18, 1939, to August 4, 1939, static tests were carried out for the purpose of applying the oxygen-gas generator that had been developed to the operation of a pump-type rocket.

Test of May 18, 1939 (P-5):
Static Test, Oxygen-Gas Generator Rocket

Turbine drive. The gas generator, as finally tested April 28, 1939, was used for the turbine drive, the gasoline and oxygen being supplied through two reducing valves from the high-pressure pump delivery tubes, and the turbines being started by 200 psi outside nitrogen pressure applied during the period of fall of the third dashpot weight. The chamber was the same as that previously used, without a tube jacket, and the pumps were the same as before except that the casing or housing of the gasoline pump was of Dowmetal. The same oxygen and gasoline tanks were again used.

Owing to the fact that the flows through the gasoline spray orifice of the gas generator, with water tests, were found to be altered somewhat each time the spray nozzle and strainer were dismantled and reassembled, they were tested with distilled water and thereafter dried with warm air, without being taken down. The flow of water at 30 psi was 4⅔ oz/min.

Checks were made subsequently, in which the use of water was avoided, by timing the pressure drop in a 9-in. sphere for air flow, the pressure falling from 30 to 20 psi in 59 sec.

Flame from the gas generator was prevented, at the end of the run, by a shutoff valve in the line to the turbines, this valve having a low resistance when opened in order not to retard the high-speed gases in this line.

Supports. The general layout of pumps and turbine drive was planned for eventual use in a flight rocket. For this reason a 3-ft distance was added between the two square-tubing mountings for the pumps and the combustion chamber, this space providing for the gas generator and reducing valves and also for bringing the center of gravity considerably toward the forward end of the rocket. Four ⅞-in.-O.D. steel tubes were used between the square frame on which the gasoline pump was mounted, and a similar square-tubing frame, from the corners of which ⅞-in. tubes extended rearward to the upper cone of the chamber.

Fire shields, of ⅛-in. iron plate, were used at the top of the chamber to protect the main oxygen and gasoline valves, and at the lowest of the three square-tubing frames to protect the gas generator and pumps; also, short pieces of angle iron were placed around the gas generator to protect the pumps.

Oxygen lines. The main oxygen line passed from the oxygen tank through a strainer to the pump, and thence to the chamber through an on-and-off valve close to the latter. A branch line just below the pump led high pressure to an oxygen reducing valve, and from this valve to the gas generator, through a ¼-in. copper tube.

The main oxygen line was cooled by gravity flow of liquid oxygen, through the pump, as far rearward as the main on-and-off valve above the chamber. The branch line down to the valve seat of the gas-generator reducing valve was similarly cooled, except that a vent tube was needed to the top of the oxygen tank because of small diameter. A small spring-loaded check valve in this vent line prevented high pressure from leaking back to the tank during the rocket operation, this spring-loaded check valve being set to close at 10 psi.

Oxygen jackets. Two low-pressure oxygen jackets were used. One enclosed the reducing valve to the part where the seat was located, and extended from this to cover the ¼-in. copper tube to the gas-generator oxygen inlet. It was a ⅝-in. corrugated or flexible tube, to permit a necessary bend in the ¼-in. tube. From the inlet end, a vent tube led to the top of the tank.

The other low-pressure jacket passed down to the short tube jacket around the part of the oxygen line within the chamber, which was used as before to cool the oxygen-inlet orifice, this jacket also being provided with a vent tube.

In order to simplify the piping, a single wide tube was used from the bottom of the oxygen tank to a manifold from which extended the 1/4-in. tubes to the reducing valve and chamber jacket. A similar manifold was used just below the oxygen tank for the three vent tubes, a single large vent tube being used above this point. All the lines were wrapped with felt and aluminum-foil strips, except for the large vent tube above the middle of the oxygen tank.

Gasoline lines. The main gasoline line extended from the bottom of the gasoline tank, through a strainer to the pump, and thence to the main on-and-off gasoline valve, just above the chamber. A side tube below the pump led high pressure to the reducing valve for the gas generator, in the same way as for the oxygen. A vent tube branched from this tube to the top of the gasoline tank, this last line including a spring-loaded check valve, similar to the oxygen spring-loaded check valve for closing the line under high pump pressure.

The tubing and nozzles for starting the turbines, and also the line for supplying tank pressures from an outside pressure supply, were the same as in the earlier static tests.

On-and-off valves. The oxygen on-and-off valve, above the chamber, consisted of steel and sheet-nickel parts and was of brazed construction. The valve opening was 3/4 in. in diameter, and the valve member that served to prevent flow before the run was a 7/8-in.-diameter brass disk on the downstream side, held closed by an outside lever and coil tension spring. The seat was metal to metal. The packing on the rod between valve member and lever arm was a 9/16-in.-O.D. bellows, this rod being pinned rather loosely to the valve member to avoid a tilting force on the latter.

The valve member to close the passage after the run was likewise a 7/8-in. disk, located on the upstream side of the valve opening, within the same valve housing. It was pinned loosely, in the same way, on a rod that held the valve closed until it was released when an outside lever arm was freed by the action of bellows pressure and a strong coil compression spring.

This method of shutoff was considered superior to an additional spring on the arm of the opening lever, since such a spring might be weakened in case of a fire, thus preventing the valve from closing at the end of a run.

The gasoline valve was of similar construction except that a ring of sheet Vellumoid was used on both the inlet and the outlet faces of the 3/4-in. valve opening.

The lever arms for the oxygen valve were made in two parts, with a bakelite strip between for heat insulation.

Reducing valves. The oxygen and gasoline reducing valves for the gas generator were designed to maintain closely 250 psi reduced pressure, regardless of variation of pump pressures, so that 180 to 200 psi pressure could be obtained from the gas generator. Such maintenance of reasonably constant pressure was attained by using small valve openings with large regulating bellows and strong springs, there being for this reason but little variation in the reduced pressure from 300 to 600 psi pump pressure.

The oxygen reducing valve was of the same general construction as that for the gasoline reducing valve. The valve opening was ³⁄₁₆ in. in diameter, and was closed by a conical brass valve member located on the downstream side of the valve opening (Figs. 24, 25).

This valve member had a ⅛-in. diameter, 1-in.-long stem, traveling in a guide, with a light compression spring tending to keep the valve closed, and a ¹⁄₁₆-in. diameter, ¼-in.-long projection on the upstream side of the valve, this being engaged by a ⅛-in. rod, also moving in a guide.

The base plate on the movable end of a 1½-in. two-ply bellows pressed against the ⅛-in. rod, thus keeping the valve open at low pressures by a strong coil compression spring above the bellows. This spring had ground ends to prevent tilting, and was adjustable for the degree of compression by three screws that engaged an aluminum end plate on the spring. A ¼-in. rod engaged a threaded boss in the above base plate, thus enabling an outside lever arm at the end of the valve device to pull this base plate against the compression of the spring and thereby to allow the valve to close before a run.

A flat bakelite ring, between flanges, located just above the side tube from the high-pressure line, served to insulate thermally the valve proper from the bellows and compression spring. In addition, bakelite bushings were used to insulate the screws in the flanges.

The gasoline valve was of similar construction except for the absence of the bakelite ring and the screw bushings.

Because of the shape of the space available for these two reducing valves, they were installed in inverted position, that is, with the 1½-in. operating bellows placed downward, or rearward.

Operation of valves. The lever arm of each of the two reducing valves was held in a notch on the end of another lever, which in turn was held by what will be termed a push-type bellows operator, to be described below. When 30-psi control pressure was relieved from this bellows operator, the lever was freed and accordingly moved, under the influence of the strong compression spring of the valve, to start the test.

At the end of the run, a pull-type bellows operator, also to be described below, released a coil tension spring that pulled the lever arm of the valve back to the initial position, thereby allowing the valve to close.

The end of the valve rod was held at all times in an eye in the end of what may be termed a slack-motion rod. This rod was provided with an enlargement at the other end, which slid in a tube, constricted at both ends. Initially the rod was telescoped into this tube. When the lever arm was released, the rod became extended from the tube. Later, when the tube to which the coil spring was attached at the end opposite the rod was released, the tube, pulling on the enlargement, pulled down the valve lever arm.

In the push-type bellows operator referred to, 30-psi control pressure compressed a 1⅛-in. bellows against a compression spring, thereby pushing outward a pin or rod on the moving end of the bellows. This rod could be held in the extended position before pressure was applied, as in the present case, by a flat spring, which engaged a notch or slot in the pin and which was freed and sprang to one side as soon as pressure was applied to the bellows, thus causing the pin to move outward a small but appreciable amount.

In the pull-type bellows operator the control pressure likewise compressed a 1⅛-in. bellows, but the pin in this case was fastened to a yoke or sleeve which telescoped, or slid, along the outside of the steel tube containing the bellows, so that a pin, on the opposite side of the device from the pin just mentioned, was pulled rather than pushed.

Turbine shutoff valve. The turbine shutoff valve was, as above explained, closed at the end of the run in order to prevent flame from the gas generator from passing to the turbines. This precaution appeared necessary, since during development of the gas generator a tendency for such a flame to appear at the end of each run had been observed.

The valve opening was ¾ in. in diameter, and the valve disk used was ⅞ in. Inasmuch as this valve disk was thin and could be swung to one side in a valve chamber or tube 1¾ in. wide, it could be moved entirely out of line of the gas flow during the run, thus causing a minimum of interference with the high-velocity flow.

Release of the rod that swung the valve member into closed position was accomplished by means of a side rod with a 9/16-in. bellows packing, similar to the rods that released the closing parts of the main oxygen and gasoline valves. The compression spring, however, was located 2 in. away from the valve housing, and the tube containing the valve rod was narrow in addition, in order to minimize heat conduction both to the spring and to the solder of the bellows.

Controls. The 12-in.-diameter, 5-ft nickel tank was again used to supply starting pressure at 200 psi. This pressure was applied during the 3-sec fall of the third dashpot. The spark for the gas generator remained on during the fall of both the second and third dashpots.

A new 30-psi reducing valve for the tanks was made, the valve orifice being ⅝ in. in diameter, and the valve member being of the flat tapered-edge type, with a ⅛ in. motion and actuated by a 5⅝-in.-diameter bellows. Six coil tension springs were used to compress the bellows.

A 35-psi safety valve was used on the 30-lb line to the tanks, and a 300-psi safety valve was used on the turbine gas line to avoid dangerous rise of pressure by residual combustion after the stop valve was closed.

As in earlier tests, a chamber-pressure contact maker, consisting of a rod hooked at the end, on a 9/16-in. bellows, was used to stop the run when the chamber pressure fell. The arm slipped off the contact spring on a rise of pressure of 75 psi, thus setting or cocking the device. The spring made contact, thus stopping the run, on a fall of chamber pressure to 50 psi, instead of 25 psi as before, in order to make certain that the chamber pressure was higher than any pressure likely to be maintained by the inertia of the gasoline pump.

Test. A strong lift was produced after the rocket was started, but the chamber split open after 2 or 3 sec, apparently as much from high pressure as from heat. It appeared likely that the pressure had risen before the gasoline flow was adequate and also that the gas-generator pressure may have risen too high. The high pump speed, possibly at the time of the flame at the end of the run, apparently had enlarged the shroud rings on the turbines.

The lift, from the second frame of the Sept camera film, was 776 lb, the turbine pressure at that time being 123 psi; chamber pressure, 328 psi; oxygen-pump pressure, 650 psi; and gasoline-pump pressure, 420 psi. The turbine pressure at the moment when the chamber opened up was observed from the 50-ft shelter to be 175 psi; and hence the maximum lift, attained at that time, was probably considerably in excess of the above figure. The gas generator appeared to operate satisfactorily.

Recommendations. Less pressure might be used to start the turbines, making certain that gasoline was present in the chamber when pressure was applied. A short bellows might be used in the high-pressure oxygen line, in order to reduce stress due to contraction when it was filled with liquid oxygen.

Test of June 3, 1939 (P-6):
Repeat Test, Reduced Starting Pressure

The object of this test was to repeat the preceding test with reduced outside starting pressure, and also with more time allowed for the initial flow of gasoline in order to avoid too high an initial pressure.

Alterations. A new chamber was constructed, of 0.050-in.-thick nickel sheet instead of 0.037, for strength. The previous conical-frustum water jacket used was again employed.

Several alterations were made in the turbine drive. The gasoline reducing valve was used in the position originally planned, namely, with the 1½-in.-diameter operating bellows at the top and the valve part at the bottom, in order to avoid air bubbles being carried to the gas generator during operation. This change required an additional on-and-off valve between the high-pressure pump line and the gasoline reducing valve. The new ¼-in.-diameter connecting line was so long, however, as to require an additional vent line and an additional spring-loaded check valve. It should be remarked that a check of the gas-generator gasoline nozzle after the previous run gave a fall of pressure from 30 to 20 psi in 58 sec, this being only 1 sec less than before.

Gas generator. A new cylindrical part was made for the gas generator, including a new tangential oxygen orifice. Although a No. 29 hole was again used, the flow of water at 30 psi was 4½ oz/sec instead of the previous 5½ oz/sec.

The gas generator was placed lower in order to make the connecting tube from the oxygen reducing valve horizontal and thus reduce the amount of bending of this tube and the consequent difficulty of installing the ⅝-in. corrugated-tube jacket. The 300-psi safety valve in the turbine gas line was discarded, since the pressure in this line did not rise at the end of the preceding run.

A gasoline shutoff valve was added in the supply line to the pump, just below the gasoline tank, for the purpose of stopping the flow in case of breakage of the line below this point.

The only changes in the controls at the tower consisted in reducing the pressure in the 5-ft starting tank from 200 to 100 psi, and in increasing the time of fall of the first dashpot weight from 2½ to 4 sec in order to make certain that gasoline had reached the chamber before turbine starting pressure was applied.

Test. A considerable flow of gasoline was observed coming from the chamber after the igniter was fired, this gasoline not burning outside the chamber. Then a rather wide and noisy whitish flame was seen, which gradually became smaller and somewhat pulsating.

An examination of the rocket showed that the gas generator had operated. The maximum pump pressures were, however, only 400 and 225 psi for the oxygen and gasoline, respectively, and fell off to zero in 3 sec. The maximum chamber pressure was 210 psi.

Conclusion. It appeared likely that the 100-psi starting pressure was too low to bring the pumps up to sufficiently high pressures for the gas generator to be put into steady operation.

Test of June 14, 1939 (P-7):
Repeat Test, Medium Starting Pressure

The object of this test was to repeat the preceding test with a turbine starting pressure halfway between those of the two preceding tests, and also with the oxygen reducing valve inverted, the bellows part being above the valve orifice, as with the gasoline reducing valve in the preceding test.

Turbine drive. An examination of the bakelite heat-insulating ring between the valve and the bellows-operator parts of the oxygen reducing valve showed that the inner exposed surface had been burned, possibly from a backflash into this valve in stopping the run. The heat thus generated had weakened the small spring on the valve-member stem.

This burning was avoided by using a perforated steel disk inside the bakelite ring, so that the inner edge of the bakelite was not exposed. Heat conduction through the steel disk was avoided by using Vellumoid washers, as before, for packing on the two flat sides of the steel disk and bakelite ring.

A check of the spray nozzle for the gasoline reducing valve gave the same time for the air flow from the 9-in. sphere as before. It was found that the levers on the valves became somewhat worn where they were held by the releasing pins. This wear was diminished, and at the same time the friction on withdrawing the pins was reduced, by casehardening the part of the levers in contact with these pins.

Reducing valves. The lever arms of the two reducing valves for the gas generator, both of which were now at the tops of the valves, were moved by a single bellows-valve operator, actuated by 30 psi from the same three-way valve cock that had been used for the double-bellows pump seal pressure. The change in location of the two reducing valves obviated the need for the on-and-off valve for the gasoline line, which had been used in the preceding test.

The bellows-valve operator just mentioned consisted of four 2-in.-O.D. bellows of $9\frac{5}{8}$ in. total length when extended. They could be contracted to the extent of 3 in., whereupon the free space inside was reduced as much as possible by a $1\frac{1}{4}$-in.-O.D. steel tube, which extended for the full inside length of the compressed bellows. The lower end of the bellows was soldered to this steel tube, to which the $\frac{1}{4}$-in. gas-supply tube for operating the bellows passed.

A plate or cap fitted the upper end of the bellows, and from this two tubes extended rearward, holding a crossbar or yoke below the fixed bellows support. At the middle of this crossbar were suspended two long screws that bore internally threaded tubes, at the lower ends of which were pins passing through the ends of the lever arms of the two reducing valves. These arms, each 6 in. long, extended in opposite directions, the bellows-valve operator being located on approximately the axis of the rocket. The valve operator weighed 34 oz complete. An operating pressure of 30 psi was used, although 20 psi gave positive upward motion.

A 9-lb force was required to compress the bellows system, this being produced by a $21\frac{7}{8}$-in. screen-door coil tension spring, hooked just below where the ends of the lever arm were held together by a cross pin, the length of this spring producing very little increase of force for the 3 in. of motion required. This spring force, however, altered the reduced pressure from the two reducing valves, and it was necessary to restore the pressures to 250 psi by adjusting the force of the strong compression springs in these valves.

Controls. The reduced pressure for starting the turbines was set at 160 psi at the time of the test, with the control pressure at 29 psi. Since it was found that opening the 30-psi reducing valve for tank pressure caused a drop to 26 psi when flow took place, this valve was set to open wider and to give 33 psi for no flow. The time interval for the first dashpot was changed from 4 sec to 3 sec.

Test. A test was attempted on June 13, but the gasoline pump was found to leak between two of the casings and certain of the casing screws, possibly owing to the presence of dust or dirt when the pump was assembled. The pump was accordingly removed and taken to the shop for reassembling, the main gasoline valve being wired shut and the hose to the gas generator being disconnected.

When the test was carried out the next day, there was a sharp report about 2 sec after the igniter was fired. Gasoline then appeared, followed by a flame and then by an explosion that broke the chamber and caused some damage to the pump mountings.

It seemed likely that leakage occurring overnight through the gasoline valve had caused the first report from the chamber. The resulting high pressure may have retarded the oxygen, thus causing a sudden rush of oxygen, with consequent explosion.

Recommendations. It would appear worth while, for a flight rocket, to use a gravity-feed oil cup, the opening to the bearing being closed by a valve rod or plug until the pump is put into operation.

Test of June 23, 1939 (P-8):
Repeat Test

The object of this test was to repeat the preceding test, under proper starting conditions.

Turbine drive. The air-flow check of the gasoline spray orifice of the gas generator gave 57 sec, as compared with 58 sec after the previous run and 59 sec after being first assembled. A change was made in the tubing between the outlet in the pump delivery line and the oxygen reducing valve. Previously this tube had been filled by gravity before the run, by means of a vent tube with a spring-loaded check valve. In the present test the tube was enclosed by a jacket, which was connected with the jacket around the tube from the reducing valve to the gas generator, a low-pressure vent line being used to the top of the oxygen tank, as usual. It appeared likely that more thorough cooling could be obtained in this way.

It was found that the main on-and-off gasoline valve had a tendency to leak slightly under pressure unless the seat was ground with Duco paint-buffing compound, which produced no lines or scratches on polishing.

Test. The run started with a noticeable pop about 2 sec after the igniter was fired, the flame being yellowish white and fairly large, and remaining steady up to the end of the run. It was accompanied by a billowy dust cloud about 50 ft high, at the rear of the sheet-iron shelter. Steam appeared from the top of the water jacket on the chamber, and a white vapor was seen close to the oxygen-pump casing, possibly due to a slight leakage in the pump casing.

From the Sept film it was seen that the oxygen and gasoline pressures rose in the first second to 500 and 320 psi, fell in the next to 370 and 220 psi, and thereafter remained, practically without change, at 600 and 470 psi; the chamber pressure rose, however, from 270 to 323 psi, and the lift rose proportionately. The turbine gas pressure became steady at 130 psi. The turbine gas temperature, however, was erratic, sometimes being above and sometimes below air temperature.

From the lift, 693 lb during the steady period, the jet velocity was estimated as 4,020 ft/sec, allowing 0.5 lb/sec for the flow to the gas generator. The rates of flow of oxygen and gasoline, obtained from the recorded rheostat readings, were 3 and 2.5 lb/sec respectively, making the mixture ratio 1.2.

Since the gas-generator pressure kept increasing until it reached 130 psi, it appeared likely that a starting pressure somewhat greater than 160 psi would avoid the drop in pump pressures before these became steady. It is probable, also, that the continued rise of chamber pressure resulted from the gradually increasing flow of oxygen as this pump became thoroughly cool. The tank pressures became steady at 26 psi, 2 sec after the start. Hence at least a 4-psi additional excess over 30-psi pressure for the reducing valve was required.

The porcelain of the gas-generator spark plug was found to be cracked, although the refractory cement lining of the upper cone was intact. A hole about 1½ in. long by 3 in. was found to have been burned in the refractory liner of the upper cone of the chamber, possibly owing to gaseous oxygen entering the chamber after the oxygen tank had become empty of liquid.

Test of July 5, 1939 (P-9):
Repeat Test

The object of this test was to repeat the preceding test with a larger fuel load.

Turbine drive. The air-check test for the gasoline spray orifice of the gas generator gave a drop from 30 to 20 psi in 44 sec, as compared with 57 sec before the last run. It was used without change, however, since the turbine pressure produced in the last test was considerably below the desired 180 psi.

Pumps. Since one of the thin outer edges of the oxygen impeller was found to have become loose, the outer ends of both impellers were pushed inward, and the space outside was filled with solder.

Controls. The 30-psi reducing valve for the liquid tanks was set at 34 psi with no flow. The turbine starting pressure remained at 160 psi.

Results. After 3 sec of strong flame, a smaller reddish flame was seen above the chamber, and the run was accordingly stopped. During these 3 sec the tank pressures rose to 29 psi, whereas the pump pressures fell from 560 and 400 psi to 200 and 120 psi. It was found that the tube from the gas generator to the turbine manifolds had burned out for a distance of about 4 in., beginning 10 in. below the gas generator.

A shop examination of the gasoline spray nozzle showed that the perforated threaded brass disk bearing on the under side that held the small cylinder with the two tangential grooves, already described, had become unscrewed 2½ turns and thereby loosened, possibly owing to jars in transit from the shop to the tower. The result had therefore been either a straight stream of gasoline or a coarse spray. This threaded disk was soldered in place and a check test from 30 to 20 psi was then made. It was found that the time had been increased from 45 to 58 sec.

Recommendation. Since it is difficult to fasten the very thin outer ends of the impeller blades to the impeller side walls, these ends may be made of U shape, with the sides of the U facing inward radially, thereby supplying a surface of considerable extent for soldering, by sweating, on each side of the outer end part of an impeller blade.

Test of July 11, 1939 (P-10):
Repeat Test, Larger Fuel Supply

Tanks. The oxygen tank, as previously used, was again employed, together with two additional gasoline tanks for increasing the fuel load. These extra tanks had 26½-in. cylinders of 0.018-in. sheet nickel strengthened by a 4-in.-wide band of 0.050-in. nickel in the middle, and were provided with 9-in. hemispherical ends. The original gasoline tank had a 27½-in.-long cylinder and was joined to the two side tanks at both the top and bottom.

Inasmuch as the level readings for the oxygen tank were found to be erratic, the two contact springs or brushes bearing against the vertical rheostat wire were bent so as to bear with greater force against this wire.

Controls. In order to prevent excessive heat in the chamber at the end of the run, the pressure contact maker was set to shut off operation on a chamber-pressure drop to 155 psi, the contact spring being cocked at a 180-psi rise.

Test. The flame showed evidence of low pressure, being yellowish and pulsating slowly. After several seconds the tube below the gas generator again became red-hot, and the run was accordingly stopped, the gas generator itself burning through at that time.

The pump pressures were found, by the Sept camera record, to have remained at zero, the chamber pressure rising to 18 psi and the turbine pressure to 5 psi.

Conclusion. The failure to obtain high pressures was apparently due to the use of two nitrogen cylinders joined together and having moderate pressures, namely 675 psi, instead of a single high-pressure nitrogen cylinder as before. Thus moderate cylinder pressure, even from a large volume, was not sufficient to maintain adequate pressure in the 5-ft nickel tank.

Recommendations. The breaking of the porcelain of the spark plug could perhaps be avoided by having the steel ring at the top or head end of the chamber concave rather than flat, in order to deflect any oxygen downward, or away from the inside of the refractory-lined upper cone.

A further means of avoiding fracture might possibly consist in preventing contact of the porcelain with liquid oxygen or gasoline after the run, using short distances between the valves and the gas generator, and having these valves closed quickly on fall of chamber pressure.

Test of July 17, 1939 (P-11):
Repeat Test

The object of this test was to repeat the preceding test, using a single full cylinder of nitrogen.

Turbine drive. It seemed desirable to permit the lever arms of the oxygen and gasoline reducing valves for the gas generator to move independently during operation of the gas generator. This procedure had not been possible with the bellows valve operator so far used, since the threaded-rod type of link on the end of each lever arm had been suspended from the same pin on the yoke of the bellows operator.

In the present test these threaded links were replaced by two links, each having a long slot which the end of the lever arm passed through. At the lower end of the slot was a roller, against which the lever arm bore when the bellows of the operator was extended, that is, when the yoke held the lever ends up so that the reducing valves could close.

During the rocket operation, the bellows of the operator was contracted, thus allowing each lever arm to move freely up and down within the slot in the link. The links themselves were prevented from slipping off the lever arms by keeping them parallel to the rocket axis. This was accomplished by using a rod extension on the bottom of each slotted part, these rods sliding up and down in holes in a small fixed plate.

Gas generator. The gas generator was repaired by making a new cylindrical part, including the No. 29 tangential oxygen orifice. The flow of water at 30 psi was, however, 5¾ oz/sec instead of 4½ oz/sec as in the preceding tests, and 5½ oz/sec for the first orifice used, the variation in flow probably being due to differences in the shape of the entrance to the No. 29 holes. An air-flow check of the gasoline spray nozzle gave the time for the usual pressure drop as 58 sec.

Test. After the usual delay of about 5 sec from the time the igniter-operated control was freed, a large yellow, or gasoline-type, flame appeared, accompanied by a loud roar and a violent vibration of the sheet-iron shelter. Thereafter the rocket operation appeared to be perfectly steady.

Steam rose from the water jacket, and vapor appeared about the pump manifolds, possibly owing to the fall of temperature of the gas on passing through the turbines.

The contact maker operating on chamber pressure did not stop the rocket, and gaseous oxygen therefore passed into the chamber for a second or two before the run was terminated manually, this oxygen probably accounting for the burning through, again, of the inverted cone of the chamber. The absence of liquid oxygen in the pump, at the same time, probably accounted also for the breaking off of the oxygen-turbine shroud ring at the end of the run. Both pump shafts turned freely after the run. The nitrogen cylinder and reduced pressures were 1900 and 155 psi before the run, and 1300 and 161, respectively, afterward.

From the data furnished by the Sept film, the pump pressures rose to 500 and 300 psi in 1 sec, and to the full 600 and 440 psi in 3 sec. Both pumps varied 20 psi or so during the run. The chamber pressure remained fairly constant at about 330 psi. The turbine pressure rose to 150 psi in 3 sec and was steady at about 100° C. The water jacket rise of temperature was 15° C. The tank pressures rose to 24 psi in 1 sec and to 28 psi, where they remained steady, in 3 sec.

From the lift, 695 lb, and the flow rates as obtained from the rheostat data, the velocity was calculated as 3200 ft/sec. This figure appeared to be low and suggested that the actual flow rates may have been less than the estimated 4 lb/sec for the oxygen and 3 lb/sec for the gasoline.

Test of August 4, 1939 (P-12):
Repeat, with Liquid Nitrogen for Tank Pressure

The object of this test was to repeat the preceding test with the addition of a liquid-nitrogen tank and a reducing valve for supplying tank pressures, the nitrogen being evaporated in a tube jacket on a thin shell-like water jacket around the chamber and nozzle.

Chamber and jacket. The chamber, after being repaired, was covered with a jacket for water circulation, to within 2¼ in. from the top of the cylindrical part and 4 in. from the bottom of the nozzle, this jacket being everywhere 1/4 in. from the nozzle and chamber walls.

Convection through this jacket space was maintained by four 1/2-in. copper tubes from the top and four from the bottom, which entered an overflow can, or reservoir, 3 in. in diameter by 4 in., located 11¾ in. above the top of the jacket.

The tube jacket for liquefying the nitrogen consisted of 12 soft aluminum tubes, ⅜₆ in. in diameter and of ¹⁄₆₄-in. wall, closely wrapped over a distance of 7 in. on the cylindrical part of the water jacket and held tight by two thin steel bands. Triangular aluminum wire was used under the tubes, as before, to provide good thermal contact, and small steel union parts were used on the flared ends of the tubes, also as before.

Turbine drive. Clearing the gasoline spray nozzle of rust increased the time for the air-flow check from 45 to 48 sec. Further rusting was avoided by replacing the steel fitting for the connection between the spray nozzle and the strainer by one of brass.

Tanks. The three gasoline tanks were again used.

The liquid-nitrogen tank consisted of a cylinder of 0.031-in. sheet nickel, 5 in. in diameter and 6 in. high, having 120-deg conical ends. The temperature of the nitrogen was prevented from dropping below that for the oxygen, and thus reducing the pressure, by brazing six 1/2-in.-diameter open-end copper tubes into the tank, between the cones, halfway between the tank axis and the cylindrical wall.

Liquefaction of gaseous nitrogen from a commercial nitrogen cylinder took place in a 5-in.-diameter, 7-coil, ⅜₆-in.-O.D. by ¹⁄₆₄-in.-wall copper tube of 9-ft length, mounted on the upper cone of the nitrogen tank. The gas from the outside could be shut off, when desired, by a small brass cock. This coil was wound in an open manner, so that a bath of liquid oxygen could reach the entire surface.

The oxygen bath was contained in a jacket within which the nitrogen tank was located, this bath being used to liquefy the nitrogen and thereafter to retain it in liquid form. Made of sheet tin, it was 1/2 in. wider in radius than the nitrogen tank, and extended 2 in. above the top of the copper liquefying coil. It was covered with 1/4-in. thick felt on which was wrapped sheet-aluminum foil. A tubular extension at the bottom of the oxygen jacket surrounded the essential parts of the nitrogen reducing valve, to be described below, which was used to maintain a constant pressure on the oxygen and gasoline tanks.

Piping and valves. The liquid nitrogen passed downward from the reducing valve through a 1/2-in.-O.D. aluminum tube to the upper end of the aluminum-tube jacket on the chamber water jacket. It entered at the upper end instead of at the lower end, as in earlier liquid-nitrogen jackets, for the reason that the temperature of the water jacket in the preceding test was greatest at or near the top.

From the aluminum-tube jacket, the evaporated nitrogen passed up through a ⅝-in. steel tube to a centrifugal liquid-nitrogen separator, above the oxygen tank, similar to the double-cone type used in the earlier liquid-nitrogen rockets of the pressure-tank type. In the present case the upper cone was of 30-deg angle, and the lower of 120 deg.

The nitrogen entered tangentially at the junction of these cones and left for the gasoline tank on the opposite side but in the same tangential direction. The tube to the oxygen tank passed out of the apex of the upper cone, from a point halfway down on the axis. As before, check valves were used close to the two tanks to avoid explosive mixtures.

The rate of flow through the nitrogen reducing valve was regulated by the tank pressure, a connection being made for this purpose in the gasoline-tank pressure line between the check valve just mentioned and the tank. With this arrangement the tank pressures could remain constant regardless of the fact that it was necessary for the reduced pressure of the nitrogen, after passing through the valve, to exceed the tank pressure by the amount required to force the liquid nitrogen through the evaporating jacket of aluminum tubing.

A 100-psi safety valve was used on the liquid-nitrogen tank, so that the pressure would not rise to a dangerous amount when there was no longer liquid oxygen in the outside jacket.

Liquid-nitrogen reducing valve. The ⅜-in.-diameter liquid-nitrogen reducing-valve opening was located 2 in. below the bottom of the nitrogen tank, this distance being as short as possible in order to reduce evaporation in the ½-in.-diameter connecting tube. The rod on the ⁷⁄₃₂-in.-wide tapered-seat valve member extended upward through a perforated block guide, below which was a small coil compression spring that tended to keep the valve pressed downward into the closed position (Figs. 26, 27).

A ⅛-in.-diameter rod, below the valve member, served to open the valve by pushing on the end of a ⅜-in.-long rodlike projection on the under side of the valve disk. This ⅛-in. rod had a ⁹⁄₁₆-in. bellows packing, the space above having a side tube for leading out the liquid nitrogen. The space below communicated, as already explained, with the gasoline-tank pressure line and was insulated thermally from the space just above by a ⅛-in.-thick bakelite ring, held between flanges fastened together with bakelite-bushed screws.

The space below the packing bellows led, further, into a steel tube containing a 2-in.-O.D. bellows. The top of this bellows was movable and was closed by a disk that moved the ⅛-in. rod just mentioned. The inside of the bellows communicated with the atmosphere and was provided with a coil compression spring.

Excess tank pressure accordingly compressed the 2-in. bellows against the compression of the spring and removed the ⅛-in. rod from engagement with the valve member, thus allowing the latter to close. A lever on a rod extending through the 2-in. bellows allowed the spring in this bellows to be compressed and thus permitted the nitrogen valve to close before the run. The lever was held firmly but yieldingly by a short coil spring, the free end passing through a removable pin.

In shop tests the nitrogen valve reduced pressure from 75 psi to 28 to 30 psi in the connection for tank pressure, with a pressure in the chamber jacket connection of 35 to 55 psi.

Oxygen starting valve. In previous pump tests frost had been observed on the slinger housing of the oxygen pump, especially if the run were delayed after the oxygen-tank filling. As a precaution against moisture freezing on the double bellows seal of the oxygen pump, an oxygen starting valve was installed in the low-pressure or suction line, to be opened not more than 5 min before the run.

This oxygen valve was constructed similar to the shutoff side of the main oxygen valve, but with as little flow resistance as possible. The 1/4-in. valve rod, on a 9/16-in. packing bellows, moved in a 17/8-in. steel tube and pressed the flat valve member, 11/8 in. wide, against the seat of the 1-in. valve opening. As usual, this member was pinned sufficiently loosely in the valve rod to permit firm seating.

Controls. The time allowed for the application of 30-psi outside pressure for the tanks was 4 sec, this interval including 1 sec of the 21/2-sec fall of the second dashpot, and the full 3 sec occupied by the fall of the third dashpot. The liquid-nitrogen valve opened by means of a lever on the third dashpot, 1/2 sec before the end of the dashpot stroke.

In order to keep gaseous oxygen from entering the chamber at the end of the run, the contact maker was set to become operative when the chamber pressure had fallen to 175 psi, having been cocked when the pressure had risen to 220 psi. In the present case the movable contact spring was bent into a hooked form at the end, so that the rod, which pulled the contact spring downward, retained the spring in this position, thus preventing a quick re-establishment of the current, which might take place on rapid fall of chamber pressure at the end of the run.

A reducing valve was tried on the commercial nitrogen cylinder that supplied the gas to be liquefied on the rocket, in order to avoid the almost continuous manual control of the cylinder valve otherwise required.

Contact along the rheostat wires used for the flow measurements was improved by scraping both the wires and the copper contact strips, using a steel scraper moved constantly in the longitudinal direction, both scraped surfaces being wiped afterward with a cloth. Motion of the scraper in this way avoided longitudinal irregularities. Emery cloth was found to be unsuitable, owing to the presence of small nonconducting particles that became embedded in the surfaces.

A saving of time in setting up the electrical controls was made by installing two 2-wire lead-covered cables in the ground, between the flight tower and both the 1000-ft and the 140-ft shelters.

Test. About 5 sec after the igniter key was pressed there was a loud explosion, possibly produced by a mixture of gasoline vapor and air inside the sheet-iron shelter surrounding the tower. The flame continued steadily after this, and was wide, yellowish white, and very noisy. The cover of the overflow can for the chamber water jacket blew off at once, and all but a quarter of the contained water left the jacket in about a second.

The rocket shut itself off as soon as a yellowish, gasoline-rich flame appeared. No frost was observed on the liquid-nitrogen jacket and piping. The refractory cement was melted from a portion of the inverted cone of the chamber, although the perforated steel backing was intact. This condition indicated that the chamber pressure contact maker should be set to make contact for stopping the run at a still higher pressure. The remainder of the chamber showed little evidence of heating.

From the data obtained from the Sept film, the pump pressures rose to 400 and 320 psi in 1 sec, and to 500 and 420 psi in 2 sec. They finally became steady at 630 and 500 psi, respectively. The chamber pressure rose to 213 psi in 1 sec, to 267 in 2 sec, and finally reached a maximum of 340 psi.

The turbine pressure rose to 90 psi in 1 sec and became fairly steady at 150 psi. The turbine gas temperature rose slowly to 150° C but remained at 100° C during most of the run.

The oxygen- and gasoline-tank pressures rose to 10 and 17 psi in 1 sec, becoming steady at 30 psi, but not until after the elapse of 11 more seconds. This slow rise may have been due to the time required to cool the mass of the tube leading liquid nitrogen from the reducing valve to the chamber jacket. The gasoline pump bearing temperature rose 15° C.

The chamber and pump pressures, in the present test, were practically the same as in the test of June 23, although the turbine pressure was slightly higher.

Recommendations. A number of general improvements might be made as a result of the static tests with pumps operated by a gas generator. First, inasmuch as there was but little water in the chamber jacket during most of the present run, it appeared that a tube jacket for the liquid nitrogen, wound directly on the chamber nozzle, would be adequate. Apparently a setting of the pressure contact maker to become cocked at about 260 psi and to stop the run at 240 psi would be needed in order to avoid overheating the inverted cone of the chamber.

The use of liquid nitrogen might be avoided by using a 30-psi reducing valve in a branch from the high-pressure oxygen line to the oxygen tank, and by using a tank of liquid hydrocarbons at moderate pressure, piped to the gasoline tank through another 30-psi reducing valve. The reducing valve used on the nitrogen cylinder in the present test was originally intended for such an oxygen valve, and in addition a reducing valve for liquid hydrocarbons was constructed. Further, through the efforts of General James Doolittle, the Shell Oil Company prepared a combination of butane and propane, for supplying gasoline-tank pressure, the mixture having a fairly constant boiling point over the temperature range likely to be required for flight rockets.

Pump pressure of about 600 psi, obtained by raising the gas-generator pressure to 300 or 350 psi, would be advantageous for a flight rocket, because the added weight would be small, consisting of the slightly heavier pumps and high-pressure tubing, and the added cylindrical weight of longer tanks. The greater part of the increase in thrust could therefore be used for increasing the fuel load. High pressures would necessitate the use of long sections of $\frac{1}{8}$-in. flexible tubing, possibly braid-covered, in place of the $\frac{9}{16}$-in. bellows so far used as valve-rod packing. Further, greater thrust with little additional rocket weight suggests the use of a spring or springs on the arms of the gas-generator reducing valves in order to decrease the acceleration during the latter part of the flight, thereby avoiding excessive air resistance.

Improvement in chamber efficiency also appeared to be desirable in view of the great heat loss evidenced by the large size of the flame issuing from the nozzle as well as the extent to which the inside surface of the concrete of the gas deflector was fused.

11

Conclusion of Pump Tests for the Purpose of Developing a Pump-driven Flight Rocket

P Series, November 18, 1939 — October 10, 1941

Unlike the previous sections, which were Dr. Goddard's own condensations of his original notes, this section has been condensed by the editors. Dr. Goddard's manuscript ends with the material of Section 10. In completing the task which he left unfinished, we have tried to follow his general method as closely as possible, but owing to the very large volume of his notes on this series of experiments, our condensations are considerably more severe in places than were Dr. Goddard's in the previous sections. We have especially omitted descriptions of apparatus which seemed generally similar to that described in connection with the earlier experiments, and have kept to a minimum details of tubing, valves, and such equipment as did not seem to have a major bearing on the results achieved.—Editors.

The purpose of this series of tests was the construction of a flight rocket of large fuel-load capacity, using the chamber, pumps, and power plant already developed.

Test of November 18, 1939 (P-13):
Static Test

The object of this test was to check the performance of a flight-model rocket of large fuel capacity, before adding the strictly flight features. Rocket propulsion and control for this model were essentially the same as for Test P-12.

Chamber. A new chamber was made, similar to that used in the preceding test. The jacket for evaporating liquid nitrogen, for supplying pressure to the oxygen and gasoline tanks, consisted of $\frac{3}{16}$-in.-O.D. copper tubing, of $\frac{1}{64}$-in. wall. Aluminum wire of triangular cross section, fitting the copper tubes, was used under the tubes on the nozzle and cylindrical part of the chamber. This wire was not used over the lower cone of the chamber because of the difficulty of winding. The turns of the jacket were held on by soldering adjacent tubes together at four places along the chamber and nozzle (Fig. 28).

The ends of the copper-jacket tubes were flared and were held in the same steel tube-fitting unions that had been used before. These were brazed to ½-in.-O.D. square tubes, having rather thick walls to avoid cracking due to closeness of brazing. The liquid nitrogen entered through straight tubes. Two tubes were used, each consisting of two halves, joined by welding to a 1-in.-long middle section. Entrance was through two %6-in.-O.D. felt-covered steel tubes, somewhat flattened at the ends.

As before, two semicircular tubes were used around the lower part of the nozzle, near the open end, to collect gas produced in the jacket.

Nitrogen tank. In order to save the weight of an oxygen jacket for the liquid-nitrogen tank, the liquid-nitrogen tanks were installed inside the bottom hemisphere of the oxygen tank. Two nitrogen tanks were used to avoid having to raise the oxygen level too high before the tank was immersed, and also so as not to interfere with the tubes that passed through the oxygen tank.

The tanks were made of ⅟₁₆-in. 3S½H sheet, welded. Six ½-in.-O.D. aluminum tubes were welded into the top and bottom of the tank to provide a circulation of oxygen to keep the liquid nitrogen up to the liquid-oxygen temperature, and hence to maintain a nitrogen pressure of about 30 lb in excess of the oxygen pressure. The tubes were bent in the middle to reduce stress accompanying temperature changes.

A coil of five turns of %6-in. aluminum tubing was used around each tank. These coils were held in four clamps, each consisting of two halves, held together by two screws. The clamps were held to the cylindrical part of the tank by wires. Gas to be liquefied entered from above the level of the tanks, through a tube, branching to the two coils, then entering the tanks. Each nitrogen tank weighed 14 oz, and the two tanks complete weighed 31 oz (Fig. 29).

Oxygen tank. The cylinder of the oxygen tank was of 3S½H ⅟₁₆-in. thick sheet. It was butt-welded along the seam. The 18-in.-diameter hemispherical ends were of 0.050 in. wall thickness, welded to the cylinder. The tank was strengthened against internal pressure by means of compressive supports (Fig. 30).

Two aluminum tubes, 1¾ in. O.D. and 1⅜ in. O.D., were welded into the oxygen tank to permit the tubing to pass through. These tubes were welded to the top hemisphere of the tank and to short sleeves welded outside the tubes on the bottom hemisphere, the sleeves having ⅟₁₆ in. radial clearance. The collecting well, on the bottom hemisphere, consisted of a 3½-in.-O.D. aluminum tube, 3 in. long, with a 30-deg cone of ⅟₁₆-in. aluminum on the bottom, to which was welded part of an aluminum ½-in. union.

The lower hemisphere of the tank was covered with ⅜-in.-thick felt at places where a steel-tubing support frame was in contact with the hemisphere. A band of ⅛-in.-thick felt, 1¼ in. wide, was glued to the upper end of the cylindrical part of the tank, and a band of 2½-in. width was glued to the lower part of the upper hemisphere.

As before, horizontal baffle plates were used inside the tank. A special baffle system was necessary for the lower hemisphere because of the presence of the two nitrogen tanks. The finished oxygen tank weighed 22¼ lb (Fig. 31).

Gasoline tank. The cylinder of the gasoline tank was of the same diameter and thickness as the oxygen tank, as were also the end hemispheres. Welding was performed in the same way. The baffle system inside the cylindrical part of the tank was similar to that for the oxygen tank. The finished tank weighed 21 lb.

Pumps. The gasoline and oxygen pumps and bearings were the same as in the preceding test. Alterations were made, however, in the supports, filters, and manifolds as explained below.

The oxygen pump was held to a 2- × 2- × ¼-in. Dowmetal angle, 10½ in. long, by means of a bracket milled from a solid piece of 17 ST aluminum. The manifold was held by a 4-in. length of 1¼- × 1¼- × ⅛-in. Dowmetal angle. These angles were bolted together, and the pump angle was bolted to the square-tubing frame of the supports by large aluminum bolts. Similar supports were provided for the gasoline pump.

The manifolds were lightened by removing the short, plugged tubes that had been retained after the turbine nozzle regulators had been discarded. The filters, or strainers, for the pumps were made lighter, and the pump units were shortened by using 17 ST filters attached directly to the pumps. The weight of the oxygen-pump unit with the mountings and manifold complete was 6¾ lb. The gasoline pump weighed 6½ lb complete.

Turbine drive. The turbine drive was essentially the same as before, the only alterations being the lightening of certain parts. Among these were the steel head of the gas generator, made 6½ oz lighter by milling off around the outside, and the long bellows operator for the two reducing valves for the gas generator, lightened by perforating the supporting plates and by making these of 17 ST instead of steel.

Oxygen lines. The low-pressure oxygen pipe was joined by a union to the well at the bottom of the oxygen tank, and to a valve for letting oxygen flow into the high-pressure piping for about five minutes before the run. The valve was joined directly to the oxygen filter on the oxygen pump by means of an aluminum union.

From the pump the high-pressure oxygen line passed to the main oxygen valve and thence to the chamber through the jacketed oxygen inlet tube. This tube, 3/4 in. O.D., of 1/32-in.-wall instead of 1/16-in. as before, withstood 700-lb nitrogen-gas pressure.

A short side tube led to a 1/4-in. aluminum tube that conveyed high-pressure oxygen to the oxygen reducing valve, for running the turbine. From the upper end of this tube a copper tube extended upward to a small check valve, from which a 1/4-in.-O.D. aluminum tube extended to an opening in the top of the oxygen tank. A reduced pressure tube, jacketed by a flexible tube, led from the reducing valve to the gas generator.

A 1/4-in. copper tube from the high-pressure oxygen line passed up through the smaller of the tubes through the oxygen tank, and was connected to the instrument board. Through the same tube in the oxygen tank passed a 1/4-in. aluminum tube leading outside nitrogen pressure at 30 lb to the gyroscope, as well as pressure to the pump locks and bellows valve operator. This tube was connected to the tube through which nitrogen gas at 30-lb pressure passed into the oxygen tank, through a small check valve. When the hoses were pulled off, this valve allowed oxygen gas to pass into the valve and bellows operating system.

Gasoline lines. The 3/4-in. low-pressure supply pipe for the gasoline passed from an aluminum union on the collecting well to an aluminum union at the gasoline-pump strainer, where it entered through an aluminum elbow. The high-pressure line, of 3/4-in.-O.D. steel, with 1/32-in. wall, passed from the gasoline pump to the main gasoline valve. From a short tube below the valve the line branched to two 7/16-in.-O.D. steel tubes to the gasoline orifices on the chamber.

From a tee about 2 in. below the pump outlet nozzle, a 1/4-in. copper tube led high pressure to the gasoline reducing valve for the gas generator. The vent line for the main high-pressure gasoline line consisted of a 1/4-in. copper tube extending to a small check valve; an aluminum tube extended from the check valve along the outside of the gasoline tank to a fitting at the top of the tank. This tube was wrapped with felt and aluminum strip where it passed through the oxygen tank.

Nitrogen lines. The main nitrogen-gas line, for supplying the oxygen and gasoline tanks with pressure, was 3/4 in. in diameter. Nitrogen at 30-lb pressure entered through the large hose valve, joining a 3/4-in.-O.D. steel tube that passed to the same liquid nitrogen separator used in the preceding test. From this separator a steel tube carried the gaseous and liquid nitrogen to the gasoline-tank pressure tube in the gasoline tank. The other tube from the separator, also of 3/4-in.-diameter steel, passed to the oxygen tank.

After the hoses were removed, pressure was supplied to the oxygen and gasoline tanks from the liquid-nitrogen tanks at the bottom of the liquid-oxygen tank. The liquid nitrogen passed out through a jacketed tube to the liquid-nitrogen reducing valve. Thence it passed out of a

½-in.-O.D. aluminum tube to the two square tubes of the jacket around the chamber, the tube branching at the level of the bottom square-tube frame of the supports. The evaporated gas passed from the two semi-circular square tubes through two ½-in. steel tubes, through suitable unions, to a large welded tee behind the hose valve. Pressure lines to operate the 30-lb pump lock and bellows operator, and various other valves, led from a similar tee.

Turbine drive and starting line. The pumps were started by leading outside nitrogen gas at 150-lb pressure through the large hose previously used. It entered through a connection of the same construction as the 30-lb connection for the large hose, but without the valve and guide. From this connection the gas passed through a ¾-in.-O.D. steel tube to two tubes, each of $^{13}\!/_{16}$-in.-diameter steel, the former leading to the two starting nozzles for the oxygen turbine, and the latter to those for the gasoline turbine. From the gas generator, after starting, the gas passed through a $^{13}\!/_{16}$-in.-O.D. steel tube branching to the oxygen manifold and the gasoline manifold.

Electric releases. In order to have the operation take place as nearly as possible like that for a flight test, the hoses were pulled off when the third dashpot reached the end of its travel, and the various controls operated at the end of the test were arranged to function automatically, except for the emergency gasoline shutoff valve, which was operated by a key, using outside batteries.

Valves. The main oxygen and gasoline valves from the preceding test were used without change except that the end of the lever on the oxygen closing valve was altered so as to be operated by a fused-wire release. The oxygen and gasoline reducing valves, for supplying the gas generator, were also used without alteration. Various other valves, including the three-way valve for operating the pump locks and bellows operator, the oxygen-pump valve, the turbine shutoff valve, and several check valves, were slightly altered, principally for weight reduction.

Two new safety valves were made, one set at 40 lb for the oxygen tank and the other set at 130 lb for the nitrogen tank. They were similar to the brass Norgren safety valves previously used, but were made of Dow-metal. The oxygen valve was modified so as to give a better exhaust.

Preparations for the test. Inasmuch as there was considerable work in preparing the tower, piping, controls, and tubing to the instrument board, the first test was not made until November 18, although the rocket was placed in the tower on the 16th. The weight of the rocket, including the lower angle-iron guides and lever support, was 160 lb (Fig. 32).

New piping for pressures was installed, and also tubing to the instrument board. The felts were tested and found to pull away satisfactorily. The valve of the third dashpot was adjusted so that the weight fell in 3 sec, as before. The circuits were tested, the tanks were rinsed with nitrogen, the controls were set, and preparations were made for filling. A steel stylus on a thin aluminum plate was used to indicate the extent of the lift, because the lift bellows permitted an upward displacement of only $3/8$ in.

Test. The igniter appeared to fire as usual, but no flame was observable from the nozzle for several seconds. A large flame then appeared in the cement gas deflector, and a smaller flame from the nozzle. The emergency shutoff valve for the gasoline was then operated, and the cord that shut off the Sept camera was pulled. A rather large pool of gasoline was burning on the ground from the drain tube from the gasoline-pump lock. The igniter was found, practically intact, in the cement gas deflector.

An examination showed that the gas generator had operated, since soot was found inside. The chamber was found to be intact. From the photographic record of the test, obtained with the Sept camera, the lift was seen to be less than the weight of the rocket plus the added force of the lever. This result was expected, since oxygen did not appear to be present in an amount sufficient to produce a strong flame.

The oxygen-tank pressure rose from 15 to 25 lb in 5 sec, and to 30 lb in 9 sec. The gasoline-tank pressure rose from 27 to 30 lb in about the same time. The gasoline-pump pressure rose to 100 lb, evidently while outside pressure was being applied. There was no oxygen-pump pressure and consequently no chamber pressure. The turbine-gas pressure also was zero. The nitrogen-gas pressure remained at 39 lb. Apparently the oxygen-opening valve did not open and, consequently, no oxygen was permitted to pass to the chamber.

Test of December 2, 1939 (P-14):
Repeat Test

The object of this test was to repeat the preceding test, with the oxygen valves and levers completely covered with felt to prevent sticking from freezing; with a large-capacity safety valve for the oxygen tank; with a higher pressure in the auxiliary tank for producing a rapid rise of fuel-tank pressures; and with arrangements to vent the oxygen tank before the gasoline tank.

Changes. The Insalute-Alundum liner of the gas generator was wiped of soot, and the time of air flow for the gasoline orifice was checked. The spark plug was adjusted to produce a more concentrated spark.

The oxygen valves were overhauled and were found to be dry and apparently in good condition. The nitrogen reducing valve on the nitrogen tank was found to leak and was overhauled. A large-capacity safety valve was made for the oxygen tank. Felt was sewed completely over the oxygen valves and cold parts of the levers, so that no gaping would occur when the valve lever was moved. Sufficient slack of felt was provided at the levers to allow motion.

Test. About 3 sec after the igniter was fired, a strong flame suddenly appeared, and remained without noticeable change until the run was stopped about 40 sec later by the oxygen-valve control on the rocket. The stop was very abrupt, and the bright flame ceased immediately, a very large smoky flame thereafter appearing for a few seconds. The flame during the run was somewhat yellowish, and appeared to be a narrow column from the nozzle, about 2½ or 3 in. wide, surrounded by a turbulent yellow flame.

After the run a small gasoline flame appeared about on a level with the top of the chamber, and the turbine gas tube below the gas generator became red-hot and burned through. The emergency gasoline shutoff key was then pressed.

Examination of the rocket in the tower showed that the lever which opened the two three-way valves at the end of the run had jammed on the valve-release lever freed by the fused-wire release. This binding prevented the two three-way valves from opening and hence prevented all the following from closing: the pump locks, the reducing valves for the gas generator, the main gasoline valve, and the turbine gas valve.

The chamber was in perfect condition after the test. The copper-tube jacket was burned through in spots, near the lower end, owing to the large gasoline flame that appeared at the end of the test. The oxygen turbine dragged at one point, and on taking the pump apart it was found that one of the impeller blades had become loose at the outer end. The gasoline turbine and the bearings were in good condition.

The Sept camera showed that the lift pressure reached 30 lb 2 sec after the start of the camera, fell to 22 lb in 4 sec, and rose steadily to 34 lb thereafter. The fall was probably due to the cooling of the pump and feed lines, which required several seconds and would be certain to produce a fall of lift unless the gas-generator pressure were increased for the first few seconds of the run.

The chamber pressure was very steady, not varying more than a pound either way from 349 lb after the oxygen line had become cool. The oxygen-pump pressure was not registered accurately, owing to dirt in the small opening in the high-pressure oxygen gauge. The gasoline-pump pressure was high and steady. The nitrogen-tank pressure was steady at about 40 lb until near the end of the run, when the pressure rose sharply. The lift lasted about 40 sec, with conditions steady soon after the start. The turbine gas temperature was steady and fairly high. The lifting force, calculated from the lift pressure, varied from 680 lb, near the start, to the maximum lift, also near the start, of 785 lb. The lift near the end was 595 lb.

Conclusions. The lift, except for a slight fall at the start, appeared to be steady, and the performance did not appear to change appreciably with the time. The oxygen shutoff valve appeared to operate sufficiently rapidly to prevent burning of the chamber. The oxygen-tank pressure appeared to be relatively low at the start, and it thus appeared likely that for a flight test either the directing vanes would need to operate well at 15- to 30-lb pressure or an auxiliary pressure tank would be needed on the rocket, initially at 30-lb pressure.

Test of February 9, 1940 (P-15): Flight Test with Pump Rocket

The object of this test was to repeat the previous test as a flight test, using the same chamber, tanks, and pumping systems, and an official barograph.

Changes. No change was made in the chamber or in the oxygen, gasoline, and liquid-nitrogen tanks. A gas-pressure tank was added to supply gas at 30 psi for the gyroscope and directing vane bellows. The pumps and bearings were overhauled. A new impeller of ½₂-in. larger diameter than before was made for the oxygen pump. The nitrogen-gas pressure lines and liquid-nitrogen line were substantially the same as in the preceding test. A new 1³⁄₁₆-in.-O.D. steel tube was fitted to the gas generator.

Two additional features were aluminum tubes for draining the leakage from the housings of the two pumps. These drain tubes extended through the outer casing of the rocket.

Pressure for the directing system. The flight controls were operated, during the first part of the flight, by dry nitrogen gas from a separator in a steel tube mounted on the oxygen tank. Nitrogen gas was used for the reason that during the early part of the period of propulsion the nitrogen-line pressure is higher than the oxygen-tank pressure, probably owing to the very low temperature of the oxygen tank. Later the oxygen pressure rises, and after a short time reaches 30 psi. After propulsion ceases, the nitrogen-gas pressure may fall considerably, owing to the cooling of the combustion chamber, whereas the pressure in the oxygen tank may rise, even if empty of liquid oxygen, owing to warming of the oxygen gas by passing through the air. For this reason a check valve was employed to allow oxygen gas to pass from the oxygen tank when the oxygen pressure exceeds the nitrogen-line pressure.

Supports, casings, and guides. The support tubes of the rocket were the same as in the preceding test except between the chamber and the lowest square-tubing frame, where changes were made to provide room for the 3-in.-diameter air- and blast-vane bellows operators.

The casings were supported by rings of 17 ST aluminum, fastened to the frame. The casing sections were not screwed to the rings but to 17 ST strips extending between the rings. A smooth outer surface was obtained at the joints by using a short 17 ST flat piece inside the ring and strip, to which the latter were held by flathead screws. The casings were painted a glossy black, except for the quadrant toward the rear of the tower, which was left bare aluminum.

Three pairs of guides were used. The additional middle pair was provided because of the long distance between the upper and lower guides in the rocket, and the likelihood that the rise from the tower would be slow. The middle pair was placed close to the bottom pair so that the rocket would be steadied until the last possible moment before leaving the tower.

Directing vanes. The four fixed air vanes were of 0.020-in. 17 ST sheet aluminum, so formed as to have an outer full diameter of 18 in., to extend upward as far as possible and yet not enough to interfere with the movable, retractable air vanes; to extend down beyond the nozzle opening as much as possible consistent with the use of a 9-in. steel thimble under the nozzle; and at the same time to be rigid and light (Fig. 33).

Rigidity was attained by having the vanes wide in the middle, using for this purpose a U-shaped piece as a spacer, riveted to the sides of the air vane. The forward edges of the sides of the fixed air vanes were each riveted to a rib of 17 ST aluminum, beveled along the top to reduce air resistance.

The movable air vanes were held by arms consisting of Dowmetal tees, held by screws to arms milled from 17 ST strip. The forward edge of each vane was beveled to reduce air resistance.

The blast vanes, of 0.037-in. stainless steel, were each mounted on an arm of square steel tubing, of 0.054-in. wall. Each arm was mounted movably on a lug on an aluminum arm, which in turn was mounted on the steel ring at the level of the nozzle. A steel lug, by means of which the vane was moved inward to operative position, was welded to the square arm, and a steel yoke was connected to it by a pin. To this yoke was brazed a rod, ending at the upper end in a second yoke. This upper yoke was moved by the 3-in. bellows operator that controlled the blast vane in question. Each vane was kept retracted by a spring under tension.

The motion of the bellows operator was $\frac{5}{16}$ in., and the weight was 16 oz. A test with air pressure showed that for pressures of 15, 20, and 30 psi, the forces to move the free end of the corresponding blast vane were 12, 18, and over 20 lb.

The travel of the corresponding bellows operator for an air vane was $\frac{15}{16}$ in. The angle made with the tapered casing was 13 deg when the vane was extended, the angle of a side of the tapered casing being 6 deg. When extended, the lower edge of the air vane was $5\frac{7}{8}$ in. from the casing and was $1\frac{7}{8}$ in. beyond the 18-in. diameter, or cross section, of the rocket.

Gyroscope. The gyroscope was as before, except for the wiring. It was believed that the enameled copper wires, as previously used on the gyroscope supporting frame, might have their enamel scraped off by vibration, thus forming a ground. The wires were therefore covered with ¹⁄₁₆-in.-O.D. white rubber tubing.

The ⅛-in.-O.D. steel tube for running the gyro had a single No. 69 hole, instead of two No. 69 holes in series, and the screen used for a strainer was a disk of 150-mesh nickel wire cloth.

Magnet-operated valves. Because of the shortness of travel (¹⁄₁₆ in.) of the magnet-operated valves previously used, together with the small diameter of the valve rod, they were employed in the present model to serve as trigger valves, operating bellows that moved considerably larger valves. Shop tests of this double set of valves showed that sufficiently rapid action could be obtained with a 10-ft length of ⅜-in.-O.D. aluminum tubing between the auxiliary valves and a pair of bellows vane operators, one for blast vane and one for air vane.

Cap and parachute release. The rocket cap, 18 in. in diameter, consisted of two spun-aluminum sections, stiffened by a band of 17 ST. The parachutes, cable, and barograph were carried in the cap.

The steel cables were all Roebling airplane cables. A ¹⁄₁₆-in. cable was looped over the two tubing rings of the barograph support, thus forming a doubled cable between these rings. From the lower end of the loop a doubled ¹⁄₁₆-in. cable extended to the 6-ft cap parachute, and from the bag of this parachute extended a single ¹⁄₁₆-in. cable to the pilot parachute for the cap. The bag of the 15-ft parachute, for the main body of the rocket, was attached by a single ¹⁄₁₆-in. cable. This bag was not attached to the parachute. The parachute itself was fastened to the rocket by a loop of ¼-in. cable, the ends of which were held by a clamp.

The barograph was held in a steel-tubing frame, the end pieces of which consisted of tubing rings. It was supported by eight rings, or eyes, on the barograph box, which were connected by music-wire loops to snap fasteners engaging loops brazed to the tubing supporting rings. Two rubber bands were used for each of the corner supports. Sidewise vibration was avoided by using a number of strips of sponge rubber in contact with each of the four sides of the barograph box.

Weights and dimensions. The length of the rocket from the open end of the nozzle to the plate on the cap release mechanism was 18 ft 10 in. The vanes extended rearward 7⅜ in. and the cap added 30 in., making the over-all length 21 ft 11⅜ in. (Fig. 34).

The weight was obtained by weighing the rocket, complete except for the cap and casings, suspended at two convenient points. The two balance readings were 132 and 78 lb. The cap weighed 16 lb 8 oz and the casings 10 lb 2 oz, making the total weight of the rocket, empty, 236 lb 10 oz.

Controls at tower. Instead of a single releasing lever, as used in previous flights, two releasing levers were used, on opposite sides of the rocket, in order to have no sidewise force on the rocket while it was lifting against the levers. The absence of such force made it possible to use a device for indicating when the lift had reached a certain amount. Such information was desirable for the reason that the weight of the rocket (236 lb) plus fuel (480 lb total, or 500 lb if 120 lb of gasoline were used) was nearly that of the initial lift (between 600 and 700 lb); hence it was feared that releasing as soon as the indicator light appeared, with the rocket lifting no more than its weight, might cause even a slight wind to tilt the rocket seriously as it left the tower. Moreover, the rocket was so long that the cap reached nearly halfway up the tower.

The remaining controls at the tower were the same as for the static test. The pin to release the gyroscope was the same as in the preceding flight tests.

Attempted test, February 6. The rocket and equipment were taken to the tower on January 30, and the rocket was placed in the tower that afternoon. The next day the remainder of the equipment was set up and adjusted, but bad weather caused the postponement of the flight until February 6. A test was attempted on this date, but the lever on the fused-wire release of the second dashpot, which opened valves and applied pressures, stuck when halfway up, due to rust that had formed in the previous wet weather. The gasoline and oxygen were drained out and the rocket was wrapped up for the night. Bad weather again intervened.

Test. On February 9 preparations for a test began at the tower at 6 A.M. The canvas covering of the rocket, as well as the entire tower, was coated with ice. It was necessary to knock the ice off the tower in two operations. Before the sun warmed the tower the worst of the ice was knocked off, and later the remainder was scraped off. Preparations and checks were made for a test, although water continued to drop from parts of the tower.

The test was carried out about 12:15 P.M. The flame at the start seemed somewhat more yellowish than usual, and the noise somewhat less. After about 2 sec a flash appeared at the level of the pumps, the casing at this place being blown off, and the white vapor produced by a stream of liquid oxygen was visible thereafter.

An examination showed that the bolts holding the casings of the oxygen pump had given way, causing the pump to break in two. The flame that appeared was forced back through the oxygen line by the chamber pressure. The oxygen starting valve came off with the oxygen filter and outer section of the pump casing, and was considerably damaged. The oxygen turbine was broken off around the hub and was not recovered. The chamber was undamaged. The tower guides were bent owing to the force with which the pump casing was blown off.

Conclusions. The breaking of the oxygen pump may best be explained by the supposition that ice particles occurred in the oxygen line and that these started clogging the oxygen orifice in the top of the chamber from the start. This explanation would account for a yellowish rather than a whitish flame at the start and for the less than usually intense noise.

Test of March 21, 1940 (P-16):
Attempted Flight Test

The object of this test was to repeat the preceding test after the rocket had been overhauled. An extension of 20 ft was added to the tower, and the right-hand guides were made sectional, so that the rocket could be placed in the tower without bending the angle-iron guides.

Chamber. The chamber was found in good condition after the preceding test, but since the oxygen pump broke in that test, apparently owing to sudden rise of pressure, a check was made on the possibility that the oxygen orifice in the chamber was clogged. No clogging was found.

Tanks. The liquid-nitrogen tank was blown out, several drops of water being thrown out, as usual. The oxygen tank appeared to be dry, but the Vellumoid gasket at the union on the bottom of the tank was moist, and there were drops of water on the lower half of the union. The oxygen and nitrogen tanks were dried out with hot air in the shop. The gasoline tank was blown out with dry air.

A new filler was welded into the gasoline tank, near the bottom of the top hemisphere, so that filling could take place from the side, with the rocket cap in place.

Pumps. A new oxygen pump was constructed, using as much of the previous pump as possible. Because the screws used in the preceding tests for holding the pump casings together had proved to be very brittle at liquid-oxygen temperature, they were replaced by 18-8-FM stainless-steel stud bolts with cold-rolled-steel nuts.

New pump casings, and also the middle section, were made of Dowmetal. The diameter was increased over that for previous pumps in order to accommodate the larger bolts. A new turbine was used, to replace that lost in the preceding test.

Directing vanes. Owing to the large force exerted on the free ends of the blast vanes in the last test, and the possibility that this force might decrease the vertical component of the lifting force of the rocket, thus causing it to fall soon after the start should the velocity be low, the force of the four bellows operators for the blast vanes was reduced.

The force of the movable air vanes was unaltered.

Test. The loading began at 7:27 A.M., and the test commenced at 8:35 A.M.

A click was heard, about 3 sec after the igniter key was pressed, followed by a yellowish flame, which at no time was noisy and which finally pulsated. The run was allowed to continue for about 8 sec, in order that the power plant might start itself, if possible. At about this time, however, there were two successive explosions, one halfway up the rocket and the other over the chamber. The emergency gasoline-valve key was pressed to stop the run.

An examination of the rocket in the tower showed that the two manifolds had exploded, denting the turbines. The edges of the fragments were not bent, indicating that the manifolds were very cold. Frost was observed on the outer half of the steel tube from the gas generator to the manifolds, and none on the gas generator. The bottom cone of the chamber was split open lengthwise, apparently more as a result of heat than of high pressure. The fused-wire release for the oxygen valve was intact, but that for the three-way valves had been fused. The pressure contact maker showed no rise of pressure.

Examination of the rocket at the shop revealed that there was no soot in the gas generator, although it was very wet with gasoline. The damage was confined to the parts near the manifolds and to those around the top of the chamber, including the air vanes. The 2000-lb reducing valve was dry and clean inside. The safety valve did not open, even at 250 lb.

Conclusions. The most reasonable assumption is that the switch on the third dashpot acted prematurely. If this closed, for example, by jar, when the first dashpot operated, the turbine and pump pressures would have been shut off as soon as they started, and the spark would have stopped before gasoline and oxygen entered the gas generator.

Test of April 12, 1940 (P-17): Static Test

The object of this test was to repeat the preceding test as a static test, with various operations and pressures recorded photographically, in order to determine what changes would be necessary to assure more positive operation.

Chamber. A new lower cone and nozzle were made and brazed on. Two patches were made on the inverted cone with Insalute-Alundum cement. A new copper-tube jacket was put on the chamber, and a new lower steel ring was made, to support the cross for the air vanes (Fig. 35).

Pumps. Extensive repairs were needed on the pumps, largely owing to the impact of the exploding manifolds in the preceding test, which sprung the shafts. The oxygen pump required a new shaft and one new bakelite bolt bushing. The gasoline pump required a new shaft and a new screen in the filter (Fig. 36).

Turbine drive. A new turbine was made for each pump, since the turbines used in the preceding test were cut on the rims and some of the blades were bent. The turbines were the same as those previously used, except that the hubs were made with $\frac{1}{16}$ in. greater radius so as to withstand the effects of gyroscopic forces in flight.

A new manifold with new steel nozzles was made for each pump. These manifolds were of $\frac{1}{16}$-in. soft sheet steel, as before, and were tested at 250-lb pressure.

The gas-generator head was taken apart, reassembled, and tested with air. Water was not used because of the danger of loosening the Insalute-Alundum lining. The air test gave 54 sec, instead of 50 as before. No dirt was observed, and hence the head was not altered.

Other repairs and changes. Two steel unions were used in the steel tube carrying liquid oxygen from the oxygen pump to the main oxygen valve above the chamber. These unions made it possible to remove and examine most of the main oxygen valve, and to remove both pumps without cutting the tubes. New bellows and a new ¼-in. copper inlet tube were installed on the bellows operator for the gas-generator reducing valves.

Test. The rocket and other equipment were set up and checked on April 10. On April 11 at 6:30 A.M. the wiring was checked, the tanks were rinsed out, and the controls were set. When the filling was being completed, however, the chamber was found to be leaking gasoline slowly. The test was stopped and the gasoline drained. Examination of the gasoline valve showed evidence of a flat particle in the Vellumoid seat ring. The valve was taken to the shop, a new ring was inserted, and the upper part of the valve was filled with gasoline to test for leakage. It was later tested with 8-lb air pressure.

Test. On the morning of April 12, after preliminary tests and checking, the tanks were filled and the test was begun.

There seemed to be several seconds between the time of the click of the release operated by the igniter and the appearance of a flame. Meanwhile the pumps were heard, and then the flame appeared, accompanied by a very loud roar. A dust cloud appeared at the rear of the tower, and the flame in the tower was very white. There was no lift light, however. After a considerable time, the chamber burned out just below the throat. The flame continued and the emergency gasoline shutoff key was pressed.

An examination of the rocket showed that the initial explosion had torn off one lift battery box and pulled the shunt connection off the other. The copper-tube jacket appeared cool and not discolored, except a short distance above the throat. The rocket had become pulled out of the angle-iron guides of the tower; both felt pieces had been frozen to the oxygen tank and had not been removed; the spark was still on, as the spark switch had not quite opened, and the ³⁄₁₆-in. copper tube from the oxygen tank to the instrument board had been broken off at the fitting on the tank. The ⅛-in. steel plate that held the thimble into which the nozzle fitted was warped by the heat, and a part of the top of the thimble had been burned away.

All the fused-wire releases on the rocket had worked, although the the lever of the lower three-way valve was prevented from completing its travel by one of the ³⁄₁₆-in. copper tubes to the instrument board.

When the bottom cone of the chamber was removed, it was found that a hole had been burned through the perforated steel of the inverted Insaluted cone. The gasoline orifices were found to be clear.

Conclusions. The violent explosion at the start was probably due to gasoline vapor, or gasoline vapor and oxygen gas, accumulating in the cement gas deflector and inside the sheet-iron shelter and being ignited when a strong flame issued from the nozzle. The explosion shook the rocket sidewise out of the angle-iron guides and also shook the sheet-iron shelter. The present explosion was more violent than usual because of the delay before the strong flame appeared.

Test of April 26, 1940 (P-18):
Repeat Static Test

The object was to repeat the preceding static test, avoiding the difficulties that were experienced in it.

Changes. A completely new chamber was made, except for the oxygen orifice, the spider for holding the oxygen deflector, and the oxygen deflector. No changes were made in the tanks.

At the end of the preceding test the pump locks were applied while power was still being applied to the turbines. The heat generated by the pump locks caused the solder on the double bellows joints to melt and also scored the sealing surfaces to such an extent as to produce chips of metal. Appropriate repairs were made to these parts.

New nozzles were made for the turbine manifolds, $\frac{1}{8}$ in. longer than those of the preceding test, to provide greater force on the turbines. The main gasoline valve was examined, cleaned, and tested.

Two braces were used to prevent the rocket from moving out from the guide angle irons of the tower in case of an explosion in the cement gas deflector or behind the sheet-iron shelter. Further, the total clearance between the guides on the rocket and the angle-iron guides was reduced from somewhat over $\frac{3}{8}$ in. to slightly under $\frac{1}{4}$ in. A new thimble for the nozzle was made, and the boxes of batteries for the lift light were placed outside the sheet-iron shelter.

Test. At the test there was a delay, as before, of several seconds between the firing of the igniter and the explosion, followed by the steady flame. The explosion seemed to be of about the same intensity as in the preceding test. The flame was very white and tapered down to a tip. The white light, indicating lift, appeared about as soon as the flame, and the red light, indicating a lift of 200 lb in excess of the weight, appeared about a second later. After about 15 sec, the chamber burned through at the top, and the emergency gasoline-valve key was pressed, although the rocket may have shut itself off before.

After the test it was found that the steel tubes at the top of the chamber, namely the oxygen line and the oxygen jacket, had been burned, but the nickel of the upper cone of the chamber was intact. Both lower fused-wire releases had been burned. The oxygen pump, and the oxygen line to the gas generator, were found to contain gasoline.

Conclusions. It appears probable that the pumps delivered unusually high pressures and that oscillations of pump pressure caused the steel tubing of the oxygen line to break where the stress was greatest. These oscillations of pump pressure may be due to the oscillations of the gas generator, which are inherent in the generator as at present constructed or with the present pressures. The pump pressures may oscillate, also, because of the vibration of the impeller.

Test of May 15, 1940 (P-19):
Repeat Static Test

The object of this test was to repeat the previous test, without using material in the high-pressure liquid-oxygen line that was brittle when cold.

Chamber. In the preceding test the oxygen line and the oxygen jacket tubes were burned to the point where they entered the chamber, and a hole about 1½ in. square was burned in the inverted cone. For the present test the same cylinder, lower cone, and nozzle were used, but monel metal was used in place of steel tubing for the oxygen entrance parts and jacket, and 0.050-in. sheet nickel was used for the upper cone because of possible high chamber pressure. The head of the oxygen nozzle was made of a solid monel rod. The main oxygen line was a monel tube, and the jacket tube was machined from a solid rod, since tubing of the desired size was not on hand.

Other changes. No change was made in the tanks. The pumps were overhauled but not changed. In repairing the tubing above the chamber, ordinary steel tubing as well as iron pipe fittings were avoided, since these are brittle at low temperatures. The oxygen valve was modified so as to avoid brittle material as far as possible, without taking too much time for reconstruction.

In an attempt to avoid the oscillations of pressure in the turbine gas line, a shock absorber was made, consisting of a 0.002-in. steel piston operating in a steel cylinder filled with oil. A threaded sleeve joined the shock absorber to the rod holding the lever of the oxygen reducing valve.

At the tower, additional electric circuits were provided, to show when the explosion in the sheet-iron shelter at the start of the outside flame took place, and also to show when the hoses were pulled off.

Test. The strong explosion in the sheet-iron shelter occurred at the usual time after the igniter key was pressed. The dust cloud produced by the flame from the nozzle was large, and the noise was loud and somewhat pulsating. After 10 or 15 sec a small white flame was seen at the bottom of the nozzle. This was later found to have been the top of the thimble burning through. About 2 sec afterward, three places were burned through the nozzle, whereupon the casings around the turbines were blown off, and flame was seen coming from the gas generator, which was covered with frost. The rim of the gasoline turbine flew off, breaking in two. Some of the Insalute lining of the gas generator was found to have been broken off. Both brass impellers of the pumps were found to have rubbed on the housings.

Conclusions. Apparently the hoses were released prematurely, when the initial explosion took place, but the turbine pressure at the time, 103 lb, was high enough to raise the pumps to full working pressure.

The chamber may have burned out because of the low and oscillating gasoline pressure at the end of the run. In order to allow for possible dropping of gasoline-pump pressure, it might be well to reduce the oxygen flow in the chamber.

Test of June 11, 1940 (P-20):
Repeat Static Test

The object of this test was to repeat the preceding test with a reduced flow of oxygen to the chamber, a steel impeller in the gasoline pump to reduce impeller vibration, fixed rims for the turbines, and a copper liner for the gas generator.

Chamber. The oxygen orifice was reduced in cross section so that the flow of water at 20-lb pressure was reduced from $9\frac{13}{16}$ to 9 oz/sec. A new Insaluted inverted cone was made, since that used in the preceding test had a hole about 1 in. square burned through it. A new nozzle and 60-deg lower cone were also made.

Other changes. In order to avoid oscillations of gasoline-pump pressure, a new impeller was made of cold-rolled steel. The new impeller weighed 68 grams, or $2\frac{1}{4}$ oz, this being 26 grams less than the brass impeller, besides being of more rigid material.

To enable the turbines to run at high speed without danger of the ring on the turbine breaking off, fixed steel rings were used for both turbines. Gas leakage between the ends of the blades and the ring was reduced as much as possible by making the radial clearance 0.015 in. New turbines, of 17 ST aluminum, were the same as those previously used, except that the blades were not drilled and tapped for screws.

The gas generator head was altered by using a copper liner in place of the Insalute-Alundum liner previously used. The liner was kept cool by liquid oxygen in contact with the flat, exposed face.

Test. The gas explosion occurred at about the usual time after the igniter was fired. The flame appeared to be more yellowish than before. The test appeared to be much longer than any previous test, and red-hot stones were seen to fly up out of the cement gas deflector at intervals. The rod or tube on the arm of the switch freed by the firing of the igniter was melted off, dropping the weight at the end. The steel thimble under the rocket was scaled outside by the heat but was undamaged inside. The rocket stopped firing suddenly, apparently shutting itself off. A yellow flame, probably from residual gasoline in the gasoline valve, burned at the nozzle for some time.

Data from the Sept camera showed that the run was the longest so far obtained. The time was 43.5 sec.

Test of June 26, 1940 (P-21):
Flight Test

The object was to repeat the flight test of March 21, 1940 (P-16), with the rocket altered as suggested by the results of the intervening static tests.

Changes. The chamber was used without change, and no alterations were made in the tanks or pumps, except that the latter were overhauled. The steel tube on the nitrogen valve, which was broken during or after the preceding test, was replaced. New cables were used for withstanding the forces of tension along the rocket and for holding the large parachute.

Four new retractable air vanes were made of Dowmetal, to replace those of 17 ST sheet aluminum. Each Dowmetal air vane weighed a little under 10 oz, whereas each aluminum vane had weighed somewhat over 14 oz.

Adjustments were made in the bellows operators for the blast vanes so that, at 26-lb air pressure, the force required to move a blast vane outward at right angles to the rocket axis was 14 lb to start and 16 lb when fully out. At 30-lb air pressure the respective forces were 16 and 18 lb. The gyroscope, magnet-operated valves, cap and parachute release, batteries, and wiring were substantially the same as in the test of March 21.

Weights and dimensions. The length of the rocket was the same as for Tests P-15 and P-16. The weight of the rocket without the casings, except the narrow band at the top of the gasoline tank, was 201 lb. The total weight, with casings, cap, parachutes, cable, and barograph, was 241½ lb.

Test. There was the usual delay after pressing the igniter key before the flame appeared. The flame was accompanied by the usual explosion. About 3 sec later the flame, which may have been a little more yellowish than usual, diminished fairly rapidly, and a tall gasoline flame ascended the left side of the rocket, evidently from the gasoline drain tube. About 3 sec later the manifolds exploded, and the emergency gasoline key was pressed.

An examination showed that the top of the gas generator had been blown off. The steel of the manifolds appeared to be brittle. There was some soot on the copper liner of the gas generator, indicating that it had operated.

Test of August 1, 1940 (P-22):
Repeat Flight Test

The object of this test was to obtain a flight under the same conditions as those of the test of June 26, 1940 (P-21).

Changes. Aside from necessary repairs, virtually no change was made in the rocket. A small leak in the jacket space around the oxygen inlet was found and repaired. A new 3/16-in.-O.D. by 1/64-in.-wall copper-tube jacket was used, since the flanges on the bottom steel unions leaked. Two new manifolds were made for the pumps, and the nozzles were carefully adjusted (Fig. 37).

Test. When the igniter key was pressed, a click was heard after the usual time, and then a flame, which was not accompanied by much noise. There were pulsations of the flame, which then diminished, and the emergency key was pressed, shutting off the gasoline.

An examination of the tower showed that the release lever had operated, although the key to operate this lever had not been pressed. No fused-wire release on the rocket had operated except that on the emergency gasoline valve. Checks were made of the electrical connections. The relays worked as before, and each switch gave current when the proper associated terminals were short-circuited. The cause of the failure could not be ascertained with certainty. Possibly the emergency gasoline-valve circuit and the main release-lever circuit were operated accidentally (Fig. 38).

Test of August 9, 1940 (P-23):
Repeat Flight Test

The object of this test was to obtain a flight under the same conditions as those of the test of August 1, 1940.

Changes. No changes were made in the chamber, tanks, or pumps, except that the pumps were overhauled and new ball bearings were installed in the oxygen pump. The turbine drive, piping and valves, gyro, batteries and wiring were all as in the previous test.

Test. The usual loud initial explosion took place after the usual delay. The white lift light soon showed, and after a second or so the red lift light showed. The main release key was pressed about a second afterward.

The rocket rose, seemed to hesitate for an instant after it had risen a short distance, and a yellow flame spread out. It then rose slowly, but apparently no more slowly than in a number of tests with the 9-in. model. It left the tower straight, but soon tilted toward the left for no apparent reason, and showed no evidence of stabilizing vane action. It continued to rise and turn, then plunged straight downward, still turning, and struck the ground about 400 ft from the observers. It exploded and a strong concussion was felt soon afterward. A dense black cloud of smoke arose.

The rocket appeared to leave the tower at about 10 to 15 mph, and rose 200 to 300 ft. The flame was rather long and yellowish, and the lower end was fuzzy. There did not appear to be much smoke. Apparently the explosion did not occur inside the rocket, since the parts were not greatly torn or scattered. It seems likely that the two tanks burst simultaneously, and that the two liquids mixed violently, igniting immediately afterward.

An examination of the tower showed that the right rear felt had frozen to the oxygen tank and had been carried along with it, pulling out the spring on the control. In addition, the wire extending up under the felt, for freeing the gyroscope, had been pulled between the felt and the tank. This was evidently what caused the delay when the rocket started to rise.

Conclusions. The pumps and gas generator evidently operated satisfactorily, even when the rocket was upside down. The inclination of the rocket after leaving the tower could hardly have been due to wind, since only a small breeze was blowing at the time of the test. It seems unlikely that the inclination could have been caused by the torque on the turbines or pumps, or by the gas flowing unevenly out of the annular space below the 18-in.-diameter casing. It therefore seems to have been due to a guide on the rocket touching an aluminum angle guide of the tower just as the rocket left the tower. The speed of the rocket appeared to be too low for the felt to deflect the rocket because of air resistance. The lack of steering appears to have been due to too small a correcting force on the blast vanes.

Test of December 18, 1940 (P-24): Static Test

The object of this test was to repeat the former test as a static test, with a half fuel load, without decreasing the force of the 3-in. blast-vane bellows, and with an additional, alternative circuit for shutting off the pumps and then closing the main valves and releasing the parachute, should the rocket tilt 90 deg from the vertical with the chamber under full pressure.

Changes. The chamber and copper-tube jacket, the oxygen and gasoline tanks, and the pumps and accessories were substantially the same as in the previous test, except for necessary repairs and strengthening or bracing.

The wiring was changed to a dual control system. The first circuit was designed to operate substantially as before, provided the automatic steering was satisfactory, the chamber pressure fell, and the rocket continued to coast up vertically. The second circuit was designed to operate if the rocket tilted through 90 deg while the chamber still fired, when the grounding of the gyroscope gimbals caused current to pass through the fused-wire release, stopping the pumps. When the chamber pressure had fallen as a result, further contacts took place, closing the main valves and releasing the parachute.

For this static test the gyro, magnet valves, directing vanes, and casings were not used. Clips were employed to hold the gyroscope gimbals in 90-deg displacement positions.

Test. There seemed to be a longer delay than usual between the pressing of the igniter key and the initial loud explosion. Gasoline was seen running out of the nozzle just before this for 1 or 2 sec. The initial explosion did not seem to be accompanied by a large flame from the cement gas deflector. Something appeared to be burning close under the liquid-oxygen tank. The tube from the gas generator then became red-hot and burned through. The test was stopped by pressing the key that closed the emergency gasoline valve.

All the operations seemed normal except that the gas generator started but did not continue to operate. On examination, all parts were found to be tight, except that the oxygen reducing valve to the gas generator leaked somewhat. The chamber was uninjured.

Test of January 6, 1941 (P-25):
Repeat Static Test

The object of this test was to repeat the previous static test, with a full fuel load, a 25-lb increase in gas-generator reducing-valve pressures, and with a measurement of the lift.

No changes were made in the chamber, tanks, or pumps. The pressures for the oxygen reducing valve and the gasoline reducing valve supplying the gas generator were raised from 250 to 275 lb.

An attempted test on December 31 disclosed leakage past the bolts that held the casings of the gasoline pump together. As a result both pumps were further tested and minor adjustments were made.

Test. The initial explosion did not appear quite so loud as usual, and the flame was long, narrow, pointed, and somewhat yellowish. There appeared to be no flame in the cement gas deflector. The flame seemed to be directed slightly toward the right. After about 10 sec a flame was seen coming from below the oxygen tank or from the top of the chamber. The rocket then stopped itself.

The lift rose rather slowly to a high value, 985 lb. The tank pressures rose as usual, but the chamber pressure varied and was not as high as before. Both oxygen and gasoline pump pressures were greater (700 and 550 lb, respectively) than in the last static test. The turbine gas pressure was 165 lb, or about 10 per cent over the previous pressure.

On examination it was found that the outer oxygen jacket tube on top of the chamber had burned through just above the top of the upper cone. The felt around the oxygen starting valve was burned. The asbestos cords or tubes on the ends of the tin jacket around the gasoline pump had been blown out, and there was soot at joints at the Vellumoid rings of the gas-generator strainer. The Insalute-Alundum cone and the outer oxygen jacket tube in the chamber had been partly burned through. The steel gasoline impeller was found to have rubbed the Dowmetal casing on one side.

Conclusions. It seems likely that extra high pressure or lack of centering caused the gasoline impeller to rub, reducing the gasoline pressure and giving a momentary excess of oxygen, which burned the Insalute cone and the oxygen jacket of the chamber. It is possible, however, that a piece of foreign substance clogged one side of the oxygen orifice, thus removing the protection of the cone of oxygen from one side of the Insaluted cone, permitting it to burn through. This explanation would account for the yellowish flame, the total oxygen flow being reduced.

Test of January 22, 1941 (P-26):
Repeat Static Test

The purpose of this test was to repeat the preceding static test with the reducing valve for the gas generator set at 250 lb as before.

Changes. The chamber was repaired, and the inlet rates of flow for oxygen and gasoline were tested, and found to be 8 and 7.75 oz/sec, respectively, for each orifice, for water at 20-lb pressure. No change was made in the tanks or pumps, except that the gasoline impeller was care-fully smoothed, and both impellers were lined up as accurately as pos-sible. Various other minor adjustments were made, and the joints were tightened with fresh Vellumoid packings, to reduce or prevent leakage.

Test. The igniter key was pressed as soon as the camera motor was observed to be in motion. There was the usual delay of several seconds. A yellow flame about 4 ft long then appeared from the nozzle. This dis-appeared and was followed a second or so afterward by a loud, bright, steady flame. The flame was long and pointed, but not so narrow as in the preceding test, and seemed yellower. The roar was steady but seemed to vibrate or pulsate. After about half a minute, a small flame appeared from the top cone of the chamber, and the test stopped itself immediately afterward.

Examination showed that the upper nickel cone of the chamber had been severely heated. Bulging evidently took place first, and then the brazing of the small steel tube that led to the contact maker and the in-strument board melted. The contact maker then stopped the operation of the rocket.

The Sept camera record indicated that the total lift was about 842 lb just after the hose was pulled off and 826 lb just before the end of the run. The time of the run was 29 sec.

The purpose of this test was to repeat the previous static test with an oxygen spray cone of smaller angle, so as to avoid, if possible, the heating and burning through of the top cone of the chamber. At the same time the gas pressure was to be increased somewhat, so as to obtain an increase in lift.

Changes. The lower cone and nozzle of the chamber were made of 0.050-in. nickel instead of 0.037-in., to withstand higher pressure, prevent bending at the throat, and strengthen the nozzle.

No change was made in the tanks. New bearings were used in both pumps. Tubing and valves were tested, and joints were tightened or were provided with new gaskets to stop leaks. The pressure for the two reducing valves was increased from 250 to 270 lb.

Test. The delay before the initial explosion appeared to be longer than usual. The flame, once started, was steady, long, pointed, and somewhat yellowish. After about 15 sec a flame appeared at the top of the chamber, followed by a large gasoline flame below the nozzle. Somewhat later a bright flame appeared under the oxygen tank, later proving to be from the felt and aluminum around the oxygen pump.

The large gasoline flame below the nozzle did not decrease when the emergency gasoline-valve key was pressed, nor when the cord was pulled which closed the switch on the tower that in turn short-circuited the switch and the contact maker on the rocket. The main release-lever key was then pressed, and on the fall of this lever the large gasoline flame ceased.

An examination showed that the monel jacket had burned through. A hole was also burned in the inverted Insaluted cone, but the upper, outer cone of the chamber was not burned or bulged.

At the shop it was found that the impeller of the oxygen pump had rubbed on the casing, chiefly on the short tube inlet. Several of the ends of the turbine blades of the gasoline pump were found to have rubbed. Since they were not adjacent, they may have been scored by an obstruction passing through the turbine.

Since, in various tests, an all-steel oxygen orifice and jacket cracked after a long series of successful tests, and the all-monel has cracked in the last three tests, it appears likely that there is a strain, due to the method of construction, which is less easily withstood by the welded and brazed monel joints.

Test of February 14, 1941 (P-28):
Repeat Static Test

The purpose of this test was to repeat the preceding static test.
Changes. The chamber was repaired, but otherwise was substantially

the same as before, except that steel parts were used for the oxygen-chamber entrance orifice and jacket, and an expansion joint was provided at the top of this jacket to relieve strain due to contraction. The oxygen impeller was modified and trued, the shaft was changed to one of aluminum, and the balance was improved.

Test. After the igniter key was pressed, there was the usual delay before the flame appeared. It was rather long, pointed, and yellowish. After 10 or 15 sec of steady firing, the intense flame suddenly stopped, and a fairly large gasoline flame appeared for a few seconds. Flames appeared immediately afterward around the pumps. The lift rose much more rapidly than in the previous test, but the pump, turbine, and chamber pressures were slightly lower.

After the test, examination showed that the gasoline-pump bearing nearer the impeller was broken up and that the other bearing was about ready to jam. It was concluded that both bearings, particularly that nearer the impeller, were dry, and should hereafter be oiled before each run.

Test of March 5, 1941 (P-29):
Repeat Static Test

The object of this test was to repeat the preceding static test, with the gasoline-pump bearings carefully oiled.

No changes were made, except to install new bearings in the gasoline pump, with the original grease, and with oil added. Felt was wrapped around the exposed places of the two pump bearings, in order to keep out dirt and dust.

Test. The initial explosion occurred after a somewhat longer delay than usual. The appearance of the flame was normal for 2 or 3 sec, whereupon a loud explosion and flame were seen at the oxygen pump.

The outlet nozzle on this pump was found to have broken off, the screws breaking in two. The interior of the pump was found to be considerably burned. The oxygen entrance to the gas generator was unsoldered. On examination at the shop it seemed evident that too much oil had been used in the oxygen-pump bearings, causing sticking of the impeller at the start.

Test of April 1, 1941 (P-30):
Repeat Static Test

The object of this test was to repeat the preceding static test, with a new oxygen pump having an improved casing and steel impeller, and with an easily detachable oxygen reducing valve.

Changes. The chamber was repaired by chipping off the loose and melted Insalute-Alundum cement and applying new cement. Aside from the new oxygen pump, virtually no changes were made in the rocket except for necessary repairs.

Oxygen pump. Since it was necessary to remake the oxygen pump completely, an improved casing design was used that had been planned for higher pressures. A steel impeller replaced one of brass (Fig. 39).

Large Dowmetal castings were used for the main parts of the pump casings. The volute was milled out of the casting with an end mill. The design provided for screwing the outlet nozzle into the pump casing, which had not been possible with the previous pump. Because of the narrow shoulder, difficulty had been experienced with the previous pump in screwing the impellers onto the impeller shaft so that the impeller and shaft axes were in line. In the new pump a wide shoulder was used. In addition, a close-fitting extension was made on the impeller, between it and the screw that held it to the impeller shaft. This extension also helped to keep the two axes in line.

The new oxygen pump was somewhat larger and heavier than the old. It weighed, together with the turbine, $5\frac{1}{4}$ lb. When complete with the supporting bracket, starting nozzles, and outlet nozzle, the weight was $6\frac{1}{2}$ lb. The steel impeller weighed 77 grams, as compared with the old brass impeller, which weighed, less solder and connecting screws, 70 grams. The moment of inertia of the steel impeller was less, however, since much of the weight was in the threaded end. The new pump had 143 parts.

Test. The run started about the usual time after the igniter key was pressed, and the flame appeared steady. It was long, yellowish white, and pointed.

The Sept camera record indicated that the lift rose slowly at the start but at the middle of the run reached 380 lb over the weight of the rocket and fuel. The period of this strong lift, from 325 to 380 lb more than the rocket weight, lasted for a total of 33 sec.

The full working pressures for the two pumps, 600 and 500 lb, were reached 7 sec after the hose was pulled off; the chamber pressure was 300 lb. After the test, considerable oil was found to have spattered from the pump bearings. Both pumps turned freely after the test. The new pump design appeared to be satisfactory.

Test of May 8, 1941 (P-31):
Flight Test

The object of this test was to obtain a flight with the model used in the preceding static test.

Changes. A new upper cone and inverted cone were necessary for the chamber. Opportunity was taken, in making the change, to increase the wall thickness of the steel-tube jacket for the oxygen entrance tube from 0.035 in. to 0.065 in.

The lower end of the nozzle was supported against sidewise displacement.

A new gasoline pump was constructed along the same general lines as the new oxygen pump, and a thicker tube was used for the turbine gas-pressure line.

The new alternative electrical circuit was used, whereby the pumps would be stopped, the main valves to the chamber closed, and the parachute released, in that order, if the rocket became inclined 90 deg from the vertical while firing.

Test. When the igniter key was pressed, a click was heard, indicating that the first dashpot had operated. Nothing happened immediately after that, and it was believed that a flight would not be made. The keys operating the emergency gasoline valve and the outside short-circuiting switch were not pressed, however.

After about 5 min the rocket was heard to start. There was no loud initial explosion, but a large gasoline flame instead. The red lift light appeared soon after the white, and the hose dropped about 3 sec later. After about 5 sec the release-lever key was pressed.

The rocket rose considerably faster than in the previous flight with the same model. It rose straight for two or three tower lengths, then heeled over rapidly away from the tower. When the axis became horizontal, the strong flame was succeeded by a small flame. After the rocket had inclined about 20 deg below the horizontal, the cap came off, and the main parachute was pulled out, being partly open when the rocket struck the ground. Immediately afterward a very large gasoline flame appeared, followed by a rather dull explosion.

Test of July 11, 1941 (P-32):
Static Test

The object of this test was to make a static test with the rocket, repaired after the previous flight test.

Changes. A new chamber was made, a replica of that used in the preceding test. The nitrogen tanks were the same as previously used but were piped together by means of aluminum-tube fittings. In place of the baffle system for the gasoline tank previously used, a hollow float was employed. This had a rack-and-pawl arrangement so that it would be inclined to descend, not to ascend. By this means it was possible to have the level surface of the gasoline practically perpendicular to the axis of the gasoline tank for all reasonable angles of tilt.

A rigid support between the tanks and the steel-tubing frame of the rocket was made, and the nozzle was carefully lined up with the axis of the rocket.

Test. When the igniter key was pressed, the igniter fired after the usual interval. Gasoline then came from the nozzle, and the high pitch of the rotors could be heard, but no flame was visible. A large cloud of white vapor then appeared from the safety valve and also from below the oxygen tank. The keys were pressed to stop the run.

On examination it was found that the fused-wire releases for the oxygen and the three-way valve had operated but that the levers thus released had stuck, being clogged with sand that had blown into them during a sudden squall just before the test.

Test of July 17, 1941 (P-33):
Repeat Static Test

The purpose of this test was to repeat the preceding static test, with the levers of the three-way valve release cleared of sand, and the valve stems of the main oxygen and gasoline valves lengthened. No other changes were made in the chamber, tanks, pumps, or other equipment, except for necessary adjustments and repairs.

Test. The igniter burned at about the usual time after the key was pressed. The flame was narrow, straight, and yellowish, and the noise was uncomfortably loud.

At the end of the run the rocket did not shut itself off, and a yellowish diverging flame appeared, apparently accompanied by some pressure in the chamber. The shutoff emergency keys were pressed about 2 sec afterward.

From the Sept film, the average thrust may be taken as 825 lb for 34 sec, making 6.5 lb total liquids used per second, the totals being 131.7 lb oxygen and 91.5 lb gasoline, a ratio of 1.43. The gas ejection velocity for 825 lb average thrust and 6.5 lb/sec is 4060, and the average thrust per pound of fuels per second 128.

The chamber, pumps, and power plant were all in good condition after the test, the only repair work necessary being replacement of the ball bearings of the pumps, which had been injured by the fire after the run. The nozzle was found to be 3 deg out of line.

Test of August 10, 1941 (P-34):
Flight Test

The purpose of this test was to obtain a flight with a rocket as constructed in the preceding test.

Changes. After the preceding test the nozzle was not only bent considerably at the throat but also was curved along its length. A new lower cone and nozzle were made, and changes were made to brace the nozzle to prevent buckling due to expansion. There were no other changes, except for necessary adjustments and repairs. The empty rocket weighed 255 lb.

Test. The rocket started with a mild explosion. Immediately afterward, the whiteness left the flame, which became large and sooty. The run was then stopped.

The porcelain on the spark plug was found to have been broken off back to about ¼ in. from the end of the core. Chips off the oxygen turbine vanes indicated that the broken piece or pieces had passed through this turbine. A slowing down of the oxygen turbine very probably produced the decrease of oxygen observed, and resulted in little or no flow through the oxygen line.

Test of August 17, 1941 (P-35):
Repeat Flight Test

The purpose of this test was to repeat the preceding flight test. Few changes were made. A new spark plug was used in the gas generator, as usual.

Test. Up to the initial explosion, the start was the same as usual. Just after this, and before the hoses had been pulled off, the oxygen flow apparently stopped, and a large gasoline flame appeared. The two shutoff keys were not pressed immediately, in the hope that the run would start up again. In the meantime a sharp explosion was heard, and the casings were blown off, probably from the mixture from the gas generator or from the pump seals. The stop keys were pressed and the gasoline flame from the nozzle soon disappeared.

Examination of the rocket at the shop disclosed faulty functioning of the shutoff part of the main oxygen valve, which probably was the cause of failure of two of the preceding tests (P-32 and P-34). A piece of porcelain from the spark plug of Test P-34, found in one of the oxygen-manifold nozzle throats, may have been a contributing factor.

Test of October 10, 1941 (P-36):
Repeat Flight Test

The object of this test was to repeat the preceding flight test. Aside from necessary repairs and adjustments, no important alterations were made.

During most of September the rocket was ready for test, and liquid oxygen was on hand. The period, however, happened to be the rainiest in New Mexico's history. Liquid oxygen in 24-liter lots, in two 15-liter containers, was obtained at intervals, but even this was delayed by washed-out roads, and on the few days when the weather was fair, the liquid-oxygen supply was low.

On October 10, even though the liquid oxygen was rather low, it was decided to make an attempt, since there was very little wind and no sign of rain.

Test. At the usual time after the igniter key was pressed, a moderately large gasoline flame appeared. There was little or no initial explosion. This flame died down, and a strong flame followed immediately. The white and red lights quickly appeared. After a wait of 4 or 5 sec, the release key was pressed. The rocket rose about a foot and stopped. Something appeared to be wrong, and the stopping keys were pressed, even though the main release lever had operated and the rocket switch and possibly also the jacks in the plug for short-circuiting had been disconnected. The flame stopped at this time, except for the Dowmetal of the gasoline pump, which continued to burn.

It was found that the lever on the control that freed the hose pull-off lever was bent. The bending was sufficient to prevent the arm moving out of the two guide or support pieces, and thus releasing the hoses. It seems likely that a flight would have been obtained if the hoses had been released, for the lift quickly exceeded the weight by at least 200 lb.

The difficulties inherent in the development of pump-driven flight rockets were made apparent in the P Series of experiments. Not only was there a comparatively new gas generator to contend with, but intricate piping and wiring were needed to make the operation, control, and release from the tower completely automatic after the igniter key was pressed.

The work had followed the usual pattern of development of new devices: a period of increasing complexity, succeeded by a stage of gradual simplification. Dr. Goddard had emerged from the difficult and trying first stage and was well into the second stage. The initial shock or starting explosion, with its attendant jar to all the adjustments, wiring, and controls, was being eliminated, and the pumps were functioning with increasing efficiency.

Following Test P-36 the work at New Mexico was terminated on account of the rapidly approaching World War II, and Dr. Goddard accepted invitations from the Army and Navy to undertake work on military applications of rockets, to be carried on in the East. He planned to resume his flight tests with pump rockets in New Mexico immediately after the war, but his death intervened.—Editors

Index

Indiana University
Northwest Campus Library